MW00559636

Revolution and Renaissance
1965 to 1975

Daniel Forbes Hauser

Foreword by Richie Furay
Rock & Roll Hall of Fame

History Publishing Company
Palisades, NY 10964

ISBN 9781951008000 Quality Paperback
ISBN 9781951008017 E-Book
ISBN 9781951008024 Hardback

History Publishing Company LLC
P.O. Box 700
Palisades, NY 10964
www.historypublishingco.com
SAN 850-5942

TABLE OF CONTENTS

FOREWORD

By Richie Furay, "Rock & Roll Hall of Fame"

Sex, drugs, and rock & roll. That certainly was the descriptive moniker of the late 60's and early 70's. During those years the American culture was in a total upheaval as young adults sought to experience what they thought to be freedom.

I had the personal privilege of experiencing those years from the vantage point of a musician traveling around the country with a rock & roll band. In 1965 I had moved to southern California with the dream of becoming an entertainer. When I got there, the scene was alive with other musicians who were also in pursuit of the same dream. It was while I was hanging out with my friend, Stephen Stills, that we re-connected with a mutual friend, Neil Young, from Winnipeg, Canada, along with Bruce Palmer on bass guitar and Dewey Martin on drums.

We were confident that we had a cohesive band with real talent, and just needed a unique name for ourselves. As fate would have it, we ultimately agreed on the name *"Buffalo Springfield."* which was a steam-roller company that was doing work on the street where we were living.

Our personalities led us to pursue a new kind of musical sound for that era. Influenced by many current bands like *"The Byrds"* and *"The Lovin' Spoonful"*, we created the first real merger of folk and rock music. That hybrid concept was later enhanced even further by a second group that I formed – *"Poco"* – and later carried "to the limit" by another L.A. group called *"The Eagles."* We started playing at some of the hottest clubs in the Hollywood area, including "Whiskey A Go Go" and others. We were chosen to share billing from time to time with such bands as *"The Doors"*, *"The Turtles"*, and *"The Beach Boys."*

It was a great adventure, and we were fortunate to have several major hits. Undoubtedly our most noted song was *"For What It's Worth (Stop, Children, What's That Sound?)."* Due to the national tensions surrounding the Viet Nam War during that time, it became one of the defining songs of the 60's. (This song was also later highlighted in the movie *"Forrest Gump"*, which chronicled the most memorable music of that era.)

We rode the crest of the cultural rebellion that we watched from the stage every night. While I can say that I never used any hallucinogenic drugs, there were always a variety of drugs and women available to us at any concert. Some club owners seemed to assume that drugs in some form were a necessary part of our performance payment, or at the very least to get us to commit to come back for another concert in the future.

In hindsight we can now see some unfortunate decisions that diminished our true potential as a major rock & roll band. We were in position for great success, but early on we were compelled to say "NO" to an invitation to be on the *"Tonight Show"* with Johnny Carson due to ongoing instability in the group, demonstrating that success has it's cost. Can you say, "Hindsight is perfect?" Emotional setbacks and conflicting egos caused our group to splinter and move in different directions. We had no idea that 32 years later we would receive the honor of being elected into the Rock & Roll Hall of Fame in 1997.

One of the greatest experiences for me personally during all those early concerts was that I met Nancy, who became the love of my life. We were married in 1967, and she immediately brought a degree of balance and perspective back into my world.

I decided to start a new band, *"Poco"*, joining forces with Randy Meisner, later replaced by Timothy Schmit, Jimmy Messina, later replaced by Paul Cotton, George Grantham, and Rusty Young. After some initial success we all agreed we wanted to move out of the congestion of L.A. At first the assumption was to move to San Francisco, but we soon changed our minds. Something compelling seemed to hover around the mention of Boulder, Colorado. There had been a strong influx of hippies into that community in the late '60's, and there was soon to be a great recording studio (Caribou Ranch) near Nederland, located in the mountains about 30 minutes west of Boulder. So it was that in 1972 Boulder became our new home. We had no idea at the time that so many other people and events were gravitating to Boulder, just like we did.

I have to admit I didn't even know what a "Chinook wind" was until we got to Boulder. But we quickly learned. Abrupt weather changes in the winter would occasionally cause the temperature to shift by more than 65 degrees within a 24-hour period. Extremely high winds would always accompany that kind of shift in the weather. And every winter would see at least 3 to 5 days with winds of more than 90 mph – and sometimes over 120 mph. I must confess . . . I absolutely love the scenery, the climate, and the culture in and around Boulder County, but to this day I detest those occasional severe winds.

Once we arrived in the splendor of the Rocky Mountains, I wrote *"A Good Feelin' To Know."* It accurately captured the surroundings in which we found ourselves. Our national success allowed us to open for major bands across the country, including our old friends, The Beach Boys. However, "real success" seemed to be allusive, and I quit Poco to start another band at the encouragement of David Geffen, a major record mogul at the time. Sadly, I was so consumed with being a rock and roll star that I didn't notice that my personal life had started to take a downward spiral that almost cost me my marriage.

The constant temptations in front of any entertainer were beyond my control, and for a time Nancy moved out of our house. There were many poor choices that I made to find myself in this predicament, and many difficult lessons were to be learned during this time. It was this valley that became a defining moment in my life, and I am thankful that I survived something that could have been the most devastating experience I would ever have to go through. So many fellow musicians and entertainers have destroyed their health, given up on their families, lost all their money, and too many even lost their lives. Both Nancy & I realized that our conflicts and confusion were beyond our own selves, and we independently chose to seek God's help in our life. I'm not saying we turned into "Jesus Freaks", which had become popular in California just a few years earlier. But the idea of a personal relationship with a personal God became real for us, and by His grace we were spared from disaster. I'm happy to say we just celebrated our 49th anniversary together, and now truly enjoy so many holidays or birthdays with our four great kids, three sons-in-law, and twelve incredible grandchildren.

So I personally observed – and also experienced first-hand – many of the dramatic changes in America (and specifically in Boulder) that my friend, Daniel Forbes Hauser, has documented in this compelling book. In hindsight it is incredible to see how often Boulder was a critical microcosm of what was happening across our nation. I happen to be another example of someone who was a part of the national trends, and who chose Boulder to be a tangible part of that experience. I am certain you are going to greatly enjoy this entertaining reflection on the decade of 1965 to 1975 because it captures so many events and issues that made this season of U.S. history so diverse and even bizarre.

It was an incredible ride.

DANIEL FORBES HAUSER

PREFACE

Between 1946 and 1964, more than 76 million babies were born in the U.S. That population spike had never been seen before in our country's history, and will never be seen again. I happened to be one of them. Involuntarily I became a member of this incredible "age wave" that has trampled over America, producing unexpected volatility and unprecedented change at every stage of its life from adolescence to retirement.

Like most teenagers and "20 somethings", I did not fully appreciate the profound changes that were occurring around us at the time. We all assumed it was just "Life", and that it carried the normal challenges of growing up. Only in our later years could we begin to reflect back on that era and recognize that something truly unusual had taken place.

I was fortunate to go through grade school, middle school, and high school in Boulder, Colorado in the 1960's. My friends and I personally experienced or observed some fascinating moments that have always provided amusing stories in social conversations over the years. Like most people, we assumed our childhood was somewhat "routine."

But something dramatic happened to me just a few years ago. Within a span of less than 30 days and in two separate conversations, I heard two friends share moments from their youth that made me shudder. These two events came from within our same community but were so polarized in their respective nature that it was difficult for me to grasp at first. These two extremes demonstrated the breadth of turmoil that was tearing at the very soul of our nation during the '60's and '70's.

At one end of that philosophical spectrum was a friend's older brother, who chose to co-found one of the most radical groups in our nation's history. The "Weather Underground" was so obsessed with the need for extreme change in America that they chose to set off multiple bombs somewhere in the U.S. every day for several years. Their vision was to destroy capitalism and start with an entirely new system. It truly was an undeclared war on our own soil, pitting radical young people against the Establishment.

At the opposite end of this spectrum was a personal friend to the former Marshall in our County. My acquaintance recounted to me that this officer of the law was so opposed to the cultural changes sweeping through the Boulder area during that time-frame that he personally and secretly killed a few hippies that were a botheration to him. At the time nobody else knew what happened. But that was his extremist response to the onslaught of "change."

I suddenly realized there was a story here, and began doing extensive historical research using those two moments as polarized "bookends" for this incredible expanse of events contained in between. And the findings have been most fascinating.

Historians and sociologists have often said that the '60's and '70's were such tumultuous times for America. I have arbitrarily concentrated on the middle 11 years of that season of time because it encompassed the steepest bell curve of volatility and upheaval. One would be hard-pressed to refute that concept after reviewing this short but unforgettable period of time.

Three primary elements in that era converged to cause a cultural explosion: the sudden and overwhelming age wave of the "baby boomers" in their teens and 20's, the entirety of the Viet Nam War, and the Civil Rights movement. Each of these factors is integral to this year-by-year review. Other issues certainly became a part of the mix, but these three were the engine that drove everything forward.

These moments offer us a dire warning for today. The same issues and convulsing demands for change in our current culture grow from the same roots of the late '60's and early '70's.

Every city across the U.S. was impacted during this window in history, but Boulder, Colorado – and the county that surrounds it – may have experienced the greatest seismic shift of all. You will see Boulder's inordinate connection and national influence in many of the issues of our current culture.

Some may dismiss it as coincidence. Others would contend that Boulder's role grew as the nation discovered what a beautiful setting it provides for work or recreation. Or maybe because it is home to a major University. Mystics have even claimed that it is one of only seven energy points in the world.

I'll let the readers choose their own conclusion on that. But the dots continually connect Boulder into the conversation surrounding so many crucial subjects from that era as well as the present.

I hope to convey two major messages here. First, this is a fast look at the chaos that confronted our country during the late '60's and early '70's. Whether you witnessed one of these many events yourself, or whether you read about it, my expectation is that you will discover numerous new and meaningful details within every chapter. I hope you find it entertaining.

But there is a second and more ominous takeaway from this review. America may be on the precipice of another season of cultural upheaval. Elements are in place that could cause a more cataclysmic shift than ever before. A cultural "Chinook" could take on new meaning for everyone.

If we learned anything from the '60's and '70's, it was that anger and protests do not in and of themselves bring about worthwhile change. Civilized dialog must replace the heated rhetoric of debate. One of the greatest legacies of our country is that whenever we have faced a crisis, we have applied mental and natural resources to uncover a solution.

I hope this book helps to move us one step in that direction.

A Word of Thanks.

I could not possibly list all of the names of the men and women that have shared some of their unique memories with me. Personal interviews with more than 60 people produced a wealth of stories. To all of you I say a heartfelt THANK YOU. As I promised every interviewee, all the names have been changed to prevent any breach of confidentiality or embarrassment. Some of the individual characters mentioned in this book are a compilation of several individual's different experiences. But I can assure you of this . . . every event recorded in this book is true.

We survived – and we can do it again . . . if we so choose.

CHAPTER 1

"APPROACHING CHINOOK"

". . . if your time to you is worth savin'
then you better start swimmin'
or you'll sink like a stone
for the times, they are a-changin.'"

Bob Dylan

Boulder, Colorado was a "garden of Eden" in the early 1960's. Nestled tightly against the Rocky Mountains, Boulder County actually straddles the mountainous foothills to the west as well as the Great Plains to the east. And the climate is just as compelling as the stunning backdrop of the snow-capped mountains that create the Continental Divide. Located at 5,400 feet above sea level, with more than 300 days of sunshine each year, low humidity, clean mountain water, and cool breezes every evening coming down from the mountain canyons, Boulder's residents understandably consider it heaven on earth.

Doctors have frequently recommended that patients with emphysema or other lung issues move to Boulder because of the exceptional air quality. The density of pine trees throughout the 24 million acres of National Forest and private land forests within Colorado produces a slightly greater concentration of pure oxygen in the air for those immediate areas, and literally creates a natural "Rocky Mountain high." The spiritual experience of "forest bathing" would not be officially labeled for another 50 years, even though its physiological, psychological, and emotional benefits were already tangibly real – reducing stress, anxiety, and diabetes. When singer John Denver discovered this phenomenon, he single-handedly raised the value of all real estate in Colorado by writing songs about his deep love for this area.

This attractive environment did not go unnoticed by the U.S. Government, spurring them to locate strategically several of their National Laboratories in the Boulder area. The National Bureau of Standards houses the nuclear clock that establishes the correct time for the entire world. The Nat'l Center for Atmospheric Research (NCAR) leads the way in global weather forecasting and studies in climate change. The Nat'l Oceanic and Atmospheric Administration (NOAA) focuses on climate, weather, and oceans. And just down the road are the Nat'l Renewable Energy Laboratory (NREL) and the Nat'l Earthquake Center. Another lab facility worthy of mention was Rocky Flats, which was a large but controversial employer in Boulder County for many years because it produced nuclear bomb triggers for the Department of Energy.

Boulder was in its infancy in having a profound influence on the culture of an entire nation. Some would say it was merely coincidence. Some would say it was the compelling beauty of its geographical location which drew adventurers, intelligentsia, and entrepreneurs into its midst. Others would say it was one of Planet Earth's Chakras, or energy centers, that serve as a link between the physical and spiritual worlds. Whatever the source, Boulder would have an inordinate role in the shifting culture that was coming to America.

The University of Colorado is also located in Boulder, founded in 1876, and renowned as a comprehensive research campus. Today it is home to more than 32,000 under-grad and graduate students, and has received international recognition for its excellence in Aerospace, Engineering, Physics, and Business. Twelve Nobel Laureates, nine MacArthur Fellows, and eighteen astronauts have called the CU campus their home.

In the early 60's this idyllic community generated a strong and steady economy for its 30,000 Boulder residents. IBM – the largest technology company in the world at that time, and the most dominant single listing on the Dow Jones Industrial Average – opened its newest Division in the northeastern outskirts of Boulder in 1964, and instantly brought more than 1000 new jobs into the County. New housing subdivisions sprang up in a matter of weeks and, as a result, the schools, restaurants, and churches were bursting.

Outdoor recreation was abundant: hiking, mountain picnics or camping, biking, the rapid rise of snow skiing, white water rafting, hunting and fishing, tennis, and golf, which – because of the unusually dry air and fast-melting snow – could be enjoyed during some portion of every month in the year.

Like most mid-western cities in the Sixties, Boulder was a "dry" town, meaning no liquor was served or sold anywhere on Sundays. Children's Little League games were not allowed on Sundays either. Instead, it was assumed that families went to a church on Sunday mornings, or at least claimed a specific church as their regular place of worship. Drugs were almost non-existent, and considered to be limited to the skid row district of downtown Denver.

Every winter, Boulder – like any city near the Rocky Mountains – experienced an occasional weather phenomenon known as "Chinook winds." These winds announce an abrupt and extreme change in the weather. Temperatures might shift up or down by 50 degrees within an hour, or 75 degrees within 24 hours. The greater the approaching temperature change, the greater the velocity of the wind. With the arrival of a new major weather system, Chinook wind gusts often reach 90 to 130 mph, and leave minor destruction in its path.

The years following WWII had been such a comfortable and neighborly time. No one in America could possibly have been prepared for the "Chinook winds" of cultural change that were about to sweep the country – and particularly Boulder – beginning in 1965.

This arrival of extreme and abrupt social upheaval was the "perfect storm" brought about by three clashing factors that swept over the entire United States simultaneously. If it is true that we can learn from history, we need to take a careful and reflective look at each of those three contributing elements, and learn from them.

In order to understand fully the first of those three components, it is necessary to go all the way back to 1945. World War II – known as the "Great War" – was finally over, and the victorious Allied Forces were able to return home. Freedom had defeated fascism on a global scale. America was jubilant. Millions of men in uniform returned to the U.S. to a heroes' welcome. These soldiers saw a flurry of parades, parties, and celebrations. They were proud, and rightly so. They were tired, and deservedly so. And as much as anything else, they were horny, and understandably so.

Moral standards of the time generally frowned on recreational sex for single men or women. Illegitimate pregnancy carried deep personal guilt and severe shame. And any idea of couples "living together" was socially unacceptable. So these healthy young men were highly motivated to get married as soon as possible. As a result, the average age for a woman of that era to get married was 21, and the vast majority of women were married by the age of 24. (Women could get married without parental consent at the age of 18, but men had to have a parent's signature on a Marriage Certificate until they reached the age of 21.) And the natural consequence of that surge in marriages was a pronounced increase in the American birth rate. Over the next 15 years there was a literal explosion in the number of babies being produced within the U.S. Once that trend was recognized, it was thereafter referred to as the "Baby Boomer Generation." By 1965 more than one-third of the U.S. population was under the age of 18. And by 1967 the number of college students had tripled from just 12 years earlier.

The unprecedented "age wave" demographic from this segment of history has continued to dominate our country ever since. Today, as these Boomers enter retirement age by tens of thousands every day, it is the driving reason that no existing model for most company pensions or our nation's Social Security system can survive under their current parameters. Currently there are three times as many adults over the age of 65 in the U.S., compared to the number of teenagers. Thanks to extended life expectancy for those Baby Boomers, within 12 years that ratio will explode to 6 : 1 from 3 : 1.

It was during the 1960's that the young men and women of this new Boomer Generation reached their critical teenage and college years, with a growing sense of self-determination. As this avalanche of humanity was developing a new independence, they were away from home and parents for the first time, and they were looking for fun or purpose as they began to consider themselves young adults. It became an opportunity to make collective demands for whatever they wanted.

This vast surge of young manpower – both men and women – was ready and waiting to follow any and all persuasive voices that offered self-discovery and uniqueness. Because of sheer volume, the usual experience of rebelling against one's parents easily transferred into a wide-spread student rebellion against authority of any kind. An unwritten rule of the day was "Don't trust anyone over 30." The second most popular bumper sticker in the mid and late 60's succinctly captured that mindset by saying, "QUESTION AUTHORITY." It was this young demographic explosion that served as the first of the three colliding components in this "perfect storm" of cultural upheaval. They were the most educated and affluent generation in American history. Their mantra for this new life-style of rebellious independence and freedom became "Sex, Drugs, and Rock & Roll." That was the guiding world-view for most young adults. A hormone-driven lifestyle of sybaritic excess became the norm. And it was this rebellious sea of human energy that quickly found its role as the driving engine for a national shift in attitudes.

The second contributing factor to this "perfect storm" crashing on our society during the '65 - '75 time-window was the Viet Nam War. While the Defense Department tried to call this a "military action" instead of a declared war, public debate became increasingly vitriolic as the body count mounted, and more and more families had to claim their son's remains in an enclosed body bag instead of a celebratory parade. It was the first time in our nation's history that soldiers returning from a war would choose to organize in collective groups to defy their superior officers or the entire Defense Department by openly stating that the war was not only a mistake but a national disaster.

In the aftermath of World War II, both our government and our Defense Department were revered with the highest of respect. But the early seeds of an underlying sense of skepticism or questioning of our government had actually begun to sprout in the early '60's. In 1960, for example, fighter pilot Gary Powers had been shot down while secretly flying a military spy plane over Russian airspace. At first the Defense Department blatantly lied about the incident, claiming it was a weather research plane that had just gone off course. They even re-painted an identical spy plane with a fake logo and colors to try to convince the world of their charade. But when the Soviet Union released pictures of Powers after he had been captured alive, as well as pictures of the wreckage of the plane itself, the gig was up. International relations took a giant step backwards, the Cold War intensified, and Americans reluctantly began to realize that their government was willing to say or print something that was not the truth if the government felt it was justified.

It was discovered that the CIA had secretly funded government coups in Africa, as well as certain student groups on University campuses. Americans began to have a twinge of caution. That growing mindset of doubting the U.S. government's storyline took another giant leap in late 1963 following the assassination of President John F. Kennedy. Although government officials tried, they soon learned they could no longer fully control information. Too many uncertainties were left hanging. Too many conspiracy theories began to gain traction. The manufactured "spin" coming out of Washington, D.C. had several logical gaps or conflicts of interest, and an ever-growing segment of the population did not want to accept blindly such sterilized claims or "managed news" that might be hiding the real truth or something even more sinister.

With such hints of suspicion growing around the Kennedy scenario, it became an easy carry-over transition in 1964 and 1965 to think twice when the government tried to put a positive slant on our national purpose in the Viet Nam conflict -- particularly when it might require young men to put on a uniform and stand in harm's way in spite of the fact that there was no deep public conviction that this was in fact a necessary military action. Why risk so many lives when our purpose was unclear? It became the perfect issue for almost all young Americans to oppose categorically. The #1 bumper sticker for the decade was displayed on cars, notebook covers, dormitory walls or any visible surface, which carried only one word: "PEACE."

Speaking out against the war individually was the prerogative of any free citizen. But the public protesting of the war functioned as a new collective identity for young adults. Opposing the establishment, pursuing a noble cause, seeking peace, and experiencing the exhilaration of freedom by expressing their own independence was a perfect recipe to catalyze this age segment, regardless of their economic stature or the color of their skin.

Because of the growing opposition to this war, there was comparatively less "pride in serving" in the military as there had been in Korea or WWII just a few years earlier. In the 1940's the deep convictions of patriotism and "doing what was right" had motivated hundreds of thousands of young men to volunteer for the army – even if they had to lie – in order to GET INTO military service for our country. Conversely, 25 years later the lacking clarity of purpose in the Viet Nam conflict caused young men to find very creative ways – even if they had to lie – to AVOID military service if at all possible.

By the late '60's television Journalism was being used for the first time as the link to bring the pain, ugliness and atrocities of war from the tropical jungle directly into American living rooms every evening with the Network News. Families were exposed to real human bloodshed that had previously been limited to the sterilized fantasy of television Westerns. The presumptive glamour of a military uniform was no longer a given. War was awful, and this one proved to be one of the greatest scars in our nation's proud history. Ultimately, 58,209 US lives were lost, an additional 153,303 were wounded, and another 1,643 were missing in action (MIA) before the Pentagon and our Commander-in-Chief finally admitted defeat and brought our remaining troops home in humiliation and disgrace. An additional statistic which the Department of Defense tried to hide was that more than 20,000 US soldiers committed suicide AFTER they had returned home from Viet Nam. What a colossal tragedy of unspeakable proportions.

The third and final variable in this trilogy of cultural crises was the Civil Rights Movement. While the demands for equality would ultimately come from numerous minority ethnicities and special interest groups, the originating voice sprang from the African American community. Emancipation was no longer sufficient. African Americans insisted on true equality, the right to vote, the right to an education, the right to equal opportunity, and in its most basic objective, the very right to be treated as a fellow human being.

But two centuries of accumulated hatred and prejudice do not simply disappear overnight with a Presidential press conference or a Congressional vote. New heroes and villains were created as those conflicting attitudes devolved into physical confrontation. And television once again became the unbiased vehicle for informing Americans in every niche of society about the true inhumanity that could surface within our own country's borders. This issue unveiled the unpleasant fact that actual "change" on any national scale might necessarily be both slow and painful.

There were several charismatic personalities who quickly rose to positions of great influence for this cause. Militant activists such as Malcomb X garnered a following of those that were willing to use violence if necessary to have their message heard. Martin Luther King, Jr., on the other hand, chose a passive approach in seeking to attain the same goals. Ironically, these civil rights leaders and the anti-war activists pursued very different objectives, but actually learned from each other how to optimize their local and national impact. Organized marches, mass sit-ins, selective boycotts, spontaneous public rallies, seizure and occupation of government or campus buildings, and even bombings of strategic buildings became the common tools for demanding change in our country's thinking and way of life. This emerging new wave of young Americans became driven to help accomplish those compelling goals of ending the war and ending racial inequality.

So it was that these three powerful factors intersected during this eleven-year period of 1965 - 1975, colliding with explosive and historic ramifications. And through it all, the city of Boulder had an unexpected and disproportionate connection with much of the drama and upheaval that was about to take place.

In one way or another, two young men were continually at the heart of all that happened in Boulder County during this timeframe of 1965 to 1975. There could hardly be a greater contrast in two individuals that called the Boulder area their home. In fact, Mark and Tom had only two things in common – they both loved playing pool, and – unfortunately – they both had very low lottery numbers for the military draft. Other than that, they appeared to be virtual opposites.

Mark grew up in a family that was dirt poor. In fact, every family that he knew was poor. They lived a few miles up Boulder Canyon, in the foothills of the Rocky Mountains, closer to Nederland than to Boulder, because his folks could not afford to live within the city limits of Boulder. Many of the men in that mountainous area were unemployed miners, fiercely independent, and strong as nails. If you looked up "Colorado redneck" in the dictionary, it would likely have their picture next to it.

College education was never a consideration for Mark. Every young man that he knew started working part-time by the age of 12 out of necessity. And once they finished high school, they were expected to choose a trade and learn a life-long skill that could provide a modest income for one's survival.

Kids in Mark's world learned to drive a car long before they could legally get a driver's license. Because of his savings from part-time jobs, Mark bought an old used car the day he turned 16. And like the rest of his friends, he had to learn to nurse that car along mechanically if he wanted transportation anywhere. Particular models of cars did not matter in Nederland, as long as it functioned well enough as "wheels" to get him where he needed to go.

Like many mountain towns, Nederland was a small community that looked like it had been forgotten in time. The town had only one grocery store and one gas station for its local patrons, but it had six bars. The men in and around the town spent much of their spare time drinking at one of those bars, or drinking at home. Fistfights were frequent. Often times one had to be willing to fight to get into a bar, and then be willing to fight to stay there. Family discipline was predictably rigid and harsh. The rustic town's only claim to fame was a notorious woman named Goldy Cameron, who had traveled with Bill Hickock's *Wild West Show*, and was the only woman in American history ever to get married in New York's Madison Square Garden while on horseback.

Frequently on cold winter days the public schools of Nederland would allow the boys and girls to bring real guns with live ammunition to school, and store those guns in their lockers. Gym class would remain indoors on those frigid days, and all the kids participated in organized target shooting competitions, firing their guns at hand-drawn bulls-eye targets that were taped to the solid cement wall in one corner of the gym. That skill of accuracy with a gun was considered worthwhile, and helped young students to learn to successfully hunt an assortment of wildlife that roamed the foothills around Boulder in order that these kids might help put meat on the family dinner table. It could be deer, elk, grouse, duck, wild turkey, rabbit, and even squirrel – if you got hungry enough. Students could actually get one or two days of excused absences in the fall if their parents said they needed to go hunting together. And few kids ever bothered to get a valid hunting license. Harvesting wild game in this manner was just a necessity of life.

It was a rough life for these youngsters. They often had to "invent" toys to occupy their time fully. While in their early teens during two successive summers, Mark and his friends entertained themselves by playing with TNT that they had found left over from a construction site for a new ski area. Stealing a few cigarettes or a can of beer from one of their parents was also a common practice.

Mark's folks both worked in hourly jobs in order to make ends meet. His father was not hesitant to get into a fight if he felt like it. The axiom of "actions speaking louder than words" was the parental role model that taught Mark to be a determined survivor, a hard worker, and fiercely loyal to those he considered his friends. There was little or no expression of love in the home – only the faithful commitment of each member of the family to do their respective part to help the family as a whole to survive.

As a student, Mark never had much time for recreational sports. By the time he reached Junior High, he was expected to get a part-time job during the summer months to help pay for his limited wardrobe, and to save $140 for a used car as soon as he got his driver's license. Mark's dreams for his future were very basic and straight-forward. Someday he would have his own cabin in the foothills near Boulder, a nice car, and a nice gun. Life was not complex.

Six months following High School graduation, Mark and his two best friends enlisted in the Army. They finished boot camp, spent their tour of duty in Viet Nam, and two of the three men quietly returned home. It just seemed matter-of-fact, that there was no other choice. There was no room for complaining. Just deal with the hard challenges of life, and get through it.

To get a change of scenery, Mark and his friends enjoyed going into Boulder – hitchhiking the few miles if necessary – often for a football game at the University of Colorado, or just to play pool at one of the two pool halls in town. The Golden Cue was located "on the hill" – a nickname for the small area of the city which housed a cluster of retail shops, cheap restaurants, a dry cleaners & laundry-mat, as well as a worn down movie theater, all within a three-block stretch adjacent to the University campus, and catering to the 20,000 students across the street. The Golden Cue had over 20 pool tables, and at its peak was open 24 hours a day. Patrons often brought in their own food and drinks, and it was a great social scene. Occasionally a few local businessmen would wander in to play pool, but it was almost exclusively a student hotspot. Along with a few food or beer establishments located nearby, it was one of the busiest social gathering spots in town for students.

Keller's Billiards was the other pool hall, located in old downtown Boulder. The creaking wood floors and 16-foot high ceilings were remnants of one of the oldest buildings in town. Built in 1908, it had at one time been the most elegant saloon the local miners and ranchers had ever seen. But now it was home to only four pool tables and one snooker table, with insufficient ventilation to handle the dank smoke that always hovered in the room. Only a few university students frequented this establishment because it was not located near the campus. Rather, this was the daily gathering place for many of the blue-collar workers of Boulder. There was a random collection of postmen, tradesmen, realtors or insurance salesmen that had no appointments that day, and maybe a policeman or two. It always had a feel and look of Floyd's Barbershop from Mayberry in *"The Andy Griffith Show."*

Mark felt comfortable at either pool hall in town, and was basically an "8-Ball" kind of a guy. That was the simplest game of pool for those that just wanted a basic game accompanied by the social interaction. The full pool table rack consists of balls numbered sequentially from one to fifteen. One person had the "solids" (numbers 1 through 7), the opponent had the "stripes" (numbers 9 through 15), and once a player had pocketed all of their assigned balls, in any random order, they must then sink the #8 ball to win. "9-Ball" was a faster game, required a little more skill, and was popular for those that wanted to play pool for money. The object was to sink the balls in sequence from 1 to 9, and there were points and or money just on the #5 and the #9 ball respectively. But the game which required the most skill and patience was "straight call", and required the shooter to "call" or declare before each shot exactly which ball was going into which pocket. The shooter received one point for each successfully completed shot, and his turn would continue until he missed his called shot. Games were usually played to 50 points. Anywhere from $1 to $20 might typically change hands in the course of playing pool for a couple of hours. Jerry learned to be very, very cautious when money was on the line because he had little cash to spare.

Tom, on the other hand, was a stark contrast to Mark in almost every way. He was certainly a more skilled pool player, and preferred playing 9-Ball or Straight Call, as long as there was the suspense of a little money on the game. Tom actually didn't need the money, but loved the adrenalin rush from the action.

Unlike Mark, Tom's family had more money than most people in town. His father was an Asian physicist, and had earned a Ph.D in Chemistry. He consulted with two research firms in Boulder, but also traveled frequently to give lectures in his field of expertise. Consumed with his work, he abdicated most of the family and parenting responsibilities to his wife. Tom's mother was exceptionally brilliant in her own right. She had earned a Master's Degree in Economics while living in Hawaii, and could have had an excellent paying job herself. But like most housewives, she chose to stay at home to cook, sew, and care for her children. Rarely could she be seen without a cigarette in her hand. And at least once or twice a day she would take a break from her housework to call the local stock brokerage firm, Boettcher & Company. She supplemented the family's income nicely by managing her investment portfolio in this way without ever needing to leave the confines of her smoke-filled home.

As a youngster it was clear that Tom had inherited more than his share of those smart genes. Although he went by "Tommy" through grade school and middle school, his I.Q. made him appear to be a young man. Even in grade school his teachers recognized that he was intellectually advanced for his age, and personally driven – not just to succeed – but to excel, so that he might gain his due respect and admiration from others. His parents were more than generous in giving him ample spending money for clothes, entertainment, skiing, and a new car every year once he had turned 16. Unlike Mark or most other Jr. High and High School students, he really did not need a job in order to have money in his pocket.

Tom greatly admired his older brother, and because that brother had been an exceptional tennis player, Tom followed in those steps as well. He earned his "athletic letter" on the Boulder High School tennis team, which finished 2nd in the Colorado State tournament two years in a row. This provided an enormous boost to his sense of identity and social acceptance. He also won awards in Junior Achievement because of his entrepreneurial creativity. His mental acuity was even sharper than his athleticism.

Even in Junior High and High School, Tom had become a news hound. As his grasp of world events grew, he consumed random facts and trends whenever possible, convinced that someday he was going to impact the world. He miraculously managed to avoid the military draft, but rather than becoming distracted with the various Viet Nam War protests shouldered by his classmates and peers on campus, he was always focused on various risk-taking business ideas that might someday generate a windfall income.

Although Mark and Tom were both residents of Boulder County, they lived and circulated in entirely different worlds. Mark was comfortable with the status quo, content with simple things, and resistant to change. Tom was driven by creativity, discontent with the status quo, and always pursuing the newest ideas for the sake of change. There were only three times when their lives happened to cross paths, and those were always at a pool hall. Yet between the two of them, these young men tasted everything – good or bad, legal or illegal – that Boulder would have to offer.

In the midst of the tranquil lifestyle for middle-America, there was one fear shared by everyone. To all Americans, Russia represented the "evil empire", and aggressively pushed the United States into a Cold War. That meant no actual troops on the ground. No guns being fired. But there was constant blustering and posturing between the two super-powers in their race toward military superiority.

Lenin and Stalin had both been seen as inhumane despots willing to do unspeakable things to their own citizens to insure their position of power. Peasants were murdered en masse, or condemned to a meaningless existence in the wasteland of Siberia.

The conclusion of WWII only heightened America's disdain for the communist mindset, and the contrast in cultures could not have been more apparent. As Allied troops and Soviet troops merged near Berlin to put a final stake into the heart of Hitler's army, American troops immediately began offering humanitarian aid to the starving citizens of Germany. Approaching from the west, Allied planes airlifted food and medical supplies into villages that had been shooting at American soldiers just a few days earlier.

The USSR's attitude was slightly different. Once a final peace was declared, it took a few days for a new German government to be defined and a system of order established. In that brief interim, Soviet generals announced to all their troops that there was a "72-hour window of NO LAW." They encouraged their men to "punish" the German people in any way they chose as an act of retaliation for their wrong choice in fighting the Soviets. Gang-rape of any German woman of any age was not only tolerated but encouraged. Looting of any remaining alcohol in the taverns. Pocketing any valuables that might be found in homes or churches. It was three days of utter mayhem. These Soviets were again perceived to be nothing more than cruel animals hidden under a military uniform.

In the years that followed, communism continued to suck every resource out of East Berlin and East Germany, sending anything of value back to their homeland. As West Berlin and West Germany began to rebuild and flourish once again, the East remained under a sterile cloud of gray and gloom. The living consequences of freedom versus communism were never more apparent.

On the world stage, the Soviets had become the "rabid dog", and world domination was their stated objective. Premier Nikita Khrushchev boldly declared to U.S. diplomats, "History is on our side. We will bury you." So when he chose to send missiles into Cuba, Americans held their breath in a moment of terror. Could this evil enemy be arming a communist dictator just 90 miles from our shore? Thankfully President Kennedy called their bluff, and those missiles returned to Russia.

But the universal fear and distrust of Russia made the impending premise of a Viet Nam takeover believable. If Russian-backed troops could get a foothold anywhere else in the world, there could be a "domino" effect, as one neighboring country after another would fall under communist control. Consequently, American anxiety was the motivating factor in so many decisions. People built bomb-shelters in their back yards. Elementary school children routinely did safety drills in the event of a nuclear bomb, which simply meant curling up in a ball under one's school desk.

Even the U.S. highway department was a beneficiary from this in-bred fear. In the late '50's a vast spider-web of Interstate Highways was proposed to the federal government. Streamlining our nation's transportation routes in this way had many apparent benefits. But the costs were astronomical. Many Senators and Congressmen were skeptical, thinking that such huge expenditures could be more wisely used elsewhere; until a new variable was added. The Interstate Highway proposal engineers were instructed to adjust their design of this national network so that within every ten miles of Interstate Highway, at least one mile of that segment had to be so flat and so straight that it could be used as an emergency landing strip for military supply planes. In this way, if there was a Russian invasion into our country, the U.S. Army could set up temporary bases in any state within a matter of a few hours. With that additional specification, the Interstate proposal passed by an overwhelming majority. Even Congress feared the Russians.

Music has always had a profound influence on its listeners. A few centuries ago, the philosopher Fletcher said, "Let me write the songs of a nation, and I care not who writes its laws." True to form, the music through the 50's and early 60's seemed to generate a blanketed sense of happiness with the listening audience. Pop love songs and folk ballads that talked of a new love, or a lost love, driving in a special car, surfing, or dancing with friends. Even if the song had a sad story, it still created happiness with an empathetic listener. AM radio stations that concentrated on music always had a "Top 40", and played a daily countdown of the most requested songs. Young people collected "45 rpm" records of their favorite songs at a cost of thirty to forty cents per single. Entire albums at 33 1/3 rpm were usually three dollars or less.

The cultural changes which swept the country during the mid-60's were subtle at first. One of the earliest and most unusual sources of this shift actually came from music originating outside the US, in what was soon called the "British Invasion". Several new music groups from England were finding great success with their albums, such as *The Dave Clark Five*", "*The Kinks*", "*The Rolling Stones*", "*Chad & Jeremy*", and "*The Animals.*" But none could compare in popularity and impact to a group called "*The Beatles.*" John, Paul, George, and Ringo became an unprecedented rage.

Their meteoric rise in influence actually came from a serendipitous component. Ed Sullivan hosted the most popular weekly Variety Show on U.S. television at the time, and a majority of all TV viewers tuned in to his hour-long program every Sunday evening. Mr. Sullivan happened to be connecting on a flight through London's Heathrow Airport in late 1963, and had noticed several hundred teen-aged girls next to the tarmac, screaming with excitement as they watched another plane taxi up to the adjacent gangway.

As four young men exited that plane, the frenzy only became louder. It was the Beatles, as they returned to London from a short gig in West Germany. Although Mr. Sullivan had never heard of this British band, he was captivated by the energy of those young female fans. On a whim, he told his personal assistant to see if they could book that quartet – whoever they were – on his show.

That decision proved to be nothing short of legendary, and just a few weeks later it happened. The viewing audience for the Sullivan show on that Sunday evening, Feb. 9, 1964, shattered all records of any TV show in history up to that point. Policemen across the country said that there was no crime in the nation for a two-hour period that night because everyone stopped everything they were doing to watch this new band from England.

Americans of all ages became familiar with the Beatles in just 10 minutes. Their clothes (suits & ties) were cut slightly different, their shoes had a slightly higher heel (and became known as "Beatle Boots"), but the most significant distinctive was their hair. Most young American men hardly had hair long enough to comb. Burr cuts, Butch cuts, Buzz cuts. And if there was any hair long enough to comb, young men often used a greasy hair wax to hold it stiffly in place. Now these Liverpool rock-and-rollers were shocking the country with hair that was long enough to hang down to their eye-brows, to hang over their ears, and also over their shirt collars in the back. And no hair wax was used – it was clean, and flowing hair.

Following the Beatle's historic evening on the Ed Sullivan Show, men's hair instantly became a new fashion conversation point, particularly for young students. And as soon as that "Beatle look" became common-place, the Beatles themselves then let their hair grow even longer, to shoulder length. For American men the chosen style or length of their hair became a new personal statement of rebellion and individualism.

The epitome of this sudden fad was captured by New York's Broadway community, who capitalized on this raging trend by producing the rock musical 'HAIR' in late 1967. The underlying philosophy of cultural contrarianism was celebrated by the image of men sporting long hair as a visible statement of opposition to any and all norms of American society. Creative, daring, and going against tradition, this Broadway production exemplified the youth's aggressive attitude of rebellion against the Establishment, incorporating the anti-war movement, experimentation with drugs, and the sexual revolution. Some of the lyrics to the theme song were:

"*Hair, hair, hair, hair*
Flow it, show it, long as God can grow it,
My hair.
Give me hair, down to there,
Shoulder length or longer , , ,
Let it fly in the breeze, get caught in the trees,
Give a home to the fleas in my hair
A hive for the bees, a nest for the birds
There ain't no words for the beauty, the splendor, the wonder of my
Hair, hair, hair, hair . . ."

Yes, a man's hair suddenly mattered. But that exterior look of hair length was just the visible tip of the iceberg. The much greater rebellion of the late 1960's was that of the hidden changing attitudes of the heart. Change at an unprecedented rate was about to unfold.

In the mid-1960's the politicians of Washington, D.C. innocently added another wild card into the early mix of this social and cultural upheaval. The Great Society under President Lyndon Johnson deemed that we needed a national government policy to assist men and women who were mentally challenged.

No one would dispute the fact that something different needed to be done. Novels and movies such as *"One Flew Over the Cuckoo's Nest"* – as well as some investigative reporting – revealed a dark world of America's institutionalized care of the mentally ill. Electric shock treatments were common. Justified experimentation with drugs that had not been fully tested or approved. Sexual molestations. Even surgical exploration. And worst of all, the unthinkable practice of medical experiments for unrelated kinds of research without the patient's knowledge or consent. As one example, African American men were intentionally given syphilis so that doctors might study the effects or results of different medications not yet on the market. The CIA also developed a secret program called Project MKUltra, injecting patients with dangerous levels of LSD, Metrazol, or other drugs.

Yes, some things certainly needed to be done differently. But the pendulum swung too far. The legislation that was passed by Congress focused on "de-institutionalization", not "treatment." As a result, thousands of mentally ill men and women were simply released and put out onto the street. Clinics could not hold them for more than 48 hours. Sadly, many of these patients with severe mental disorders had nowhere else to go.

The logical outcome was a spike in the number of homeless people living under bridges, in city parks, or behind industrial buildings. Petty crimes also rose abruptly, as these men and women were frequently charged with trespassing, theft, and harassment. In their drive for survival, they searched for any welcoming accommodations, and unexpectedly found at least two new sources.

First was a national migration pattern that followed the weather from one sanctuary city to another while crossing the entire U.S. Boulder happened to be on that list. Groups of these people began to pass through Colorado for a month or so during every spring and summer, when the weather was at its best, knowing that the police would be more tolerant than other places. Most of these mental patients moved by hitchhiking or jumping a ride on a freight train. A few were able to reconfigure an old school bus or VW van as a mobile residence. In doing so they were able to eke out a meager mode of existence.

The second "welcome mat" for these transients was with the new communities of "flower children." Offering unconditional love and peace, the communal living of hippies provided a practical haven where they would not be hassled. It became an easy choice to join a way of life that had no normal constraints.

Although government agencies thought they were solving a mounting social problem in this way, they inadvertently enlarged another. The volatility and vulnerability of this group of people added fuel to the growing flame of dissent against traditional authority.

Television had not yet fully discovered the power and influence it was capable of wielding over the cultural fabric of our country. Most TV sets projected only in black & white, because the majority of broadcast programming did not even film in color until 1965. A number of these early successful shows were simply popular radio talk shows or radio game shows now being placed in front of a single camera.

A common genre for the three networks was situation comedies involving All-American families. Ozzie & Harriet, Father Knows Best, Dick Van Dyke, and Andy Griffith were dominant in their weekly time slots. The television studios were well ahead of the cultural curve by giving a few women their own shows as well, including Ann Southern, Eve Arden, Marlo Thomas, and – at the top of the ratings chart – Lucille Ball.

Program content was always wholesome and uplifting. No crude language. No inappropriate sexual innuendos of any kind. Social drinking was not a common backdrop to those shows, but cigarette and cigar smoking was a normal part of any and all television families. Any scenes that might take place in a bedroom would always show that married couples slept in twin beds, generously spaced at least six to eight feet apart.

Variety shows became the second most popular format for evening viewing. Circus acts, animal tricks, singers, dancers, comedians, and a sprinkling of inane sketches would fill the hour. Numerous stars were given a chance to host such a program, but the ratings showed that it was Jackie Gleason, Dean Martin, and Red Skelton who were always fighting for second place, pursuing the "King of Variety Shows" in the person of Ed Sullivan. His show, for example, consistently maintained its #1 status before and after having the Beatles make their American debut on his stage.

Network news was carried every evening, and was dominated by two options. Chet Huntley and David Brinkley co-anchored one news desk, and Walter Cronkite played solo on the other. There was no such thing as "news and commentary." No such thing as entire networks devoted to a political bias. No personal opinions from reporters. No political satire or subtly slanted editorials. No pundits trying to simultaneously talk over each other. No reporters trying to "create a news story" to further their own name-recognition. No rants from the Left or the Right. Just solid news reporting. There was an unwritten ethical standard which held that politicians and news reporters would carry a mutual respect for each other.

It was these television news cameras that began to capture a new trend of such things as daily scenes of rebelling university students, live action from reporters embedded in the war in Viet Nam, or Civil Rights protests across the U.S. Being live and on site, these news cameras allowed the American public to begin to simultaneously "experience" anything of importance that was happening around the country and even around the world. Thus it was television news coverage that began to influence or deepen private opinions, and accelerated the social and political polarization that was beginning to surface. Television itself was on the verge of some dramatic changes, just like the rest of the country.

Mark found his "manhood" for the first time during his junior year of high school. He took Karen to the Holiday Drive-In Theatre, which was a favorite place for young Boulder couples to fog up the car windows. Mark wasn't sure where the evening was going until she suggested they watch the remainder of the movie from the comfort of the back seat of his '55 Chevy.

Having sex in the back seat of a car was anything but comfortable. Determination had to overcome a great deal of awkwardness. But the deed was accomplished, and Mark would forever remember the movie *"In the Heat of the Night"* as historic in his life, even though he only saw a few portions of it.

Tom, on the other hand, did not have his first sexual experience until his sophomore year at the University of Colorado. By his high school graduation he determined that girls might take him more seriously if he went by "Tom" instead of "Tommy." Although he had many casual female friends throughout high school, he had very few actual dates. But on that particular wintry night he stopped by Tulagi's, a favorite campus hangout bar that served only 3.2 beer and burgers. In fact, Tulagi's proudly boasted that it had broken the national record for the number of beers sold in one day at any U.S. establishment.

As he was about to leave, Tom noticed Wendy, a good friend and classmate from Boulder High School days. After some friendly conversation, they shared one last beer before paying the tab and getting their ski jackets. As they stood to leave, Tom took a chance. "I've got a couple of joints in my car," he whispered, "if that sounds of interest to you."

Wendy smiled, thought for a moment, and replied, "Better yet, my roommate is gone this week. So let's smoke them at my apartment."

Once in her apartment, Wendy put on a couple of Bob Dylan albums as background to their conversation. After patiently finishing both joints while reclining on Wendy's giant beanbag chairs, Tom thought it might be time to leave. Instead, much to his astonishment, she sat up and began to disrobe. Tom had two memories cemented in his mind from that evening. First, sex was much easier than he had always imagined. And second – unfortunately – it was over much more quickly than he had always imagined.

When that semester ended four months later, Wendy's roommate moved out and Tom moved in.

On a national scale the 1950's and early '60's had been a carefree time for most Americans. Society was guided by a clear sense of traditional morality, respect for religion, and an adherence to the rule of law. Our country was not at war, and industry was booming. The United States enjoyed a large and bustling Middle Class, and a particularly strong agricultural sector. Men chose a career path and stayed with it, often working for the same company their entire adult life. Companies in return provided a strong degree of loyalty to their employees. IBM, for example, proudly stated that they would never lay off an employee, and promised to re-train any person for another position within the company if their previous job became unnecessary.

Most large corporations offered a full pension as part of their employee benefits. If a person worked for their company for 30 or more years, upon reaching the age of 55 they could retire with 100% salary for the rest of their life. Average age expectancy for a healthy male at that time was 68. Job security was extremely high because corporate mergers or acquisitions were virtually non-existent.

Norman Rockwell captured the soul of our country as he painted diverse human portraits of national pride for the covers of 'Life Magazine.' Two-parent families seated at the dinner table with their heads bowed in prayer before eating. Leather-skinned farmers with tanned, wrinkled faces and gnarled fingers that reflected a lifetime of hard work in the cornfields. Young boys and girls at play outside, knowing it was safe to ride all over town on their Schwinn bicycles. At least one steepled church anchored every community scene. Those Rockwell paintings encompassed the essence of a nation of people who for the most part were content and thriving.

The vast majority of women did not choose to – or need to – work outside of the home. Being a housewife was a noble calling. A Fuller-Brush salesman could make a good living for his family because most ladies were at home every day as he made his door-to-door sales calls.

America – in general – was happy and carefree. Everyone tended to feel safe from everything except the evil Soviet Union. People trusted each other and the companies they worked for with a somewhat blind and blissful naivete. There was a quiet sense of national pride that permeated the hearts of men and women, convinced that America was truly great because its people were truly good.

Health concerns were virtually a non-issue. A majority of adults smoked cigarettes, and this habit was acceptable in any public restaurant or commercial airline flight. Cigarette ads flooded both TV and print media. Smokers were told by the manufacturers that smoking was good for one's health. Any correlation with lung cancer was remote. Even professional athletes were frequently smoking while on the side-lines or during a half-time break of their particular sport.

Citizens seemed to be oblivious to the dangers that threatened their health or their life. Some gas station attendants would unknowingly fill up a car's gas tank while they held a lit cigarette in the other hand. Pesticides and insect spray were used in abundance, not only on agricultural crops, but also up and down a city's residential streets during the summer months to curb the mosquito and fly populations. Children would frolic in the spray as they followed the municipal insecticide trucks through neighborhoods, splashing in the toxic mist as if it were a new game at the water park. Everyone assumed that all such things must be totally safe for people or they would never have been developed.

An early warning regarding dangerous pesticides was offered by scientist Rachel Carson, in her book, *"Silent Spring."* Her research documented how DDT and other chemicals were not only killing the targeted insects, but killing birds and other life forms in the process. For that reason she claimed these products should be called "biocides" instead of "pesticides." However, the public tended to ignore her warnings because chemical companies and the FDA were quick to denounce her claims, and instead assured users that their products were effective and safe. For more than ten years Americans gave a collective shrug and continued to use those products with little or no concern.

Anti-pollution or environmental awareness was also non-existent. There was no such thing as "unleaded gasoline." There was no industry for "fuel emissions testing." Every vehicle was belching exhaust fumes into what was perceived to be an infinite atmosphere. There was no weekly residential garbage pick-up. Almost every household burned their own garbage in a cement incinerator located in their back yard. The smoke generated in those incinerators was never perceived as a problem.

Construction companies incorporated asbestos as a primary material for building insulation. Their employees handled these asbestos materials and breathed in these fibers with no concern for any adverse effects. Mercury was also used as a bonding agent for floor surfaces in commercial structures. No connection was immediately made between the men on those work crews and the life-threatening health issues that began to occur.

Soda pop of any kind was an acceptable beverage for any meal. The only diet option was Tab, which enjoyed modest market success until it was later discovered that its sweetener ingredient caused cancer. Again, the public assumed it must be safe because it was on the grocery shelf. Most people exclusively drank whole milk, although 2% was becoming available in a few grocery stores.

Conservation or recycling of any resource was of no concern. While rationing of a few commodities had been necessary during World War II, now everything was perceived to be limitless in availability. Almost every car had an 8-cylinder engine. Those vehicles got 11 to 16 miles per gallon, but fuel consumption was irrelevant since gasoline was typically priced at 24 cents per gallon. And unleaded gasoline was non-existent until the early '70's. Seatbelts – without a shoulder strap – were factory installed in some of the newer cars, but few people bothered to use them. Even at highway speeds, young children typically played in the back seats without any restraints.

Ethnic slurs of all kinds were common. People rationalized with themselves that they could do so without any true prejudices as long as they picked equally on everyone. Genuine racism toward blacks was considered a regional issue relegated to the Southern States, even though every ethnic group tended to live in their own tight communities regardless of what area of the country they may be. Racial barriers might have fallen in Hollywood and in professional sports, but "Main Street America" was slow to follow. As an example, Chicago had very specific and exclusive neighborhoods designated for Blacks, Italians, Poles, Swedes, Germans, Chinese, Greeks, and the Irish respectively. Quiet ignorance typically held sway over any blatant hostility.

Residents in the mountain states know what a "Chinook wind" can be, bringing a sudden change in the weather. Within ten minutes the temperature can shift 30 degrees. Within 24 hours it can shift 75 degrees. This abrupt change in weather is invisible, unannounced, extreme, and often times destructive. Now a cultural Chinook was brewing in America, unlike anything the country had ever seen, and everything was about to change in sudden and dramatic fashion. Everything.

This small and "Eden-like" town of Boulder was about to play an inordinate and major role in the shifting culture of America. From the far Left would come the most radical voices in America, demanding the complete destruction of capitalism and its traditional thinking in order to make room for a new order. And from the far Right would come the most rigid voices for protecting the present, and resisting at all costs those persons or groups that promoted such changes. A collision was about to occur between these two polarized mindsets – the adventure of the "new world" versus the familiarity of the "old west."

Yes, a cultural storm was stirring, and dramatic change was coming . . .

22

Dr. Martin Luther King's "I Have a Dream" Speech

Early Beatles

Aerial view of Boulder, Colorado

Fans at a Beatle Concert

CHAPTER 2

"1965 – THE ONSET"

"Somethin' happenin' here, what it is ain't exactly clear,
there's a man with a gun over there,
tellin' me I got to beware.
He's sayin' "STOP, HEY, what's that sound?
Everyone look what's goin' round."

Buffalo Springfield

1965 actually began with a celebratory atmosphere. Lyndon Baines Johnson had abruptly "inherited" the White House 14 months earlier following the assassination of President John F. Kennedy. Now he was duly elected and inaugurated into office in January for his first full term as our President. Declaring America as the "Great Society", LBJ cast a vision of peace and prosperity for the country, seeking a unified war against poverty as our nation's highest priority. The government's philosophy in this period was intended to be the greatest force for progress in human history. His desire as President was to maintain a national mindset of hope and promise, seeking social climbing and economic growth for everyone. His façade of optimism, however, hid one of the two greatest deceptions of the 20th Century foisted on the American public by our government.

Just five months earlier, the destroyer ship USS Maddox had moved through the Gulf of Tonkin on a routine intelligence patrol. U.S. naval officers claimed they were fired upon in two separate incidents in the span of three days by three North Vietnamese torpedo boats. The Maddox returned fire, damaging all three torpedo boats. There were no U.S. casualties, nor was there any damage to the ship itself. (Forty years later, former Secretary of Defense Robert McNamara admitted that much of this reported incident was untrue. And in 1995 Vietnamese General Vo Nguyen Giap met with McNamara and told him "the alleged attack had been imaginary.")

These details were unimportant to President Johnson. Using the rationale that our ship had been fired upon first, this incident gave him the platform to ram through Congress the "Tonkin Resolution", a piece of legislation which granted the Commander-in-Chief the authority to assist any Southeast Asian country whose government might be jeopardized by the threat of "communist aggression."

Johnson wasted no time in mobilizing a military presence there. In March the U.S. Army established a new base of operation in South Viet Nam with 3500 troops. The Defense Department saw this Viet Nam presence as a necessary extension of our Cold War with Russia. Viet Nam, on the other hand, only saw the U.S. as another nation trying to colonize their country, just as the French had done decades earlier.

The confusion and conflict of purpose could not have been greater. American forces were convinced that U.S. military support was necessary to help a small country find its independence, and to prevent a potential domino effect of the entire region quickly falling under Communist control. Conversely, the Vietnamese saw this as a slippery slope toward slavery to the U.S. Such lack of clarity could only be destined for some kind of monumental failure.

During the next ten years the Viet Nam engagement would prove to be the greatest military embarrassment that our country had ever experienced. Prior to this, America had only been familiar with military success. As the national perception of our military presence in Viet Nam slowly disintegrated from "national savior" to "bully without a cause", Americans from both political parties slowly became more and more incensed. Thousands of lives were lost in the rice paddies of Viet Nam, billions of dollars were spent, and at home our country was torn apart by a multitude of protests and hostilities. All for an undeclared war that was secretly but knowingly predicated on false information. That shame should never be forgotten.

Life in Boulder was humming. The new IBM plant on the edge of town was spurring the local economy unlike anything since the gold rush days one hundred years earlier. Numerous other small businesses were springing up to try to service the enormous needs of such a corporate giant.

Astronaut Scott Carpenter returned home to Boulder for a local hero's welcome, and was given a confetti parade. As one of the original seven astronauts, he had been carefully selected to be the 2nd American to ride into space and orbit the earth, following on the coattails of John Glenn. The newest city park and municipal swimming pool were also named in his honor.

Boulder High School had just won the previous year's State Championship football game, and students, parents, and local fans alike were eagerly anticipating the potential opportunity to repeat that accomplishment in the coming school season. Athletes from any of the major sports were the studs at school, and willingly followed the team rules of no smoking, no drinking, no hair long enough to touch one's shirt collar, and no breaking curfew.

It seemed to be an idyllic time for the entire community.

But a sudden change began to appear in Boulder in the late spring and early summer of '65, like unexpected ripples on what had been a glassy-surfaced body of water. Strange looking young people began to show up in town. First it was on the edges of the University of Colorado campus. But soon these strangers were also at the main shopping mall or the city parks as well.

The oddest looking group called themselves "Hare Krishnas." Some with very long pony tails, some with heads completely shaved, but all with bizarre or foreign-looking clothes. Most were bare-footed or in sandals. They would dance for hours at a time on a street corner with only the accompaniment of a tambourine. And there were always a few that aggressively pan-handled for money from the curious onlookers that might be walking by.

Soon to follow was another group of new arrivals comprised of young men and women that just wanted to be known as "hippies." The men sported very long hair, bell-bottomed blue jeans, tie-dyed T-shirts, and generous displays of facial hair. The women might wear the same clothes combination, but more often wore very loose-fitting, ankle-length dresses.

Whatever the outfit, they were always braless. These hippies all enjoyed sitting on the CU campus lawn or any unused athletic field while they waived posters that said "MAKE LOVE – NOT WAR", or "PEACE."

Most of these young people were college drop-outs from prosperous middle-class families who had simply grown tired of the routine of their parents. One common thread shared by all of these transplanted Californians was a youthful idealism that centered on complete freedom of self-expression. That focus gave them a comfort level to freely experiment with relationships, drugs, and styles of music. It would later be known as the "age of selfishness", and an obsession with anything counter to existing culture.

The Mayor, City Council, and local Police force had to scramble to determine how to accommodate these new residents coming in by the hundreds. Boulder's city leaders had no idea that this was only the front wave of what would soon become a tsunami of young men and women relocating from California and around the country. Primarily moving from the Haight-Ashbury section of San Francisco, these new arrivals were initially motivated to make the necessary transition to Colorado because of their fear of the San Andreas Fault – a scientific discovery suggesting that a major portion of California could suddenly slide into the ocean if this massive land fault were to give way from a major earthquake.

Most of the local citizenry were tolerant but skeptical at first. It no longer seemed safe to let their young children play in the city parks unless at least one adult was accompanying them. In the mild weather these new "foreigners" were living under street bridges and overpasses. But when chillier temperatures arrived, they began sneaking into unoccupied houses or mountain cabins where they would stay until discovered by the owner and then evicted.

The general appearance of Boulder had noticeably shifted within a matter of weeks. But this was just the pre-cursor. Changes of much greater consequence were just around the corner. Young people's appearance was one thing. But attitudes, values, and morals were also about to be assaulted.

For the majority of Americans, the Civil Rights Movement was seen as a regional issue, relegated to the Southern States. Residents of Northern and Western states were content to be preoccupied with other social or economic factors because they had no real awareness of the deplorable conditions that remained for southern Blacks. More than 4,000 lynchings had taken place since slavery had officially ended. Segregated seating was required in any restaurant or city bus. In most southern cities Blacks were not allowed to vote, attend public schools, or swim in a pool with white people.

The North naively assumed that the "Emancipation Proclamation" of 100 years earlier was sufficient, that "Negro people" were FREE, and any residual issues were minor. That mindset began to change in the spring of 1965. National television had begun to reveal the inhumane treatment of African Americans in southern communities where that was considered "normal." Very brave men and women were leading the way in seeking civil rights and equality. In the national courts, Black attorneys argued that the culture of "separate but equal" guaranteed that the school systems were separate but NOT equal.

Malcomb X was one of the earliest and most charismatic voices in the Civil Rights arena. As an activist he spoke wherever he could on the unfair positioning of black people as sub-human. Dr. Martin Luther King echoed his call for change. However, where King continually pleaded for peaceful civil disobedience in their cause, Malcomb X openly endorsed violence if necessary to achieve progress. His message was "Sad people don't do anything. They just cry over their situation. But when people get ANGRY, they bring about change." Where King sought equality and racial integration, Malcomb X promoted black supremacy while seeking separation of white and black Americans.

His devotion to black pride drew him to support a young boxer named Cassius Clay. Clay had won the Gold Medal for boxing in the 1960 Olympics, and had recently won the Heavyweight Title from Sonny Liston in an amazing upset. Clay was good looking, articulate, brash, and secretly preparing to join the black segment of the Nation of Islam. Now Clay and Liston were scheduled for a rematch in May of this year. Malcolm X saw Clay as someone that could become another needed voice for his message of black supremacy.

Sonny Liston was a quiet brute that had served time in prison. In spite of his prestigious sports title as the heavyweight champion, he was anything but a role model. The boxing world knew that he was owned by organized crime. In the initial title match with Clay, his ring managers soon realized that Liston might be stronger physically, but was not nearly as athletic as his younger opponent. A couple of rounds into the fight, they put an illegal astringent on Liston's boxing gloves which made Clay's skin feel like it was burning, and made his eyes begin to swell shut. Clay almost had to forfeit the fight during the middle rounds, and repeatedly had to have his eyes washed out with a sponge in the short breaks between rounds. Clay recovered and won the fight and the new title from the champion.

The mob took a huge financial loss betting on Liston in that first title match. To re-coup their losses, they waited until the betting odds for the rematch were 7 to 1, and then "bet the farm" on the underdog opponent Clay. They instructed Liston to "take a dive" in the first round to make sure there was no mistake in the needed outcome. Thus, a phantom punch ended the fight less than two minutes after the opening bell. After that rematch bout, Liston slid into obscurity, and Clay – more than any other black athlete in history – became an icon for the mindset of black pride that Malcolm X was preaching.

For a time Malcomb X had also affiliated himself with the Nation of Islam, thinking that association could leverage his opportunity for greater influence. He coined the phrase "Black is Beautiful", which single-handedly raised the self-esteem of the black community nationally for the next decade. But he soon became disenchanted with the leadership of the Nation of Islam, and publicly repudiated them as hypocrites to the true cause that they preached. As an act of retaliation, three members of the Nation of Islam assassinated Malcomb X that February while he was speaking to a large crowd in a Manhattan auditorium. His violent death elevated his legacy to that of a martyr for the cause of human rights.

Just two weeks later, Martin Luther King brought the Civil Rights Movement to the national stage once again. Leading a peaceful march toward Selma, Alabama, King and 525 other demonstrators were met by the Alabama State Patrol. The marchers' only purpose was to seek equal rights and voting privileges for black Americans. When the protesters refused to disperse and turn around, the State Patrol began to mercilessly beat them with their billy clubs and fists. Many were hospitalized. King and a few others were arrested for disturbing the peace and for trying to incite a riot.

What made this particular protest uniquely different was that media cameras were present that afternoon. Ensuing television news reports for the next few days were carried into every living room in America, putting white bigotry and hatred on display. The ugly story of white racists on the Selma bridge became known as "Bloody Sunday." The unrecognized power of live television created a heightened public outcry for justice on a national scale. Sadly, it would be many years before the majority of white residents in the south would agree.

Every nation or culture in recorded history has had some ethnic bias, or some general attitude of superiority toward another nation or culture. The human condition seems to find it necessary as a means of propping up one's own sense of self-worth. America is no different in that regard. Yet that offers no valid rationalization for what has occurred on our soil. Two centuries of slavery, continued racial bigotry, and economic suppression of our African American citizens remains as one of the two greatest scars in our nation's history.

Fist-fights had become a routine part of the community life which surrounded Mark and his friends. Often times these were not just a tussle or a fight, but a full-fledged beating. As young boys growing up just outside of Boulder, there were numerous occasions when they watched their dads come home from the Pioneer Inn bar with bloody knuckles or an eye swollen shut. This mountain community was "red neck" to the core, and didn't appreciate strangers of any kind coming into town.

Mark's first real serious fight – oddly enough – came in that summer of '65 prior to his junior year of high school, at the insistence of his father. One peaceful afternoon a couple of bikers with very long hair rode into town on their Harley-Davidsons. They were members of a Denver biker gang known as "Brothers Fast", and anyone who had dealings with them always described them as "real mean bastards." The two men stopped for a beer at the Pioneer Inn, and their timing could not have been worse.

Mark's dad and a few of his co-workers had just gotten off work at the County highway maintenance shop. From across the bar the locals started taunting the bikers for their unusual appearance.

"Hey, Suzie," one of them sneered, "Would you like some help gettin' a haircut?"

"Aw, shut your face," one of the bikers retorted.

That was all that was necessary. Mark's dad and five of his friends stood up and slowly walked over to the long-haired visitors. "I think it's time you boys just got back on your bikes and headed down the mountain where you came from," he said.

The bikers hesitated, took one last sip on their beers, and eased themselves off of their barstools. They were out-numbered six to two, so there was no point in trying to be a hero. As they walked out the door, one of them turned and glared at Mark's dad.

"We'll be back tomorrow – same time," he snarled, " – and with friends!" Without waiting for any further response, they kick-started their

31

bikes and roared out of town.

Mark's dad looked out through the bar window to make sure they were gone. "Well, I think we just got ourselves a real fight," he said with a satisfied sigh.

Throughout the evening, as well as the next day at work, the men diligently recruited others to join them. Mark and a couple of his friends agreed to show up with his dad, not fully knowing what to expect.

What did happen the following afternoon would be forever etched in Mark's mind. Almost 50 men from Nederland and the surrounding foothills of Boulder County converged at the Pioneer Inn immediately after work. Many started debating if those bikers would be foolish enough to show up. Within a few minutes, all doubts were removed. On such a still summer day in the mountains, the rumble of a train or the growl of a semi-trailer down shifting could be heard more than five miles away. Today it was the faint roar of Harley-Davidson motorcycles as they echoed up the canyon. For the next few minutes that roar became louder and louder as the gang of bikers approached Nederland. Finally, a double-file line of Harleys turned the corner and pulled into the parking lot. Mark quit counting at 30, but knew there were a few more.

Everyone that had been in the bar now joined the others outside. This looked like it was going to be a "rumble of biblical proportions." The bikers stayed in a group on one side of the dirt parking lot. The apparent leader for the biker gang – a huge, barrel-chested man – stepped forward.

"I understand that a couple of my brothers were run out of town yesterday, even though they were causing no trouble," he said. He paused to look around at the 'welcoming committee', and then added, "Does anyone here want to apologize for that?"

It was deathly quiet for a moment. "Yeah, I'm sorry," one of the locals finally said. "I'm sorry I didn't cut off your friend's hair yesterday when I had the chance."

The conversation was over. Within seconds everyone was in a one-on-one confrontation with someone. A few had clubs of some sort. At least two bikers had knives. Some were wrestling their opponent to the ground, but most were just trying to throw fists. Mark's adrenalin skyrocketed, but he also kept his head. He noticed a black Ford Fairlane that had been parked in the direct sunlight all afternoon. He knew the hood of that car had to be steaming hot. Mark rushed at a shirtless biker standing in front of the car, and pushed him backward onto the hood. The man shrieked in pain, and as he stood up, a layer of skin peeled off of his back and stuck to the car.

He ran away, still screaming and cursing, till he found a small stream across the road where he could lay down and soothe his back in the cold water.

Mark spun around, and targeted his next opponent. A biker caught his eye and willingly obliged. They circled each other for a minute, flailing fists into the air a bit, but without really landing any serious punches. This biker seemed quick and agile, and Mark was beginning to think he would stand a better chance if he could wrestle this guy to the ground and then go for a chokehold.

Suddenly three loud shots were fired from a 12-gauge shotgun. Everyone stopped and froze where they were. Standing on the edge of the parking lot was the local Marshall, holding a smoldering sawed-off shot gun. He glared from man to man for a few moments to make sure everyone was paying attention. "All right, listen up, everyone," the Marshall yelled with authority, as he loaded another shell into the chamber. "Everybody back away and head home! And the next person who even thinks of throwing a punch is goin' to be pickin' buckshot out of his butt!"

It was only then that Mark noticed several bikers as well as a few local friends lying on the ground, with varying degrees of injuries. The bikers cautiously complied, picked up their comrades, and moved toward their Harleys. The Marshall slowly walked into the middle of the parking lot, positioning himself between the bikers and the locals, and continued to wave his gun as a gesture for everyone to keep moving back.

Considering all that might have happened, the mayhem was over rather quickly. But Mark had learned what it meant to fight rather than back down. It made it so much easier for him in the coming months to confront hippies that frequently tried to steal gasoline or snack food from the gas station where he worked. He chose to carry a small tire iron or a baling hook in his back pocket every time a customer pulled in for gas. He found that these hippies talked about "peace" and "love" all the time, but they weren't opposed to stealing or making threats if it was necessary for their survival. Every hippie that he fought – or merely challenged to fight – seemed soft and non-athletic. They all soon learned not to mess with Mark or anyone else in his gas station.

Mark – and his community of friends – did nothing to make these "hippie foreigners" feel welcome. He didn't like them. He didn't like what they stood for. Their professed way of life was too much of a total contrast to the quiet community that Mark wanted to live in. There were just too many changes that Mark was not ready to make. And he was willing to fight to keep things the way they were.

For some, change of any kind was not welcome.

Confusion. If there could be one word to describe America's attitude on Viet Nam by late summer, it would have to be "confusion." All previous wars involving the United States had clearly been "geographic." It had always been clear WHERE the enemy lines were located. It was also clear WHO the enemy was. Neither of those factors were necessarily true with this war. This war was "psychographic." Any boundaries were invisible. There could be no assurance who was a trusted ally or who might be a secret spy for the enemy. Consequently the military strategies on the ground frequently operated in a state of confusion as well.

Fighter pilots were the most frustrated. Every target had to be approved by the White House before they could bomb it. Their instructions were to "protect" South Viet Nam, not to "attack" North Viet Nam. From their aerial vantage point, pilots could frequently see lines of supply trucks on the Ho Chi Minh Trail, waiting just north of the border. But the pilots were told those vehicles and soldiers were off-limits because they had not actually entered South Viet Nam. One pilot radioed in that he was watching a large Soviet helicopter that had crossed into South Viet Nam airspace. However, he was told not to fire, because we didn't want to create a declared war with the Russians. When they did receive permission to bomb a specific location, they had to fly 50 ft. above the ground at 730 m.p.h., not knowing if there were any anti-aircraft weapons in the jungle below.

In July, President Johnson abruptly announced a 67% increase from 75,000 to 125,000 American troops stationed in Viet Nam as a necessary step to protect the South Vietnamese people from a communist takeover. He also more than doubled the military Draft from 17,000 to 35,000 new inductees per month. Our country responded with increased confusion and debate.

In the past, the general citizenry of the U.S. had always proudly supported all of our men in uniform. After all, we had just saved the entire world from Nazi aggression 20 years earlier. As a nation we had willingly rationed our critical resources, we bought war bonds to share the cost of the war, and every citizen voluntarily sacrificed all that was necessary in order to collectively win World War II. Every man, woman, and child in the United States felt they had played a small part in the ultimate victory.

This war in southeast Asia was completely different. Suddenly America had large groups of people publicly gathering to protest our nation's involvement there. In early summer 25,000 protesters marched through Washington, D.C., demanding our complete withdrawal from Viet Nam. In October, a coordinated protest in 80 cities saw several hundred thousand people simultaneously marching in opposition to the war on the same day.

Whereas young men had gladly volunteered to enter World War II – even lied about their age if necessary to get into the service – now 18 to 30 year old men were publicly burning their Draft cards as a visible statement of defiance against the Pentagon. Even the President and Secretary of Defense were privately stunned and confused by what was happening. In the fall of the year, 40,000 men and women picketed the White House, waving signs that read "PEACE," "BRING 'EM HOME," or "NO MORE WAR."

In the middle of so much opposition, there were also those patriotic souls that felt that it was a matter of national duty to support our troops with blind optimism. In October more than 25,000 people marched through the Mall in Washington, D.C. to declare their favorable stance on the war, and their complete support of our government leaders that put us there. That further revealed the growing environment of conflict and confusion that permeated the country.

In South Viet Nam, our soldiers expected to be treated as liberators by the Vietnamese people. To be welcomed as heroes. To be embraced as saviors of their nation. Protectors of their freedom. Instead, there was great confusion there as well, and South Viet Nam was at odds with itself. To the shock of our troops, Buddhist monks on several occasions calmly walked into the middle of a main street in Saigon, sat down on the ground, drenched themselves with gasoline, and struck a match. That was their way of protesting America's presence there, and protesting the lack of any Buddhist representation in the South Vietnamese government. *How could this be?,* our military brass thought. *We're here to save them, and they're willing to burn themselves alive if needs be to make a statement that they don't want us here.* Confusing, to say the least.

Embedded news reporters captured those moments, which became regular cover photos for *Time, Newsweek, U.S. News and World Report* and every other news publication back in America. Those images of monks burning themselves alive, or innocent women and children killed by gunfire, or entire villages destroyed by napalm all served to accelerate the growing sense of "doubt" throughout the U.S. Were these large marches or campus protests around our country merely rebellious students that were trying to refuse to perform their patriotic duty? Or was this in fact a war that had no clear purpose, no clear direction, and no clear definition of victory? In 1965 the only honest answer was one of uncertainty and confusion.

Comedian Jerry Seinfeld has made many humorous – and wonderfully accurate – observations about life. One such example is this: "Men and women are very different. Women need a REASON to have sex. Men only need a PLACE."

By the mid-60's young men and women were becoming more and more adventurous or more and more brazen in what constituted an acceptable "place." The Sink was one of the two most popular bars for University of Colorado students to frequent. About once a month the manager would go into the storage closet behind the fireplace at closing time, only to find a couple engaged in the "horizontal pretzel." He would softly say, "I'll be back in ten minutes," close the door, and quietly leave, giving the couple time to finish what was started.

A similar pattern was true for the night watchman at the CU campus. While making his midnight rounds, Rick would regularly discover couples having sex in one of the darkened corners of the Student Union building. Reinforced by the lifestyles of Hollywood or Rock & Roll bands, most college students – as well as many high school students – determined that the choice of pre-marital sex had lost its sense of "moral taboo." Morality standards rapidly shifted from "abstaining" to "random experimentation." The freedom to do so appeared to be driven by the disappearance of "guilt."

Prior to this generation of young adults, a general sociological rule-of-thumb was that women would "play at sex in order to find LOVE," while conversely, men would "play at love in order to get SEX." But morality was now becoming a gray area that could be defined by each individual according to his or her own choice. No longer were there any moral absolutes. These rebellious young adults chose to separate guilt from sex, to separate sex from love, and to separate love from marriage. The more outspoken or liberated students promoted the mindset of "If it feels good, do it." And "Free Love" became the dominant philosophy because this "ME Generation" was beginning to demand complete freedom in every aspect of their lives.

Media and entertainment began to have a more noticeable – but unanticipated – influence on the culture of young adults. Their parents' generation had merely admired and adored their favorite stars from a distance. Now these Baby Boomers wanted to emulate those celebrities – and their lifestyles as well. If entertainers talked about multiple sexual partners, their fans wanted that too. If musicians talked about using drugs as a means to new sensual experiences or new realms of enlightenment, their followers wanted to experience that as well.

In early 1965 Helen Gurley Brown was promoted to be the new editor and publisher of *Cosmopolitan Magazine*. A sudden shift took place in the general content of this women's periodical. Kitchen recipes or practical fashion ideas now took a back seat to relationships, sexual experiences, and "how-to's" of what specific looks or actions were appealing to men. The unofficial slogan for the magazine was, "Good Girls Go To Heaven – Bad Girls Go Everywhere They Want." Monthly circulation numbers exploded. Ms. Brown's editorial shift caught the beginning of the sexual revolution as well as the "women's liberation movement" and rode those trends to a position of unparalleled dominance. As a result, in the ensuing years *"Cosmo"* greatly accelerated the acceptance of the loosening of sexual attitudes and behaviors among younger women.

For the opposite gender, *Playboy Magazine* had already staked its claim as the exclusive "Gentlemen's Magazine." As its publisher, Hugh Hefner was changing America's perception about female nudity as an appropriate form of entertainment, the freedom of recreational sex, and seeking the epitome of decadence in any and all forms. Some thought he reached that pinnacle when he customized a DC-9 to be his company's flying playground, with décor that included a circular bed covered with a blanket made of Tasmanian opossum.

But success invites competition, and in 1965 *Penthouse Magazine* was established to seek its share of those profits from printed erotica. Publisher Bob Guccione had to find aggressive ways to distinguish his publication from *Playboy*. He did so by including more photos of naked women in each issue, adding reader's sexually explicit letters to the editor, and deeper editorial content that sought to expose corporate and governmental scandals. Guccione also broke new barriers by going pubic" on his photos, and offering the entire magazine in high-gloss, cologne-scented paper. An industry that had previously been labeled as "smut" was now being given a position of normality and even subtle elegance.

This was also the year that comedian Lenny Bruce died. Bruce had become the national poster child for the attitude of utter rebellion against any and all cultural norms and moral standards of decency for public entertainment. His simple agenda was "no limits," and wrote a book entitled *"How to Talk Dirty and Influence People."* In his live performances, he was the first entertainer to use extreme profanity and explicit sexual references as a routine part of his show. As a consequence he repeatedly was arrested for public indecency. The last few years of his career were dotted with courtroom appearances, as he countered his charges with lawsuits of his own against the government, demanding complete freedom of speech. Judges and jurors alike were appalled at his courtroom language, but the highest courts of the land eventually had to admit that the U.S. Constitution guaranteed him the very rights that he was demanding. Although he exhausted all of his personal financial resources to get there, he ultimately won.

Every entertainer since 1965 must be eternally indebted to Lenny Bruce for their current freedom to write song lyrics or tell jokes on any subject whatsoever. Bruce's rebellious form of entertainment forever shattered the language parameters on public expression in our country. Song writers and movie scripts quickly began to take advantage of the doors that Bruce had busted open. Suddenly record companies, radio stations, and the TV networks all had to employ censors for the first time, to try to manage the onslaught of new freedoms with blatant sexual references and profanity.

James Bond had quickly become a ground-breaking movie phenomena with the drama and suspense of an international spy, but interspersed with recreational sex. Hedonism – as portrayed by Sean Connery – became an admirable role-model. His brand – and the other Bond actors that have followed him – remains the greatest movie franchise in all of history.

Sometimes actions can speak louder than words. Peter Yarrow, Paul Stookey, and Mary Travis formed a folk singing trio known simply as "Peter, Paul & Mary," and reached the top of their musical genre. Their hits such as *"If I Had a Hammer," "Blowin' In The Wind," "Puff, the Magic Dragon"* and *"Leaving On a Jet Plane"* were songs that every young person in America could sing verbatim. The folk trio took a risk by being at the forefront in protesting the Viet Nam war, as well as numerous other causes, such as Civil Rights, the rights of migrant workers, and in future years such issues as nuclear energy risks or the civil war in El Salvador. Their consistent presence at such protest events became synonymous with the public cries for the support of any cause that might benefit "the little guy." Although their record company privately cautioned them that such appearances might have a negative impact on their total album sales, the threesome continued to participate in demonstrations based on their conscience. Whether their songs spoke directly to the plight of those fighting for a particular cause, or whether they sang other light-hearted folk tunes, their very presence was a morale boost to every audience seeking to speak out on a specific social issue by using a coordinated protest as their channel of communication.

It was their unexpected and unspoken message for rebellion and cultural change, however, that came from a much more subtle path. As the trio continued to perform in their many television appearances and public concerts that year, fans noticed that Mary Travis was pregnant. Single – and pregnant. That non-verbalized statement was shocking and dramatic – a statement that said there was no assumed shame or guilt for an unmarried woman to become pregnant. In the past, if a single woman "made a mistake," she had two acceptable social options. The first assumption was that she "had to" get married. The cultural expectation was to establish a home with the father of that child, and face life together in order to salvage any respectability.

The only other option for a woman was to drop out of school, move out of town and live in obscurity with a family relative until she gave birth, then relinquish the baby to an adoption agency before returning home to resume her life. If she did anything other than that, there was a severe social stigma of shame and guilt to stain her character. Back-alley abortions were whispered about, but rarely utilized. Verbally or non-verbally, entertainers such as Mary Travis helped to shift that cultural attitude on to a new course. The onus of guilt and shame was fading when it came to sexual choices.

A rare moment of national pride and unity came during that summer. No matter the age, no matter the political persuasion, no matter the ethnicity. Everyone in America was proud of NASA and America's Space Program.

Alan Shepherd had been the first American to ride into space. John Glenn had been the first to orbit the earth. And in the summer of '65, Ed White became the first man to "space walk." Men and women across the country broke into spontaneous applause as they watched pictures from space that showed Mr. White on a tethered cord, floating in space more than 30 feet from the capsule hatch.

It was another brief moment for any and all polarized opinions to be forgotten, to come together as common citizens for the purpose of celebrating the greatest successes of America's technological leadership on a world-wide scale.

Sadly, just two years later Ed White and two of his fellow astronauts would be burned alive while seated in their space capsule on the launch pad. It would be one of only two great tragedies in all of our space endeavors.

One of President Lyndon Johnson's most satisfying accomplishments during his years in office came in 1965 when our Congress passed a complicated piece of legislation known as the "Voting Rights Act." While national in its scope, the intended target was the block of southern states where blatant segregation was still the norm, where African Americans could not use public restrooms or public drinking fountains, and could not sit where they wanted in a restaurant or city bus. The basic privilege of voting had often been withheld from black men and women due to random exceptions created at the whim of local precinct authorities. This legislative bill created a landmark shift in legalities or limitations at the County level.

To date, the growing Civil Rights conflict had been almost exclusively played out in the southern states, where the atrocities of prejudice had been most visible. But that "rule" took another dramatic turn in mid- August. All of America was given a wake-up call, and the beautiful city of Los Angeles unexpectedly became the focal point for racial tensions when it was briefly reduced to a combat zone.

L.A. was a sprawling metropolis that covered more square miles than any city in the U.S., yet it still operated under firm residential covenants that prevented Mexican Americans and African Americans from renting or buying property in most neighborhoods. The L.A. police were careful to enforce such a system long after the U.S. courts had declared these covenants to be illegal. Frequent criticism of police brutality and discrimination would surface, but a vast majority of the city's citizens would just look the other way.

On the evening of August 11th, a routine traffic stop became monumental and historic. A white L.A. police officer on a motorcycle pulled over a young African American man for reckless driving through a black neighborhood known as Watts. A few residents came out of their houses as eyewitnesses. Another police car pulled in as backup. Shouting led to shoving. Shoving led to physical force and the arrest of the driver. Some of the neighbors tried to help the young man before he was taken away to jail. Rumors quickly spread that the officers had used unnecessary force, and even kicked a pregnant woman.

The painful years of accumulated abuse and prejudicial treatment at the hands of the L.A. police finally erupted, and African Americans of all ages decided it was time to react. A crowd quickly gathered on the street. When other police came to break things up, they were greeted by flying bricks and chunks of concrete. Within minutes the city suddenly had a war on its hands – a war that would last six days. Random shooting became frequent, as well as extensive looting, and the burning of specific businesses if they were known to be owned by white people.

The uprising rapidly escalated beyond anything that the L.A. police department could handle. By the fourth day, more than 18,000 police and National Guardsmen were walking the streets of Watts. A policy of mass-arrest was implemented. Six days after the riot began, the last fire was put out, and the last resistance was over. In the aftermath 34 people had been killed, more than 1,000 were injured, and more than 3,400 arrested.

America realized that every metropolitan city was now on notice. Not just in the south. Or in the north. Or on either coast. It no longer mattered. Racial strife could not be relegated to a small region of the country anymore. True equality and human rights would have to be addressed in every neighborhood and in every corner of our land.

Music began to take a dominant role in the counter-culture community. Sales of record albums, as well as single-song records known as "45's", were growing faster than the age wave itself. Record companies went to great lengths – illegal if necessary – to promote their artists into the "Top 40" playlist each week. Manipulation of radio air-time or inflated numbers of record sales became a cutthroat business for those working behind the scenes on behalf of their contracted recording artists. But all of them were fighting for 2nd place.

The Beatles dominated the music charts as no other band has done before or since. Throughout the mid-sixties they consistently produced a prolific assembly line of hit songs, and often times simultaneously had four or five of their songs in America's Top Ten on any given week. In the summer of '65 a creative promoter took a chance by booking the Beatles to play at Shea Stadium, home of baseball's New York Mets. It appeared to be a big gamble, since no band had ever played in such a large venue. But once the concert was announced, the entire stadium was sold out within a few hours. The frenzied crowd screamed at a deafening pitch throughout the concert, drowning out most of the songs coming through a mediocre sound-system meant for baseball's play-by-play announcing rather than music.

Another dimension of music was created by the Beatles in 1965. They released a movie entitled *"A Hard Days Night"*, which had a minimal plot, but gave a new avenue to showcase their songs. The idea became the early precursor for the use of video as a vehicle for selling individual songs.

Music itself also began a dramatic transition this year by splintering into new styles. A hybrid began to appear by inter-mingling traditional folk music with rock and roll, and aptly named it "folk rock." Jazz fans began to discover a new niche called "samba." When African American artists realized they were being shunned by many record companies and music stations, they created their own universe for music and performance. Motown Records was specifically established to market talented African American musicians such as *"The Supremes"* and *"The Temptations"* exclusively to an African American audience. Stellar careers were created in a wide spectrum of musical styles as young adults began buying albums at an unprecedented rate, and listening to their favorite radio music station whenever possible. And the single newest and greatest creation of the 1965 music scene was that of "protest songs."

Rebellion against any and every form of tradition was taking place in America, and musicians joined the trend. Their hair, their outfits, and even the variety of sounds from their instruments were all seeking new limits. But the most profound evidence of protest music was in the lyrics themselves. These stood out in stark contrast to the familiar themes of love songs by pop and rock & roll artists, or the gentle ballads from folk singers.

Singer and song-writer Barry McGuire tried to touch on multiple issues confronting the American youth with his hit single, *"Eve of Destruction."* Some of his lyrics are as follows:

"The eastern world it's exploding', Violence flarin', bullets loadin;
You're old enough to kill, but not for voting
You don't believe in war, but what's that gun you're totin'
And you don't believe we're on the eve of destruction.
Think of all the hate there is in Red China,
Then take a look around to Selma, Alabama,
Ah, you may leave here for four days in space,
But when you return it's the same old place.
The poundin' of the drums, the pride and disgrace,
You can bury your dead, but don't leave a trace,
Hate your next door neighbor, but don't forget to say Grace,

And you tell me over and over and over and over again my friend,
You don't believe we're on the eve of destruction."

Tom Paxton chose to focus strictly on a protest to the issue of the Viet Nam war, with his song *"Lyndon Johnson Told the Nation."*

"I got a letter from LBJ, it said 'this is your lucky day'
It's time to put your khaki trousers on.
Though it may seem very queer, we've got no jobs to give you here,
So we're sending you to Viet Nam.
Lyndon Johnson told the nation, have no fear of escalation,
I am trying everyone to please.
Though it isn't really war, we're sending fifty thousand more
To help save Viet Nam from the Vietnamese.
Every night the local gentry slips out past the sleeping sentry,
They go to join the old VC *
In their nightly little dramas, they put on their black pajamas
And are lobbing mortar shells at me.
We go 'round in helicopters like a bunch of grasshoppers
Searching for the Viet Cong in vain.
They left a note that they had gone, they had to get down to Saigon,
Their government positions to maintain.
Well, here I sit in this rice paddy, wondering about Big Daddy,
And I know that Lyndon loves me so.
Yet how sadly I remember, way back yonder in November
When he said I'd never have to go."

(* the North Vietnamese enemy was known as the Viet Cong, or just "V.C.")

Another Viet Nam war protest song written that year was almost tongue-in-cheek, created by Phil Ochs, as a desperate plea to offer every conceivable excuse to his draft board. He called it *"Draft Dodger Rag."*

"Sarge, I'm only eighteen, I've got a ruptured spleen,
And I always carry a purse.
I got eyes like a bat, and my feet are flat,
And my asthma's getting worse.
Yes, think of my career, my sweetheart dear,
And my poor old invalid aunt.
Besides I ain't no fool, I'm goin' to school
And I'm working in a Defense plant.
I got a dislocated disc and a wrecked up back,
I'm allergic to flowers and bugs.

And when the bombshell hits, I get epileptic fits
And I'm addicted to a thousand drugs.
I got the weakness woes, I can't touch my toes,
I can hardly reach my knees, and if the enemy came close to me
I'd probably start to sneeze.
Oh, I hate Chou En-Lai, and I hope he dies,
One thing you gotta' see
That someone's gotta' go over there, and that someone isn't me.
So I wish you well, Sarge, give 'em hell
Kill me a thousand or so
And if you ever get a war without blood and gore
I'll be the first to go."

In contrast to this witty tune, J. B. Lenoir wrote a painful and angry protest song this year that cried out against the disparity of civil rights in the south. The lyrics to *"Alabama Blues"* include the following:

"I never will go back to Alabama, that is not the place to be
You know they killed my sister and my brother
And the whole world let them peoples down there go free.
I never will love Alabama, Alabama seem to never have loved poor me
O God, I wish you would rise up one day
Lead my peoples to the land of pea'
My brother was taken up for my mother, & a police officer shot him down
I can't help but sit down and cry sometimes
Think about how my poor brother lost his life.
Alabama, Alabama, why you wanna' be so mean?
You got my people behind a barb wire fence
Now you tryin' to take my freedom away from me."

Any protest song that was written to confront the status quo had a welcoming audience. The emotional experience of opposing the Establishment in every way possible was exhilarating. Thus there would be many more songs of protest that were quick to follow.

It took center stage with Al Capone. Organized crime in Chicago had first become notorious during Prohibition days when the mob made hundreds of millions of dollars by selling illegal alcohol. Elliot Ness and his "Untouchables" may have put a stop to Capone himself, but Chicago's crime network continued to flourish.

Frank Nitti led the "Outfit" into other revenue channels, including illegal gambling and "running numbers", which became so profitable that the government eventually copied them and created the state lotteries. To protect themselves from the risks of possible arrests or jail time, the Outfit always kept several key police captains and district judges on their payroll.

By the early '60's the Chicago mob had solidified their strategic relationships all the way to the White House. President John F. Kennedy was indebted to the Chicago crime network because they had delivered on their promise to manipulate the 1960 voting results just enough so that Illinois went to Kennedy instead of Richard Nixon, and those vital electoral votes were the incremental difference needed to give him a narrow margin of victory. Those kind of favors from a crime family always come with a price. But as soon as John Kennedy was in office he appointed his brother, Bobby, to be the U.S. Attorney General. To the shock of organized crime in every city, Bobby announced that his #1 job on behalf of the American people was to destroy the mob. With such blatant confrontation, the mob began to make plans to remove both of the Kennedys from office.

The tension lasted for four years, but following the assassination of the President, Bobby Kennedy resigned his position as Attorney General at the end of 1964, and then served one term as Senator from New York beginning the following year. In early 1965 President Johnson appointed Nicholas Katzenbach as the new Attorney General. His focus was different than that of Bobby Kennedy, and the mob was able to return to "normal." In Chicago, they made up for lost time.

Unlike organized crime in other cities such as New York, Philadelphia, or Detroit, the turf wars were over in Chicago, and the singular structure of their unified mob allowed them to become more successfully entrenched in political and business circles as a cover for their illegal operations. In the political arena, as the new boss of the Chicago Outfit, Sam Giancana gained unparalleled admiration and respect from his crime organization because he was able to make a most unusual connection with the White House.

Obviously there was no texting or email available, and high-ranking political officials could never be seen with a known member of organized crime. Thus any clandestine communication had to be done in person or with a trusted middleman that would not raise suspicions. Giancana's solution? He shared two mistresses with President Kennedy. One of those two was Judy Campbell, who relayed secret information back and forth on behalf of Kennedy regarding such things as the possible assassination of Fidel Castro in Cuba. Kennedy wanted Castro removed because of the new presence of a Communist government only 90 miles from the U.S. border. Organized Crime wanted Castro out because he had ruined their burgeoning casino and hotel business there. With Kennedy's secret blessing, two members of the Chicago Outfit were given that assignment, and made more than six attempts at inserting poison pills into Castro's food, but never succeeded in doing so.

On the local level, the Outfit controlled the major elections as well as the support of several Aldermen in key districts of Chicago. "Fast Eddie" was an Alderman from the south side of the city that lived in a $300,000. mansion and rode to and from his City Hall office every day in a chauffeured limousine while living on his $25,000 salary as an Alderman. Do the math. The Outfit knew that Chicago was unique in that the position of Mayor of the city was far more powerful than that of Governor of the state. The political influence of organized crime on City Hall would increase dramatically in the late '60's and early '70's.

On the business side, the Outfit had gone underground, and now owned numerous legitimate Chicago storefronts such as casualty insurance offices, restaurants, dry cleaners, and major shipping and trucking companies which provided goods into the city. Control of those businesses allowed them to launder the vast amounts of cash that were being generated from their illegal operations. By '65 they were functioning as a well-tuned machine, and even had complete control of which businesses anywhere in Chicago were able to receive a liquor license or not.

The city would pay an enormous price in the late '60's and early '70's due to the presence of the Outfit. The Italian leadership of the mob did not like African Americans, and influenced the police to continue to treat the black neighborhoods as second-rate citizens that were only good as customers for the prostitution, gambling, or drugs that they offered. Mayor Richard Daley allowed the Outfit to peacefully co-exist, and would only call on them for a favor on rare occasions. He had his favorite Bible verse framed on his office wall, which read, *"Be ye doers of the Word, and not hearers only."* Daley applied that to his local government, using worthwhile ends to justify questionable means, even using the Outfit if necessary. Together, they wanted a city that "worked." But it had to be within their rules, and consequently the growing demands for change in America would not find a welcome mat in Chicago. The "Chicago Machine" rigidly opposed any change that would threaten their system of control.

During the summer, Patrick Moynihan was one of the first sociologists to recognize and write about an alarming new trend. (This was the same Moynihan that 11 years later would become the four-term Democratic Senator from New York.) Appointed as the Asst. Secretary of Labor under LBJ, Mr. Moynihan concentrated his work in trying to understand the changes occurring within the African American community. President Johnson had declared a national "war on poverty" as a public relations ploy to divert the country's attention away from Viet Nam, and in so doing desperately wanted to identify a cause that every American man and woman could readily support.

Carefree sex among young unmarried adults was beginning to produce a spike in the number of illegitimate children. Moynihan was particularly interested in that statistical shift among minorities in the inner-city. Research specifically showed that 24% of African American children were being born into a single-parent home, and – often by necessity – were then being raised by a grandparent.

Moynihan identified several likely consequences and expected outcomes from this trend – none of which were desirable. He concluded that poverty would begin to increase on a wider scale because of the high rate of families headed by single mothers. Such a trend was exactly what the President was trying to avoid. The growing crisis would also be fueled by continued discrimination as well as a "ghetto-culture" adopted as an African American mindset, and such an outlook would further prevent any chance for economic or political equality.

His findings defied the traditional thinking of the day regarding the existing structure or contributing causes to poverty, and daringly posited that the existing welfare system was backfiring. His writings suggested that the steady expansion of welfare programs would only increase and propel the collapse of the nuclear family particularly among the African American lower class. The current process as he saw it would also enlarge the problem of poverty, and incentivize single mothers to have more and more illegitimate children in order to receive a greater monthly income from the government. He determined that the gap between African Americans and whites in terms of economic and social opportunity would not only be preserved, but would actually widen.

If that phenomena were to continue, his sociological reasoning led him to predict that there would be a dire lack of male role models within the African American community at large, as well as a lack of any male authority in a family unit. If he were accurate in those statements, the anticipated consequences would include an epidemic rise in crime, drug abuse, and gang involvement.

His findings were widely criticized by Civil Rights leaders such as Chicago's Rev. Jesse Jackson, as well as the early leadership of the Women's Rights movement. Jackson and others were angered by the implication that the primary cause for rampant poverty among blacks could be due largely to personal behavior and cultural choices of the poor, rather than exclusively resting on an external social structure based on more than a century of national racism and discrimination. Women's Rights leaders, on the other hand, decried this conclusion as belittling to women because it painted the female gender as being inadequate or less than capable in properly raising their children in a single-parent environment.

While history may show elements of truth on all sides of the debate, there is no question that Moynihan was quite prescient in most of his findings. Poverty, crime, drug usage, and gang violence have all increased within our major cities. The quality of public education particularly in our inner-cities is often deplorable. Today 93% of black children are born to a mother that is not married. Our government – while certainly well-intended – has utterly failed in Lyndon Johnson's vision for a war on poverty because they have been striving to offer political solutions to moral problems.

Lyndon Johnson was nothing if not a shrewd politician. In his zeal to pass any desired legislation he had become a master in brokering deals and manipulating relationships to get where he wanted. He had several sexual affairs while in office, but was much more discreet than his predecessor. As soon as the news cameras and microphones were off, he was known in the inner circles of Washington to use language that could make a longshoreman blush. He even tried to use Rev. Billy Graham to his political advantage, hoping to gain support from the enormous block of voters that identified themselves as Christians.

Rev. Graham had become an American phenomenon as a mass-evangelist for Christianity. Much of his early success was due to the heavy promotion that Randolph Hearst provided in his newspapers. As Graham traveled from one metropolis to another, his city-wide "crusades" would draw 50 – 100,000 people every night. Such influence was extremely attractive to any politician. During his lifetime, Graham became known as "America's pastor," and was invited to the White House for private conversations with every President from Truman through Obama.

LBJ was no exception, and had Billy Graham come to his office more than once, but while he was there always insisted on some "photo ops" as well. Johnson knew that he needed influence and support from the conservative Christian voting block, and thought that a friendship with Graham might help to accomplish that. Late in the evening after their first meeting in the Oval Office, the President and Rev. Graham went skinny-dipping in the White House pool located indoors on the lower level, under the watchful eye of the Secret Service. It was a "spur-of-the-moment" idea that Graham would never forget.

Rev. Graham was careful never to fall victim to the trappings of power and money that were constantly available to him. Throughout his lifetime he went to great lengths to remain "non-political", so that he might befriend Democrats and Republicans alike. Johnson tried to change that, but could not. He would have to find some common ground with conservative voters through some other source.

By the end of the year, the entire country suddenly felt a sense of uneasiness. The satisfaction created from a growing economy for the previous 20 years in a row and a flourishing middle-class was abruptly overtaken by unforeseen challenges. University students were rebelling in large numbers as never before. Public opinion was polarized on whether or not to support our military personnel in Southeast Asia. Minorities were no longer quietly accepting their position as second-class citizens. The fabric of America appeared frayed for the first time since the end of World War II. Media pundits were asking if this was a short-term blip before things returned to normal, or was this an early warning trend of unrest that might get even worse . . .

President Lyndon Baines Johnson

Playboy Magazine logo

Hugh Hefner, founder of Playboy

Buffalo Springfield

Viet Nam War Protest

Malcomb X

Folk trio Peter, Paul, and Mary

Buddhist Monk

CHAPTER 3

"1966 - ESCALATION ON ALL FRONTS"

"Come on, all you big strong men
Uncle Sam needs your help again.
He's got himself in a terrible jam
Way down yonder in Viet Nam.
So put down your books and pick up a gun
We're gonna' have a whole lotta' fun.
And it's One, two, three,
What are we fightin' for?
Don't ask me, I don't give a damn!
Next stop is Viet Nam
And it's five, six, seven,
Open up the pearly gates
Well, there ain't no time to wonder why
Whoopee! We're all gonna' die."

Country Joe and the Fish

Anti-war protesters welcomed the New Year of 1966 with a sense of optimism, thinking this would be the year that their voice would finally have an impact on our nation's decision makers. Major organized marches in cities throughout the country were more and more frequent, and participation levels were growing by tens of thousands. Senator Fulbright held hearings on Capitol Hill regarding the Viet Nam War, to provide a platform for constructive debate. Although little was accomplished, it gave renewed legitimacy to all those protesting the war. *"Why wouldn't we be heard?"* was the overriding attitude of the protesters.

But those dreams were quickly – and repeatedly – smashed under the boot of the U.S. Defense Department. In January America's troop level in Viet Nam was increased to 190,000. If superior weaponry could not win this war, maybe sheer volume of man-power could. Or so the Pentagon thought. Just three months later, LBJ again ordered the troop count to be increased to 250,000. Consequently the weekly "body bag" count of corpses coming back to America continued to increase as well.

The "invisible enemy" in Viet Nam was completely at home within the jungle environment, and thus could withstand any increase of American ground troops because they had only to choose selectively where they were willing to engage. But the Vietnamese had nothing to compete with the American airpower. Unprecedented numbers of Huey helicopters were ordered by the U.S. Army, because these served as an ideal method of moving men in and out of jungle skirmishes where there was no defined "battle front." The unique topography combined with guerilla warfare made this the first "helicopter war" in military history. American Generals authorized more aggressive air tactics in the hope that the enemy would voluntarily retreat. They had a growing sense of desperation since the official government of Saigon had changed for the 10th time in just 30 months. In early June, U.S.

B-52 bombers were sent for the first time to destroy large sections of North Viet Nam's capital city of Hanoi, in hopes of severing major supply channels. Even though it was apparent that non-military citizens would also be killed in this process, the bombers followed their instructions.

A new weapon known as "Agent Orange" was also introduced in Viet Nam at this time. This toxic chemical spray was initially used exclusively as a defoliant over large portions of the jungle so that U.S. troops could move more efficiently, and simultaneously to deprive the enemy of cover. Eventually it was also used over North Vietnamese agricultural land as an attempt to expel enemy troops by destroying the source of their food supplies. The chemical was increasingly used from 1966 to 1969 even though its long-term effects were still unknown.

Both winged bombers and helicopters were used in this defoliation effort, because these aircraft could carry large spray booms mounted under the wings or the belly of the aircraft, and effectively impact a wide swath of plant life with every pass. Eventually more than 12,000 square miles of Viet Nam was sprayed with Agent Orange in this way. Preliminary usage was considered a success, because the chemical did in fact perform as advertised, rapidly destroying any vegetation in its path. But unanticipated and undesirable results were also discovered later.

During the '60's most of our country was very naïve regarding the toxicity of products in any sector of business. Parents used popular insect sprays and farmers used crop fertilizers that were eventually found to be very damaging to humans. Agent Orange was one such chemical, and ultimately proved to be so devastating it would one day be listed by name in an international military ban against the usage of chemical warfare.

Almost 20% of the total forested area of Viet Nam was completely destroyed with this chemical during its four years of use. The elimination of vegetation was so great that it disrupted the ecological balance of the entire country. Forest regeneration became unlikely, and bird or animal species were greatly reduced in every effected area. Within a few years excessive soil erosion became a new problem due to the lack of sufficient plant life that was needed to hold the soil in place. Because this toxic chemical does not break down or dissipate, contamination within the soil continued to be absorbed into new plant life, and thus threatened the local food chain. Horrible consequences for the environment, to say the least, yet miniscule compared to the destruction of human lives.

Four million Vietnamese were directly exposed to this silent killer, and 3,000,000 began to experience an ugly grocery list of maladies. The Red Cross of Viet Nam today estimates that more than 1,000,000 of its citizens are now disabled or suffer severe health problems because of Agent Orange contamination. Direct contact with the spray would cause portions of the human skin to become enflamed to a dark red, and even peel away. A three-fold increase in disabilities occurred, including cleft palate, mental disabilities, children born with extra fingers or toes, increases in serious skin diseases, and a rapid rise in cancers of the lungs, larynx, and prostate. Higher rates of miscarriages, congenital birth defects, and infant mortality were also attributed to this effective but horrific product.

Our own military was not immune to this chemical's destructive capability, because many soldiers were involved in the storage, transfer, or actual dispersal of Agent Orange. While on active duty in Viet Nam, our soldiers were consistently reassured by government officials telling them that exposure to this product was completely harmless. Once these nurses and soldiers had returned home, however, the frequency of unwelcome health issues began to surface. Increased numbers of miscarriages. Increased numbers of children born with birth defects. Increases of general ill health. Over the next 25 years more than 39,000 U.S. veterans of Viet Nam filed disability claims for having been exposed to Agent Orange. Yet less than 1.4% ever received any compensation.

Class action suits on behalf of our Viet Nam veterans were ultimately brought against seven major chemical companies, including Monsanto and Dow Chemical. Sadly, before the trial was complete, a cash settlement was reached out of court which stipulated a lump sum to be paid by the chemical manufacturers, but only on the condition that any and all health claims against them would be dropped. In vintage fashion, the attorneys won, and the government as well as the chemical companies were never truly held accountable. The big losers were the innocent men and women in uniform who simply obeyed orders without being given accurate or honest information.

What a pathetic disgrace, once again, in the treatment of our soldiers.

The quality of America's public education was slipping, due in no small part to the coaching of Dr. Benjamin Spock. As a self-anointed guru on parenting and child-rearing, he espoused a concept of "adolescent freedom", allowing a child to find his or her personal interests as well as individual limits on right and wrong. As a result, comprehensive test scores began to plummet as this parental leniency moved children away from core curriculum into personal interests such as drama, choir, band and orchestra, or school sanctioned athletics.

One of the greatest status symbols for any high school boy was to earn a "Letter" in athletic competition. Boulder High School was no exception. The exclusive privilege of wearing the school lettermen's jacket was a great source of pride and personal identity. Not only did a young man need to make the cut in tryouts for his chosen sport, he also needed to get a specific minimal amount of competitive playing time in order to qualify for that honor. Football and basketball carried the greatest perception of athletic success because of their large crowd appeal. But male students could also letter in other sports, including tennis, cross-country, wrestling, baseball, and track.

Through a process of logic, Tom's older brother, Brian, convinced him to pursue the sport of tennis. Fewer people would try out for this sport, the risk of injury was almost non-existent, and the excellent conditioning would serve him well for the winter ski season. Tom was a shrewd thinker, and all of this made sense.

Tom not only made the tennis squad, but also contributed to their team's success when they finished in 2nd place in the Colorado State tournament two years in a row. Playing on the #1 doubles team, he and his partner were undefeated in their conference matches one year. The frequent recognition in the student assemblies was most gratifying.

Consequently, earning his athletic letter was assured. The anticipation was well worth the hours of sweat and toil. But what he was not fully prepared for was the secret lettermen's initiation event that had to take place.

In the spring of the school year, each of the newly qualified lettermen for all of the various sports was invited to the two-hour event, which took place behind closed doors in the men's field house and locker room. All the previous lettermen administered the initiation activities, under the complicit but disinterested eye of a couple of the athletic coaches. Fifty or sixty upperclassmen would induct the thirty to forty new lettermen.

Any expectations for a mild or casual evening were erased immediately upon arrival. Tom and his fellow inductees were told to strip completely naked and put on a full blindfold. Each new letterman was then told to reach forward with one arm, and with the other arm reach backward through his legs to the person behind him, and link hands. Thus they created a most odd-looking human chain, slowly marching around the locker room in the nude in a stooped over posture.

Although the coaches' only instructions were to injure no one, the "ceremony" was anything but pleasant.

"Tough-Skin" was a thick, syrupy product that athletes often smeared on to their feet in an effort to prevent blisters. It created an extremely stiff, leathery skin condition that could take weeks or even a few months to wear off. But on this night it was not used on anyone's feet. A 4" paint brush was repeatedly dipped into buckets of the honey-colored substance, and then slapped into every naked armpit and butt-crack as each rookie inductee crawled by. It would be five months before every remnant of Tough-Skin was fully removed from the hair of Tom's crevasses.

From time to time those being initiated were individually removed from the circle to receive personal attention. At some point each young man was carefully escorted to an individual whirlpool filled with ice water and crushed ice cubes, and instructed to submerge fully his entire person for just a split-second while remaining blindfolded. Because of the potential for muscle cramps or spasms in the dangerously frigid water, spotters were on hand in case any new lettermen lurched out of the tub too far or too fast.

Others were led on to the surface of a wooden tabletop, and were told they were standing three feet off the ground, even though in reality they were only three inches above the floor surface. A piece of string was gently tied around their penis, and they were told that the other end of the string was tied around a brick. The instruction was given that at the count of three, the brick would be dropped, and they had to jump off the table while still blindfolded and beat the brick to the floor to avoid any painful damage to their "member." Although no brick was actually attached, the trauma of jumping from an unknown height while blindfolded was certainly jolting and unforgettable.

Hazing of some sort was universal with high school and college sports teams, and also almost every Sorority and Fraternity. If the reward is perceived to be great enough, any human being will put up with a certain amount of humiliation or even demeaning treatment for a period of time in exchange for attaining that honor. For Tom – and all other athletes to receive a "Boulder High School Letter" for the first time that spring – this evening was considered totally worth it.

His June graduation from high school provided little fanfare for Mark. A few offers for a free beer at the Pioneer Inn, a few cards of celebration with a couple of bucks enclosed, or more often just a congratulatory slap on the back. That was about it. None of those six guys in his senior class planned on college. Most expected to be drafted anyway. And everyone just wanted to find a job and get on with life.

Mark started working more hours at the local gas station, thanks to the fact that there were no self-service gas stations in existence. He had become accustomed to the occasional hippies that would get their car or VW van filled with gas, and then try to "skip out" without paying. His solution was to carry a small crowbar or a baling hook attached to a loop on his blue jeans, and threaten any driver that hinted at leaving without paying. Only once did he actually have to break a rear car window to convince the driver that he was not going to leave without payment in full.

One evening after work Mark and a couple of friends decided to drive into Boulder to play some "8-Ball" at the Golden Cue. He didn't realize until they were half way to town that he still had the baler hook at his side. But he decided to leave it there, since he thought it made him look tough – and maybe even a little bit cool.

Less than an hour into their pool game, it happened. As Mark was leaning over the pool table to take his turn, he felt a hand deftly remove the baler hook from the side loop on his jeans. As he stood and turned, he found himself face to face with Sampson.

"Sampson" was only a nick-name, but nobody ever dared to question it. Sampson was an African-American man with a shocking and intimidating physique. His exaggerated muscle definition gave him a body shape of an upside-down Christmas tree. Lots and lots of steroids, no doubt. He was a regular customer at the Golden Cue, and always had at least one – if not two – attractive white co-eds accompanying him. Inter-racial dating had become a status symbol for every black man, and certainly a fun form of rebellion for white girls, particularly those from any of the southern states. Now Mark's pencil- thin body looked almost comical standing next to such a stunning physical specimen.

"Is this what you use on niggers?" Sampson inquired with a frozen glare, as he waved the tool in front of him.

Mark hesitated, somewhat in awe and somewhat in fear at this uninvited predicament. "I'm not here to cause any trouble," he finally stammered.

"That's good," Sampson said with a nod. "I think I'll hang on to this just to make sure, and then we know there ain't gonna' be no trouble. OK?"

Mark sighed, and mustered enough courage to respond again. "You can hang on to that for a little while if you want to," he said, "but I want it back when I leave. I need that for my work."

Sampson studied him for a minute, and determined he was clean-cut and harmless. "OK," he said with a little snort, "I'll be over at that table in the far corner." And with that he quietly walked away with Mark's baler hook.

Mark quickly processed what had just happened. He really had no racial bias – blacks, Mexicans, or any other ethnicity for that matter. But he did have a strong dislike for long-haired hippies, bikers, and anyone else who didn't think they needed to work. Otherwise he could get along with just about any person that pulled his own weight.

An hour later Mark hung up his pool cue, went to the far corner of the "Cue" to get his baling hook, and left without saying another word to

Sampson. Both men were trying to avoid trouble in their own way.

The city of Boulder – and particularly the University of Colorado – had very few African American men and women. There seemed to be no need or little value for racial protests or civil rights marches in this community. That just wasn't perceived as a primary issue.

On the national scene, however, racial tensions continued to escalate into frequent clashes as African Americans became more vocal and more organized in their demands for equality. James Meredith had already grown accustomed to national attention when he became the first black student to attend the University of Mississippi. In order to walk safely into that classroom, it took 500 U.S. Marshalls to protect him and enforce the new Civil Rights Law that LBJ had enacted the previous year. That new-found name recognition had given him a platform for speaking at civil rights rallies throughout the south.

But in the summer of '66 Meredith decided to take it to another level. He notified the media that he would be leading a few other black men on a 220-mile march from Memphis, Tennessee, to Jackson, Mississippi. The two-fold purpose of the march was to draw attention to the continued racism that existed in direct opposition to newly passed laws, and also to generate public support for black men and women to be able to register to vote.

As the march got underway, media support and public awareness was tepid at best. But on the 2nd day, James Meredith was shot several times in broad daylight by a drive-by motorist. During his hospitalization for the next two days, the national media coverage catapulted this to front-page news. Organizations from around the country sent financial support, and other marchers galvanized to participate with him in person.

The following week Meredith re-joined the group, and by the time they entered Jackson a week later, more than 15,000 marchers clogged the highway as they made their way toward City Hall. It was the largest march in the history of Mississippi. Of greater importance, more than 4,000 African American men and women registered to vote for the first time that week.

Any such gains in the civil rights debate were attained in small and painful increments such as this. Legislation alone can never change a heart of hatred. Conflicts and violence of this nature – ugly as they were – would only become more common.

The music industry was beginning to generate a bigger and bigger role of influence on young people. Lyrics continued to push the limits, celebrating the freedoms of sex and drugs. A quartet called *"The Mama's and the Papa's"* epitomized that thinking with a new hit single, which stated:

> *"You gotta' go where you want to go*
>
> *Do what you want to do*
>
> *·With whoever you want to do it with."*

But by the mid-60's the influence of musicians moved beyond the lyrics, and played out in ways far beyond the mere choice of which radio station one might select. Trends in hair styles, clothing, and shoe fashions were driven by specific looks of specific bands. Social and moral standards were shifting toward complete license and leniency with no boundaries as teenagers and "twenty-somethings" tried to emulate the life-style of rock & roll bands. "Marketing and Merchandising" emerged as an explosive new industry to magnify the success of those in the music industry.

At a press conference that spring, John Lennon declared that the Beatles "had become more popular than Jesus". That was undoubtedly true in some circles, but the public outcry and backlash was unexpectedly strong and forceful. Newspaper ads, TV talk shows, and many churches declared that idea to be blasphemous. Three months later during another press interview Lennon felt it was necessary to issue a public apology for what he had said.

At the end of that summer the Beatles secretly decided to hold their last LIVE concert. They had become too frustrated with the constant screaming from the audiences during their live performances, which totally drowned out the skilled nuances of their music. The band wanted to be able to focus on their love for their music so that it could be heard and enjoyed for its true musicianship. Candlestick Park in San Francisco hosted the sold-out event. At the time ticket holders had no idea that they were witnessing something so historic. There would never be – nor could there ever be – another band in all of history that held the dominance which was their legacy. The Beatles continued to do studio work for the next few years, and produced many more great songs, but never returned to the live stage. Album sales alone generated far more money than they had ever dreamed.

The creative production of music reached an inventive new pinnacle in the fall of this year. An ad appeared in two Hollywood magazines, asking for male applicants to try out for a TV cartoon show that would portray a

British band that wanted to be just like the Beatles. Over 400 quasi-actors or musicians showed up for the screen test.

This imaginary band was to be "manufactured" in a TV film studio, with a strategy of reaching pre-teens and teens with a combination of animated comedy, sketch bits, and sprinkled with a light portion of music. The name chosen for the band as well as the Saturday morning cartoon show was *"The Monkees."*

The as yet unrecognized power and potential of the media once again displayed itself. This experimental TV show was met with unprecedented success, and a cult following of these four "musicians" erupted across America, even though the band often times was not actually playing their own instruments or doing the actual vocals on the filmed music scenes. Davey Jones, Peter Tork, Micky Dolenz, and Michael Nesmith were sudden stars. In spite of their lack of any particular musical skills, the popularity of their TV show produced numerous best-selling hit songs, including *"Last Train to Clarksville"*, and *"I'm a Believer."*

This runaway success forced their TV producers to scramble in order to create a few live concerts that could satisfy the demands of their fans. The Monkees were so popular, even Jimi Hendrix was included as the opening act for several of their live concerts. Over the next three years the band sold an unbelievable sum of more than 75,000,000 albums, and in one year actually outsold the Beatles and the Rolling Stones combined. Although the financial success of the Monkees was in the stratosphere, their critics and other rock & roll bands were quick to pan their results, insisting that they were "fakes", and an actual detriment to the true artistry of the music world.

Jealousies may have played a part in such criticism. Competition for album sales definitely played a part. But one thing was certain . . . the phenomena of the Monkees made every musician more keenly aware of the value of "visibility", "marketing" and "image" as a part of the desired success of any band. The music world would never be the same because of an experimental cartoon show.

One of Boulder's earliest documented statements of protest against the Viet Nam War was insignificantly small and almost comical in nature. Claudia "Lady Bird" Johnson served as the First Lady during the nearly six years her husband was in the White House. In the summer of '66 she was sent on a brief public relations tour around the country, making appearances and short speeches at any location where the President and his team felt they might gain some political mileage.

Her itinerary brought her to Boulder for a quick tour through one of the Government Laboratories located there. Following a brief statement of thanks for all the good work that was taking place at the lab, her security team escorted her for an even shorter stop at Crossroads Mall, one of the first enclosed shopping centers in the country, for a photo op that could reflect the booming economy. While walking past the various retail stores and shaking hands with many of the surprised local shoppers that happened to be there, Lady Bird decided she needed to call her husband back in Washington, D.C. with an important question.

Of course not even the most powerful government figures in the world had cell phones at the time, and none of the security guards happened to have any loose change for a pay phone. Apparently that need had never come up before. So Lady Bird politely approached one of the proprietors in the mall and quietly asked if she could use the store's phone to call the White House, and assured him that she would reverse the charges.

The store owner thought carefully for a moment and then responded with a cordial but firm "NO." He explained that he could not in good conscience assist our government in any way when that same government insisted on escalating an immoral war. Lady Bird's question would have to wait until she was back on Air Force One.

In traditional fashion the national media chose not to report this minor incident. (unlike today's reporters that may be looking for any "dirt" or controversy to help create a story) Out of respect for the office of the Presidency, the media had knowingly looked away from President Kennedy's numerous affairs. In like manner they were now careful not to report LBJ's extremely foul language. Their perceived job was not just to deliver the news, but also to help create a positive image of our leaders whenever possible for the sake of the country. And they knew that if they did otherwise, they would immediately lose their access to the White House. This somewhat comical conversation in Boulder was never heard by the rest of the country, but in an amusing way it demonstrated the ever-increasing passion of opposition against the war that was taking place in the public sector.

In late July, suburban Chicago made national news in an embarrassing fashion.

George Rockwell had served in the U.S. Navy during WWII and Korea, and retired with honors. He loved the rigid discipline of the military, on the verge of mind control. He was also greatly influenced by Senator Joseph McCarthy, and shared his adamant stance against communism. Rockwell developed a deep respect for Nazism, and created a shrine to Hitler in his basement.

Early in this year he founded a group that he called the "World Union of Free Enterprise National Socialists." A few months later he changed the name to the "American Nazi Party." Their general charter was to seek an end to any national efforts for racial equality or integration. Rockwell preached a message of hatred and white supremacy, and claimed the Holocaust had never actually happened. His strategy was to follow the itinerary of Martin Luther King, and offer an opposite vision for America. Not unexpectedly, he found quick support from Ku Klux Klan members. But somewhat shockingly, he also received support from Malcolm X and other militant Black leaders that wanted segregation for the purpose of achieving Black supremacy.

Their first "march" was in July of 1966, in Cicero, Illinois, where Rockwell and his followers stood at attention in their own "military uniforms" while he addressed the crowd. His message stated that integration was a Jewish plot to rule the white population around the world. Much of the Polish neighborhood came to watch out of curiosity. A few yelled derogatory epithets at the Nazi members. A couple of short fist-fights broke out, but no one was hospitalized. Throughout the afternoon the local news media captured every minute.

Although George Rockwell's vision for an active Nazi Party in America became a reality, he did not live long to enjoy it. Less than a year later he was assassinated by a disgruntled member of his new Party. His martyrdom lifted the cause, and membership increased. Over the next decade the Nazi Party had 40 marches in the United States, and annually held a march in the Chicago suburbs of either Skokie or Cicero.

It's sad but true that in some circles "hatred sells."

The summer could not go by fast enough for Tom's best friend, David. Turning 16 in August, he was counting the days until he could get his Driver's License. Earlier that summer he had worked for two months on a farm in Nebraska, so he had become quite skilled at driving any vehicle, including tractors, trucks, pickups, and cars. Taking a driver's test was going to be a snap, even with a manual transmission.

When the big day arrived, Tom went with David to the Department of Motor Vehicles. There were no other applicants in the waiting room when they arrived, so the sole DMV employee stepped from behind the counter and ushered David to a corner desk, and then offered a few practical instructions for his written exam. Take your time. Carefully fill in each multiple-choice answer with pencil, so that you could erase if needed. And make sure you complete all four pages. The actual driving test would follow.

While the DMV clerk was momentarily pre-occupied helping David, Tom had stayed by the customer service counter. Glancing over the counter top, Tom noticed three stacks of blank Driver's License forms. Each license was in triplicate, with carbon paper between the 3" x 4" pieces of paper. Once a person had successfully passed the written test as well as the driving test, the service clerk would then complete the appropriate license on a manual typewriter. One copy was given to the new driver, the other two were filed with different departments of local government, and the carbon inserts were tossed into the garbage. There were no photos or holograms to worry about, yet it was a very cumbersome and messy process.

The first stack of forms had a large number "16-17" superimposed over the spaces reserved for all the personal information. That form was for drivers that were only 16 or 17 years old. The second stack had the large numbers "18-20", and the third stack just read "21 +."

Tom was never shy about taking a risk, and this was an unexpected opportunity that he could not pass up. With a quick glance over his shoulder, he made sure that the DMV employee was still busy talking with David. Tom quickly reached over the counter, and grabbed a fist-full of the "18-20" license forms, and stuffed them into his windbreaker pocket.

David aced the written test, and made only one small mistake on the driving portion. He passed with very high marks, and his license was filled out and signed by the clerk. He now could legally drive on his own. What a sense of freedom! Together David and Tom chose to go to the local McDonald's for a chocolate milk shake to celebrate.

Only after they were enjoying their shakes did Tom reveal what he had done. At first, David thought it was silly, and they would probably just throw the blank forms into the trash.

"Do you realize what this means?" Tom said with a mischievous grin. "Seriously? Do you?"

"I guess not," David responded, with a look of confusion.

"How hard would it be to use our own typewriter, and fill these out for whoever we want?" Tom said with a tone of confidence.

"Oh, wow," David exclaimed. "We could then buy our own beer if we wanted to."

"That's just the beginning," Tom added. "There is Tulagi's and the Sink up on the Hill. Think of how many bars and nightclubs there are where you have to be 18 to get in. Think of the live music & entertainment venues in Denver that require an 18-year-old ID because of their liquor license. These are GOLD!"

David was nodding in agreement. "That could be really cool. But why so many? We only need one for each of us."

Tom shook his head, realizing he was much more of a big-thinker. "Look," he said, lowering his voice, "everyone that we know would want this. We can sell these to whoever we choose."

And that is what they did. Over the next few months, they quietly accepted $10 or $15 dollars from about 30 of their sophomore and junior classmates at Boulder High School. Typing the personal information on to the form and adding a bogus signature on the bottom meant that another student instantly had all the rights of an 18-year-old. In hindsight it may not have been his proudest moment, but it proved that Tom was an incredibly creative and fast thinker who was willing to take some risk. Those innate characteristics would serve him well all of his life.

Margaret Sanger died in September. As the creator of the term "birth control", her writings and speeches had rocked American culture for decades. Sanger not only wanted to reduce the birth rate in America, but also wanted to reduce *WHO* should be able to breed. In her book *"Family Limitation"*, Sanger's contention was that intelligent men and women had a responsibility to reproduce, but the "feebleminded and insane" should receive government-mandated sterilization. Her worldview also embraced eugenics as a necessary means of improving the general quality of life for society.

Sanger helped to legalize contraception in the U.S. Her motive was to help women choose when to have children so that they might strengthen their social standing. For many years her term "birth control" held an evil or dark connotation by most Americans, and for some time she feared for her life. Although she opened the first birth control clinic in the United States, and founded organizations that eventually became "Planned Parenthood of America", she made a careful distinction between birth control – which she strongly advocated – and abortion, which she opposed, as long as contraception was available to prevent unwanted pregnancies.

As the sexual revolution gained traction in the late '60's, "birth control" began to carry an acceptable and even positive image as a necessary partner with sexual freedom. It represented another major change in the thinking of young adults. Sanger eventually became a hero for those who championed women's equality, family planning, and a woman's right to choose an abortion.

The "fad" of public protests was gaining traction in all sectors of the country. Viet Nam always garnered the most raucous crowds. Sit-ins or large rallies were frequent. The Civil Rights activists tended to focus on marches that terminated at a courthouse in order to generate maximum effect for media coverage on their demands for equality. But this year three other special interest groups began to emulate those tactics for their own purposes, utilizing protests of various kinds in hopes of causing a similar public outcry on their behalf.

On the West Coast, Cesar Chavez led marches and public rallies in support of the migrant farm workers that moved in and out of California every year from Mexico. He coordinated various strategies to build a public platform for the unionization of those laborers. He brought media awareness to the inhumane treatment of his Mexican co-workers, which included such factors as long days of back-breaking manual labor in the California sun for only $2. in pay, no clean drinking water, no restroom facilities, and no available housing.

Initially the efforts of Chavez appeared to garner mere lip-service in response until he challenged the migrant workers as well as his Caucasian supporters specifically to boycott the Californian grape industry. The immediate financial impact caused a rapid response, and conditions for those workers suddenly began to improve. Chavez had learned from the Viet Nam and Civil Rights activists how to gain media attention for the benefit of migrant farm workers, and in turn he taught the other protest groups the aggressive "tool" of selective boycotting to accelerate a desired response.

On the opposite coast Gloria Steinem established herself as the new champion for the Women's Movement. She had worked "undercover" at a Playboy Club to compile evidence of sexism and unequal pay for women. Now it was time for the female gender to have a voice in the public square, demanding equality and independence. In a calculated step toward perceived balance in the media, Marlo Thomas, daughter of the popular comedian Danny Thomas, was given her own situation-comedy TV show. A small step, but a step in the right direction none the less.

Public bra-burning became an easy strategy for the women's rights leadership to guarantee themselves instant media coverage. Emotionally charged speeches and public rallies were held in all major cities. But traction was slow compared to other causes. Many women in America felt comfortable being a housewife and homemaker. They could not identify with Steinem, who famously said, "A woman needs a man like a fish needs a bicycle." Only on rare occasions was a woman elected to public office. In the corporate world, a "glass ceiling" continued to exist, limiting women to lesser titles and lesser pay in the company's organizational structure.

Similar to the Civil Rights initiative, the women's movement sought national legislation that would quickly obligate public compliance. An "Equal Rights Amendment" was drawn up, and grass roots supporters began lobbying for its passage in every state. Although the name sounded straight-forward, the bill struggled to gain any needed momentum due to conflicts in the actual details and definitions that were included. As a result, other women's groups were created that worked in direct opposition to this legislative attempt. It would take many years to see any substantive or tangible progress in those areas that Steinem and her followers were seeking.

A third special interest group that began to raise its voice this year was the gay and lesbian community, and referred to themselves as the "last minority." In major U.S. cities the police offered $10 as a "reward" for anyone that would turn in a practicing homosexual. In New York City police would frequently raid gay bars, making arrests or physically beating the patrons. Throughout government agencies as well as all branches of the military, homosexuality was considered a mental illness. Comedians derogatorily used these "faggots" as an easy target for a quick laugh. But this year for the first time the gay community decided to fight back. Individual voices were very rare and very isolated at first, but a new demand for equality had been established. The growing contentiousness for gay rights – like all of the other protesting groups – began to swirl with increasing hatred. An explosion of some kind was imminent.

The autumn of 1966 recorded the first evidence of portions of traditional American society organizing in their effort to counter these young adults and their obsession with total rebellious freedom. The blatant disregard for any previous moral standards or decency had begun to produce an opposing force, a new galvanizing of a more conservative expression, a movement as a felt need to offer a direct alternative to the drug culture and civil disobedience that had become so commonplace.

Senator Barry Goldwater and his ultra-conservative supporters had suffered a crushing defeat in his run for the office of President two years earlier. But in the fall of this year, a Hollywood movie star decided to run for Governor of California, pushing a campaign of patriotism, conservative fiscal planning, and a complete rejection of the "drug culture" that threatened America's traditional values. Ronald Reagan was swept into office, and for the next three decades became the hero and the standard-bearer for those who strove to retain the principles of the past that his supporters so ardently believed had made America great.

A firm beachhead for traditionalism had been re-established, and the polarization from the vast majority of the "baby boomers" would only continue to widen in the coming years. And the disagreements of these two camps would ramp up in volume.

Another "first" began to surface that fall in Boulder as a different and unique reaction against the perceived shift in cultural standards.

The MacKenzie family had two lovely daughters, ages 9 and 12. Cheryl and Connie were excellent students, socially well-rounded, and active in after-school hobbies. But their parents had become convinced that the public school system was no longer providing a thorough education, and even worse, was creating a decaying environment that was not wholesome for young women such as their daughters. Blind acceptance of other students' substandard homework, sex education in earlier grades, tolerance of dirty language among students during recess, lack of personalized attention for accelerated students, and providing immoral rock & roll music at school dances. These were the factors that led the MacKenzie parents to make a very difficult decision – they asked to remove their girls from the Boulder Valley public school system, with the commitment to personally educate them within the confines of their own home.

"Home-schooling" was not only unheard of since America's pioneer days, but was presumed to be illegal when a public system of education was available. Two private meetings were held with the local school board. Neither the threats of possible jail time for child neglect nor the warning of a sizeable court fee could deter the parents. There were no legal grounds for either threat, and no penalties were ever levied against the family.

The Daily Camera – Boulder's local newspaper – carried numerous articles on the evolving story, documenting the School Board's frustration as well as the young girls' sense of shame and social alienation. Other parents and classmates alike shook their heads with a sense of sadness. It seemed so unnecessary, so extreme, so naïve.

But throughout history those who initiate change are often misunderstood. No one could have predicted the trend that was coming. In the following years, more and more parents would make that same decision. Diminishing educational standards, safety concerns due to bullying or gang intimidation, and lack of any teaching of healthy social skills eventually caused millions of parents to opt for home-schooling instead of their public classroom system.

By the end of the 20th century, 3% of all grade school students were home-schooled by their parents. Slightly more were attending private schools, charter schools, or faith-based schools. As one sad example, more than 50% of Chicago's School Board members send their own children to private schools.

Today our inner-city schools in particular are suffering. We have long ago lost our position as the world's leader in quality of education. It's no wonder that geniuses such as Steve Jobs or Bill Gates have sought to provide a complete overhaul of our public education system. Any tolerance or contentment with the status quo serves to delay needed improvements, and suggests that a greater crisis may be looming if sweeping changes are not adopted.

As the "party culture" at the University of Colorado began to expand, Fraternities and Sororities had to find new and creative ways to enjoy themselves without getting suspended from school. One such invention that found great traction was to throw a "woodsey." The name simply referenced holding a large party in the woods just outside of town, with ample booze and drugs on hand.

The forested foothills of the Rocky Mountains border the city of Boulder, and there are a plethora of public picnic grounds or meadows in the midst of those trees that could serve perfectly for this purpose. Several kegs of beer, loud music through some crude system of amplification, and an abundant supply of mescaline, LSD, or marijuana were available. Those were the only ingredients needed for an all-night party. A large bonfire was the central gathering point, and once a person paid the $5 entrance fee, they could partake in whatever beer or drugs they could find.

If a high school student were lucky enough to find one of these woodseys, he or she discovered that there rarely was any security or screening for I.D.'s. It was just a big crazy party in the woods, and anyone could feel welcome.

On a beautiful fall evening Tom's classmate, Scott, happened to find one such woodsey, and cautiously made his way into the gathering of about 200 young men and women. He had his illegal Driver's License with him just in case any cops might show up. He nervously hung around the fringes of the crowd, sipping on a plastic glass of Coors beer, not wanting to draw attention to himself. He had heard some bizarre tales that some hippies occasionally would use hallucinogenic drugs and then dance naked in front of the fire, or that couples might sneak into the darkness of the trees to have sex.

On this particular evening Scott witnessed all of that and more. He heard a crescendo of cheers, and then a small portion of the crowd began chanting "GO, GO, GO," from the other side of the bonfire. He quickly made a sweeping arc around the fire and worked his way through the maze of bodies. To his utter amazement, he almost stumbled on to a couple on the ground only six feet in front of him and everyone else, having sex on a blanket adjacent to the fire. They had not fully undressed, but both had their jeans down around their knees.

Once they had finished, the woman reached into her jeans pocket for a Kleenex to clean herself, as the crowd applauded and resumed their drinking. Scott was transfixed, and did not leave for some time, unsure if he was sexually aroused or merely grossed out.

But the next day he was the most popular guy at Boulder High School, as he shared all of the graphic details with his classmates.

Oh, the strange oxymoron of what constituted "military action" in the Viet Nam War.

Vern enlisted in the Navy, because that is what his dad had done in WWII. Thanks to his math degree, he was assigned a role as inventory manager, and landed on a supply ship cruising up and down the coastal waters of Viet Nam, replenishing food, munitions, and hard goods for the other U.S. military ships and ground troops stationed there. Every few weeks they would make another midnight run to the Philippines to re-fill every corner of their ship with the next round of supplies. His specific responsibilities were to handle payroll and materials requisitions for the entire crew. Their most valuable inventory on board was a ready stock of beer, cigarettes, and condoms.

He secretly felt a small degree of guilt because he was so insulated from the war itself. From the upper decks of their supply ship, Vern and his naval associates could watch Huey helicopters shuttling U.S. ground troops back and forth on the countryside. With high-powered binoculars they could see Marines landing on a beach north of the DMZ. Yet Vern's biggest issue of the entire war was that the lens of his camera kept fogging over due to the high humidity that permeated the area.

His fellow sailors occasionally talked about this artificial separation from the war that they were experiencing. Every week they heard news snippets of the latest total U.S. and enemy casualties. It was somewhat like suspended animation, working in the heart of the war effort but never being under the direct threat of enemy fire. His biggest danger in the war was merely embarking and disembarking from the ship. To a man, every sailor he knew was anti-war, but not anti-patriotic. In spite of their individual opposition to this specific war effort, the politics of military service meant that you do what you are asked to do.

As another American ship would pull along side to receive supplies, one of Vern's unwritten responsibilities was to radio the quarters of the approaching Captain, and compare what movies he had on board. A virtual library of movies existed among all the ships, and it was a simple matter of continually swapping with each other. Old Westerns were the most popular, but anything that had not yet been seen a few times was a welcome trade.

Payday came once a month, and Vern distributed more than $80,000. in cash every pay cycle. Lowest ranking sailors received just less than $300 and it ramped up from there. He was so excited to make a presentation to the officers about a new payroll option called "direct deposit". He stressed the convenience, the safety, and the perfect timeliness of this opportunity. To him it seemed like a "no-brainer" because of all of the benefits. But to his surprise, the proposal fell on deaf ears. During a break, the Captain pulled him aside and explained their reluctance. Every married man on board was sending funds home to his wife and family – after he secretly kept some discretionary spending money for himself. And every wife assumed she was receiving the entire paycheck. If the system of "direct deposit" were to be implemented, the men would have no pocket money for their own choices of entertainment. Vern reluctantly acquiesced, and cash payroll remained the norm for the duration of the war.

During shore leave on every trip back to the Philippines, some of the sailors would stock up on cameras and "boom-boxes." To save on the cost of batteries that those items required, the seamen had learned that they could cannibalize batteries from their Navy-issued life jackets. Those jacket batteries were intended to power a radio beacon and a flashing light, in case a crew member ever accidentally landed in the water at night. But the perceived lack of such a risk motivated the men to utilize the batteries for their own "more important" purposes.

Oh, the strange oxymoron of what constituted "military action" in the Viet Nam War.

Mark's mother was fortunate to land a great job that fall. She was hired as a cook for the Caribou Ranch, a rustic cluster of buildings located between Nederland and Boulder. She had no idea of the excitement for her that would take place there. The pay was modest, but the occasional tips were incredible. Here's why.

Caribou Ranch had only three guest houses and a community dining room, but it also included an elaborate state-of-the-art recording studio. Not only was the quality of sound production equal to any studio in New York, Chicago, or L.A., but the unique bonus with this mountain setting was the secluded privacy. A wide assortment of drugs was always available, and in open display on the countertops. The remote location meant no scrutiny from the police or the press.

Word quickly spread amongst musicians and celebrities alike. It became a haven for Hollywood's wealthy quietly to bring a mistress in secret, or a few musicians to work on an album while being high for several days at a time. Drugs were certainly available in any other city in the U.S., but they were always accompanied with the risk of discovery. Caribou Ranch offered an unparalleled sense of peace and security in an idyllic setting. Guests often said there was more "snow" in the lodge than on the mountainside that surrounded it.

Every week Mark's mother would come home with a giddy smile, as she invited her family to play the game, "Guess Who I Cooked For Today?"

Ann Margaret, Chuck Connors, Stephanie Powers, David Crosby

and Steven Stills, just to mention a few. Bands such as The Beach Boys, Poco, and Chicago. When the movie *"Stagecoach"* was being filled nearby, John Wayne and Bing Crosby stopped in. The secluded ranch had quickly become a revolving door for the rich and famous.

Boulder, Colorado, and the surrounding mountains suddenly began to take on a national reputation as an ideal destination for America's "party crowd." A person no longer needed to ski in order to enjoy a Rocky Mountain high. Playboy magazine always included the University of Colorado in its "Top Ten Party Campuses", based on the perceived availability of alcohol, sex, and drugs. Time Magazine declared Boulder to be the #1 city in the country for drug usage on a per capita basis. In rapid fashion Boulder was becoming a mecca for hedonism in any form. The city would never be the same.

During the '40's and '50's, Edward Lansdale had developed into an extraordinary secret espionage agent for the U.S. military. First in World War II, then in Korea and the Philippines, he had learned the priceless value of propaganda and psychological warfare as tools far more valuable in winning a war than using bombs and mortar shells. Particularly in the communist-driven Huk Rebellion, Lansdale observed that if a superior military system used only brute force to counter an inferior enemy, the resultant killing of guerrilla soldiers and civilians would only harden the hearts of the out-numbered enemy, and ultimately produce a sure formula for an embarrassing defeat of the greater military entity.

Secretary of Defense Robert McNamara summoned Lansdale to his office in Washington, D.C., in late 1966, seeking what strategic advice he might offer in the growing confrontation in Viet Nam. McNamara could already see some of the similarities to the recent communist efforts in the Philippines. McNamara was a certified genius, and absolutely convinced that every problem – in business, government, and warfare – could be analyzed and ultimately solved with a precise equation. One writer described him as having an IQ that could boil water, and a personality that could freeze the tropics. Like many geniuses, he had an ego the size of the Louisiana Purchase, and a correspondingly miniscule level of patience for anyone that might be his intellectual inferior – which was just about everyone.

As Lansdale entered the opulent office, McNamara told him he had 15 minutes to share any insights he might have. To McNamara's utter surprise, Lansdale dumped the contents of a gunny sack onto his nicely polished desk. A variety of "dirty weapons" smeared with mud and blood slid across the surface, including French rifles with no sights on the barrels, hand-made knives and pistols, and bamboo spears.

"What the hell is the meaning of this?" the Secretary said in a startled voice.

"Look closely," said his guest. "These are the primary weapons of your enemy. Most of those soldiers are bare-footed or wear nothing more than sandals. Yet they are kicking your ass every day of the week. And if you don't understand that the nature of this war is not about geographical 'turf' but rather about ideas and ideals, your only military result can be tragedy."

With little more to be said, Lansdale gathered his display and quietly left. The short conversation could not change the "equation" already sketched on McNamara's note pad. Logic could not be wrong. America was vastly superior in ground weaponry to that of the North Vietnamese. The enemy's naval and air force capability was almost non-existent. This battle should be short-lived, and America's victory seemed assured.

Ignoring the input from Edward Lansdale, McNamara continued to pursue a futile path the next few years that would require the lives of more than 58,000 Americans and billions in Defense Department expenditures. And in the end, the outcome could only be described in the one, single word that Lansdale had predicted . . . "tragedy."

Cezar Chavez

Gloria Steinem

The Monkees

James Meredith

U.S. troops in Viet Nam

Secretary of Defense Robert McNamara

Anti-war Protest

CHAPTER 4

"1967 – FROM TABOO TO RECREATION"

"Wouldn't it be nice if we were older,
Then we wouldn't have to wait so long. . . .
You know its gonna' make it that much better
When we can say goodnight and stay together . . ."

Beach Boys

"Why don't we do it in the road?
No one will be watching us,
Why don't we do it in the road."

Beatles

On a frigid Saturday morning in January, Mark decided to go big-game hunting for a couple of hours. *'Even the deer and elk won't feel like moving around much on a cold day like today,'* he thought, *'so maybe I'll find one.'*

As he quietly followed an old jeep trail through the timber toward an abandoned mine, his eye caught a movement against the snow-covered hillside across the ravine. Gazing through the lens of his rifle scope he studied the movement for a moment. It certainly wasn't an animal, but something was slowly shifting back and forth. He had to investigate.

Approaching with caution, Mark discovered the movement to be a large tarp flapping gently in the wind. It was military grade with a camouflage pattern, and seemed very much out of place in such a remote corner of the National Forest. As he pulled back the corner, he understood why. He found himself staring at almost 100 bales of marijuana, neatly stacked, and well-hidden. It was enough to fill a couple of large passenger vans. And certainly enough value to buy his own house if he wanted to.

Boulder had become a common destination for rented Winnebagos coming in from Miami or Tucson with a load of "Columbian Red", a popular strain of marijuana. Typically a man and woman would pose as a married couple to avoid suspicion, and transport a ton or more at a time in those RV's. Much of this product originated in Mexico, or in the remote corners of Arizona and New Mexico.

Mark sat down in the snow and pondered what to do. There certainly was a huge cash value to what was sitting there. For a moment he thought about how he might re-locate this cache one bale at a time, and then sell it himself. But common sense kicked in. *I've never needed to steal anything before. And anyone moving this kind of volume was probably capable of creating a whole lot of trouble for me later.'*

As he left he neatly tucked the corner of the tarp back under the bales so that it no longer flapped in the wind. He didn't even bother to take a small sample for himself. He continued his hunt, convinced that if he lived by the Golden Rule, he may never get rich but at least he would be OK.

Martin Luther King, Jr. was a charismatic pastor who had become the most visible spokesperson for the equal rights of all African Americans. Not just the right to vote. Not just the right to sit on the same bus. Not just the right to an education. King advocated being treated as equal human beings in any and every regard. He had become an international icon because of his "I Have A Dream" speech four years earlier, when 250,000 gathered at the Washington Monument in Washington, D.C. to hear his vision for mankind. In retrospect he may very well have been the most important American since Abraham Lincoln.

"I have a dream," he had said, "that one day our children will live in a nation where they will not be judged by the color of their skin, but rather by the content of their character." That speech became widely regarded as the most well-written — and also the most well-delivered — speech of the 20th Century. It was certainly the defining moment for the Civil Rights Movement. Of all the advocates and champions in support of equal rights, that speech put King at the top of the list.

Going from city to city in the south, King would lead large crowds in peaceful marches or sit-ins as a means of garnering media attention to the problems of inequality and racial hatred. Cynics and racists referred to him as "MARTIN LUCIFER KOON", not only due to their inbred attitudes against blacks, but also because too often he would lead a peaceful protest, and then violence and bloodshed would break out as soon as he left town.

In April of 1967, Martin Luther King took a new approach, which once again shocked the nation. While the Civil Rights effort to date had been concentrated in southern states, he noticed that the anti-war movement extended to every corner of the country. Protests against Viet Nam could pop up anywhere, and seemed to be much more universal in stimulating people to action. King chose to try to integrate those two issues for the first time, as a way to broaden his audience with those that might support racial equality. It would prove to be a shrewd and successful strategy.

While in New York City, King helped to arrange a peaceful march from Central Park to the United Nations Building. There he delivered a speech entitled "Beyond Viet Nam: A Time to Break Silence." The final destination point was chosen in hopes that it might help to bring international pressure on public opinion as well as political leaders. In coming out against the war in Viet Nam that afternoon, as well opposing the government's policies that created that war, he sought to demonstrate that both issues fell under the umbrella of "what is truly right or wrong for humanity", not merely personal whims or traditions. Both issues were positioned to be above any particular political party affiliation, reaching into the hearts of every man or woman that held a moral compass.

Any immediate reaction was mixed. Many of his fellow black leaders felt it was a mistake, because it appeared to move King off of his core message. But those closest to him realized that it just might be his most important speech ever, because it successfully engaged a much wider audience from that point forward. University students in northern and western states found a new opportunity to be a part of something else that had a grand purpose. Frequent protesting simply for the sake of protesting had become captivating entertainment for many students. And Martin Luther King managed to tap into that energy by showing the over-lap of those two issues. America would see the heightened results for the next several years.

In response to King's influence, the first noticeable national trend among African American activists was the outward demonstration of their pride in their African heritage. Blacks began studying Swahili at city colleges, and wearing brightly colored African clothing. As with their white counterparts, hair became a major statement. Large "Afros" were worn as a proud representation of the unique kinky nature of their hair. Black History Week was instituted on most campuses across the country, giving African American students an opportunity to celebrate their cultural flavor, and to speak at various student gatherings regarding their historical distinctives in food, clothes, music, and traditions.

Before African American men and women could ask to be treated equally, they needed to truly believe in themselves as equal. Martin Luther King instilled that conviction in their hearts, and all of America would slowly have to come to grips with that truth.

Cassius Clay had won the Gold Medal for boxing at the 1960 Olympics, and the Heavyweight Title in 1964. By now he had changed his name to Mohammad Ali, and had become the poster child for the Black Nation of Islam religion. He remained undefeated for the next several years, and without question still holds the position as the most celebrated international celebrity of all time for the sport of boxing, and may very well have become the most famous athlete in the world for any sport.

But Ali's most unexpected "fight" came in the spring of this year. His hometown draft board delivered the papers telling him that he was being drafted into the U.S. Army. Ali's abrupt response was simply, "No, I ain't going."

The U.S. government was forced to step in, because the integrity of the entire military system was at stake if a professional athlete or celebrity could flatly refuse to serve merely because "they didn't feel like it." Yet even the immensity of the Defense Department was not ready for the conflict that ensued.

Ali said that he was willing to accept any imposed jail time if necessary, but continued to refuse to appear for his Army physical. That was not an acceptable solution to the government, because a precedent would be set where every young man in America could then choose jail, and there would be no military system at all.

The government thought they had played their ultimate trump card when they brought pressure to bear on the U.S. Boxing Commission.

Government officials privately threatened the commission with non-renewal of all licenses if they did not in turn threaten to strip Ali of his Heavyweight Boxing Title, and prohibit him from any future boxing until he had complied with his military duty. Surely he would not surrender something so dear as his passion and his very lucrative livelihood.

However Ali was not only a man of deep convictions and principles, but often a man of great surprises as well. Instead of buckling to such strong-arm tactics, he held a national press conference of his own. He invited other African American athletes of great public stature to join him. Jim Brown, the most feared running back in professional football history, accompanied him at the press table. Bill Russell, winner of more professional basketball titles than any other player in the history of the NBA, also joined him at the press table. Their presence alone helped to make a powerful statement, and the public relations war was over, much to the chagrin of the Defense Department. Regardless of what the courts might decide, Ali had won the hearts of the general public.

At the press conference, Ali reiterated his refusal to serve in the military. How could he support a country that continued to allow the racial inequities in the south to go unabated? If he were to serve in the Army, he would be no different than a slave that was forced into labor against his will.

Painted into a corner, the government had no choice but to follow through with their original threat. They had Ali arrested, and declared guilty of draft evasion. They required that Ali forfeit his heavyweight boxing title, and also to be banned from any future association with professional boxing. Reactions were strongly divided. Even the notorious sports broadcaster, Howard Cosell, voluntarily came to his side and declared that Ali had been unethically stripped of his title. Cosell risked his own career as a boxing announcer when he stood by Ali in this fight. In so doing, Cosell ushered in a new realm for all sportscasters to begin to make social commentary rather than just reporting the score of a specific game. It would be four years of legal appeals before Ali's case was ultimately taken to the Supreme Court, and his sentence was finally revoked. Ali was free to box once again.

But both sides lost in this much-publicized confrontation. Ali suffered great financial hardship during this season of time, because he missed out on four years of opportunity while in his prime as the world's greatest fighter. The U.S. government and the Defense Department lost as well. They lost respect and credibility among many Americans. Not only was their entire military personnel fighting a futile battle in southeast Asia, but they were now losing their own "public relations war" at home. And their public image never fully recovered.

That spring Tom, David, and two of their other classmates from Boulder High School decided to try out their fake ID's at a music club in Denver, called "Hal Baby Moore's." The liquor license at the venue required that ticket holders must be 18 or older, and these 17-year old high school juniors had now created the false drivers licenses that said they qualified.

They drove to Denver with great anticipation, looking forward to hearing a local band called the *"Boenzee Cryque"*, who were getting frequent playing time on both of Denver's rock & roll radio stations. That band was performing on this particular evening as the opening set for some headliner group from California called *"Buffalo Springfield."*

The entire night was perfect. The bouncers never questioned their ID's, the energy in the packed room was great, everyone in their group stayed sober, and – to their surprise – the headliner band from California was phenomenal. Somehow that west-coast music group was creating an entirely new genre of music by playing a hybrid mix of country folk music and rock & roll. It was a great show.

David drove everyone home filling his usual role as the designated driver. As they left Denver, each of the other guys bought another beer at a liquor store for half the price of what beers cost in the club. The fake ID's worked flawlessly once again.

Tom was unusually quiet for the entire ride back to Boulder. His imagination had been stirred, and he would never forget this evening. Although he could play more than a dozen chords on his Goya guitar, he knew he really did not have what it would take to be a professional musician or entertainer. But this night had opened his eyes to other alternatives. Maybe he could own his own nightclub. Maybe he could manage a band. He knew he was smart enough to make a lot of money, and have fun doing it. Working behind the scenes in the music and entertainment field just might be his ticket. *Somehow,* he thought, *he was going to change the world.*

The hippie culture of the late '60's had a very spiritual component for many as part of their desperate search for meaning. Various gurus began creating their own private following, which splintered in many directions. The vacuum created by the "God is Dead" movement created a surge in eastern religions, mysticism, sorcery and witchcraft, meditation, and shamanism. Young adults would frequently go camping in the mountains by themselves for a few days to "commune with nature." Others came full circle to start "Jesus-freak" communities. In Boulder, about 30 to 40 hippies gathered every Sunday evening for a meal and conversation that was called "God's Thing."

Jane was a bright student at the University of Colorado. While she tried her best to abstain from the sex and drugs that were so prevalent in her circle of friends, she went to Tulagi's a couple of times a week because she loved to dance. Huge speakers hung from the ceiling, amplifying the best of psychedelic rock albums. One evening as she was dancing with a friend, she felt the tap on her shoulder of someone wanting to cut in. As she turned, she found herself dancing with Jesus. She knew she was not stoned, but felt completely mesmerized in the moment.

For the rest of her life, Jane would clearly describe what happened in those next few minutes. She had a clear sense of how He cupped her hand in His as they danced. When the song was over, she found herself standing alone in the middle of Tulagi's dance floor. In the ecstasy of that experience, she began to leap from chair to chair, from table to sofa, from the floor to the top of a railing. She could not contain her emotional high. And because of that evening, she chose to teach Dance for the rest of her life.

As a result of so many young people looking for new spiritual connection, a dramatic shift began to take place throughout the established religious institutions of our country. Harvard University was originally founded almost 400 years ago as the first University in the United States, with a close connection to mainline Protestant churches. Its primary function in those early years was to prepare men for the clergy in Congregational or Unitarian churches. By the spring semester of '67, for the first time in its esteemed history, Harvard had more incoming students identify themselves as atheists or agnostics than Protestants and Catholics combined.

The rebellious attitude begun amongst college students to "Question Authority" was now permeating the Catholic Church. Young adults were searching for "truth" and "relevance", and the traditional Mass being given in Latin did nothing to accomplish that. The Church desperately tried to adapt as congregants became more and more restless. The Cardinals found it necessary to facilitate a lengthy debate on the pro's and con's of contraceptives. Married parishioners were demanding church approval, and spoke openly of wanting to remain faithful to the church but at the same time wanting the freedom of spontaneous and recreational sex within the privacy of their home. The "absolute" authority of the priesthood was suddenly in doubt.

Attendance at Mass eroded further when hundreds of priests collectively walked away from the Catholic Church because of the continued constraints of celibacy on the priesthood. Many of their close friends followed them out the door as a show of support.

Pragmatism ultimately ruled the day for all of Catholicism, or else the clergy knew that they risked not only their weekly attendance but also their entire financial base of support in the future. New lines of clarification were drawn. Sex within marriage was no longer primarily for "procreation." It was God's gift, and should be enjoyed as marital "recreation" as well. For the first time, contraception was permissible within those constraints. Sex before marriage, however, was still labeled as "taboo", and the sudden new issue of elective abortion was declared an abomination – an act of voluntary murder – in the eyes of God as well as the church.

Protestant churches were also experiencing a seismic upheaval. The complete freedom of experimentation among young adults was spilling into the arena of one's worldview. The Maharishi Yogi had become the spiritual advisor to the Beatles, and that role model suddenly motivated young adults to be creative in their spiritual pursuits. Theism and Deism were being replaced by varieties of pantheism, the occult, or even nihilistic philosophies. A demographic gap quickly appeared in the church pews as the majority of young adults abruptly stopped attending their houses of worship.

The chosen solutions for mainline Protestant churches took on a dramatically different face compared to that of Catholic leadership. Protestantism chose to become much more secularized, i.e. to concentrate on social causes such as civil rights and poverty. These issues were certainly consistent with their foundational conviction of Biblical principles, but offered an opportunity to remain "fresh" or "relevant" in an effort to retain young adults and young families who shared those progressive social values. After all, their future survival would depend on it as well.

America's youth were suddenly instigating national changes in places such as the church that they had not intentionally considered. But their "age wave" affected everything, and that demographic was now just too big to ignore.

In the spring, 20-year-old Kathrine Switzer added her voice to the chorus of women seeking gender equality in all areas of American culture. As a competitive distance runner, she chose to attempt to participate in the

Boston Marathon, even though women were not officially allowed to enter that most prestigious distance race in America.

To circumvent the registration process, she used only her first initial "K. Switzer" on her entry form. No suspicions were aroused, and she was assigned bib number 261. A hooded sweatshirt hid her long hair as she and thousands of other runners gathered at the starting line. Once past the starter's platform and underway, she and several of her close friends assumed they home free.

Not so.

Boston Marathon officials happened to be riding in the Media truck as it slowly drove among the runners through the entire course, taking live news video of the many contestants. A few miles into the race, a cameraman commented on the fact that he noticed a woman running in the midst of several men just to the right of the truck. One of the race officials hurriedly got off the back of the truck and began running after them in his leather shoes and street clothes. As he approached, he began yelling "Get outta' my race!!", and was frantically trying to clutch her racing bib to tear it off of her sweatshirt.

Kathrine felt a surge of adrenalin as the man yanked on her shirt, unable to tear off the bib on his first attempt. Her race would have been over had it not been for two of the men that were jogging with her. They placed two well-aimed body blocks into the side of the racing official, looking as if they played for the Green Bay Packer's offensive front line. The marathon official went sprawling to the other side of the street, and the runners slowly continued.

Cameramen along the route began looking for Switzer as the race continued. They knew history was in the making. A little more than four hours after she started, Kathrine Switzer not only broke the finish line of the Boston Marathon, but she also broke another barrier in the quest for equal rights for women. Her bib "#261" became a rallying symbol for women to follow in that step of courage. Avon Cosmetics partnered with her to sponsor a series of "women's only races" around the world. It would be another five years of petitions and planning meetings, however, before the Boston Marathon Commission officially allowed women to register and run in their race.

Some movies are certain to be box-office hits before they are ever released. Other big-budget productions are total flops. But every now and then a low-budget "throw away" movie unexpectedly becomes a monster success. 1967 witnessed one of the greatest such surprises in Hollywood's history.

Donald Sutherland and Elliott Gould anchored a zany cast of would-be medical staff men and women that were assigned to serve in the Medical Army Surgical Hospital (M.A.S.H.) unit of the Viet Nam War. The shrewd timing of this comedy spoof could not have been better.

The message resonated perfectly with the growing rebellion of young Americans. Mocking the idea of "military intelligence" as a contradiction in terms, satirically opposing the atrocities war, celebrating recreational sex and drug use. It landed superbly on every targeted issue. "M.A.S.H." as a movie was an over-night success, much to the chagrin of the U.S. Defense Department.

As the war itself dragged on in coming years, the monetary opportunity for leveraging the "M.A.S.H." concept was too great to pass up. Television producers put together a TV show under the same name. The Viet Nam setting, however, had to be shifted slightly to that of South Korea to satisfy TV censors that wanted to avoid any direct appearance of implied reality and anti-Americanism. The "fictional" situation comedy was able to dodge any such accusations by those slight story-line adjustments. But the underlying message was ever so clear, and a major slap to the military as well as any of its proponents. Ex-Viet Nam soldiers and medical personnel were hired to help develop some of the plot lines and predicaments for the show to insure authenticity. Both the gravity and futility of such a war could not be missed.

"M.A.S.H." overwhelmed the TV ratings as the #1 show in their time-slot for nine straight years. When the finale was finally aired, it was the most watched program in television history. 77% of all TV's in the U.S. were tuned in to see that last show – a market share that could never be equaled again because of the future dilution of cable TV viewers that would occur in subsequent years. Since there were no VCR's or DVR's at the time, anyone who chose to watch the show by necessity watched it live at the same time. An interesting note in that regard . . . during the airing of the final M.A.S.H. episode, so many people used their bathrooms at the same time during the commercial breaks that the entire sewer system of New York City broke down.

That dominance also helped to break the public relations back of the White House and the Pentagon. "M.A.S.H." steadily helped to destroy any last vestiges for America's will to win in southeast Asia.

Steve was one of Tom's classmates at Boulder High School who was lucky enough to receive one of the fake I.D.'s. In late May Steve took advantage of that document by getting into a memorable concert in the Student Union Building at the University of Colorado campus. The *"Grateful Dead"* was booked to provide the music on that particular evening.

It was a terrible setting for such an event. Held indoors, with a low ceiling, and a patch-worked sound system that almost crushed people in the front of the room, but very poor acoustics in the back. It didn't matter too much. Most of the students were drunk or stoned before they entered. Everyone was yelling throughout the concert, which added to the distortion of the musical sound. Psychedelic lights were moving on the walls and ceiling in an attempt to create an environment of craziness.

But it was some of the noteworthy "props" that made the concert so memorable for Steve. Near the front of the stage was an old bathtub filled with jell-o. Lying on top of the jell-o was an attractive young woman who was totally naked. Her job was to stay there for the duration of the concert, and let some of the waving lights slowly roll over her body.

The concert concluded just prior to midnight. Students headed toward their respective fraternities or sororities, and assumed the band was probably staying at a nice hotel nearby. What they didn't notice was that the "Grateful Dead" tour bus was carefully parked directly behind the campus building.

The manager and stage crew for the band had come into town a day ahead of time, and in addition to their responsibilities for setting up the necessary sound equipment, they also took it upon themselves to arrange for women to "take care" of the band members after the concert. The musicians ended up being introduced to a set of twins with beautiful long blonde hair, who had agreed to some pre-determined amount as payment to service the entire band.

It was not until 6 a.m. the next morning before the twins tip-toed out of the band's tour bus, and took a taxi to their own apartment. Every member of the band and the crew had had their turn – one or two at a time – and the bus slowly rolled out of town with a bunch of very exhausted but satisfied band members. The lifestyle of a touring rock & roll group was often beyond surreal.

The sudden success of the "James Bond" brand as an invincible secret agent generated a flurry of TV copycats. Viewers were captivated by the scenario of impeccably dressed spies with proprietary technology bordering on science-fiction at their disposal, who were able to travel the world to counter the forces of evil in its most inventive forms. *"Secret Agent Man"*, *"Charlie's Angels"*, *"I Spy"*, *"Mission: Impossible"*, *"The Saint"*, and *"The Avengers"* were examples of some of the successful clones to that theme. Comedian Mel Brooks even created a comedy spoof of the entire government spy concept with another successful TV series, called *"Get Smart."*

But none of these shows had the obsessed fan base and dedicated following as that of *"The Man From U.N.C.L.E."* With cheeky dialog and outstanding music, this show dominated television in its weekly time slot. Actor Robert Vaughn had previously been in numerous Hollywood movies, but his lead role as an agent with this "United Network Command for Law Enforcement" catapulted him to stardom at the highest levels.

Vaughn chose to use that celebrity status to convey his heart. He spoke out publicly against the war wherever an opportunity presented itself. In the middle of 1967 he approached an organization called "Dissenting Democrats", and asked if he could help in their anti-war efforts. He was quickly voted as their national chairman, and joined the loose network of those people or entities that were producing newsletters, campus fliers, or public appearances for the purpose of urging all Americans to oppose our country's involvement in Viet Nam.

The idol worship of Robert Vaughn – as well as other activist Hollywood elite – and what he had to say against the war was another example of the impossible task our government had in trying to convince Americans otherwise. Celebrity influence had now become a new and invisible enemy of the war effort.

In October, a few celebrities once again made national news – not for their entertainment skills – but for their opposition to the war. Joan Baez, noted folk singer, and 39 of her friends were arrested in Oakland for blocking the entrance to a military induction center. Baez had gained notoriety for her protest folk songs and frequent speeches against America's presence in Viet Nam. The media collected another short sound-bite from her as she was being hand-cuffed and escorted into a police car.

Just five days later, on the opposite coast, Allen Ginsberg led 30,000 people on a march through the streets of Washington, D.C. as another protest to the war. Ginsberg was a poet who had gained a national following because of his radical counter-cultural views against capitalism, materialism, and traditional sexual parameters. His message of opposition was embraced by all those baby-boomers that wanted to participate in "radical change."

Celebrity involvement and influence was now contagious. Without the need for a ballot box, these musicians, writers, and entertainers were quietly moving the heart of America much faster than traditional legislators or educators could possibly have done.

Tom was fascinated with the international news that was taking place in early June. Egypt and other Arab countries had attacked Israel with their full onslaught of military aggression, but were soundly defeated in only six days by the much smaller Israeli army. The rest of the world also watched their televisions in awe as General Moshe Dayan walked up the steps at the Dome of the Rock with his nephew, Amazia Dayan, and not only declared that the war was over, but also that the holy city of Jerusalem in its entirety now belonged to the Jewish people once again.

Ensuing news stories began to reveal the vast superiority of Israel's secret intelligence. A classic example was an Egyptian military airfield that was dotted with dozens of fighter planes and mixed with an equal number of decoy planes for the purpose of generating a façade of a very large air force at the ready. Israeli commandos had chosen to destroy every real fighter plane while they sat on the ground, but also very careful to leave every decoy plane in perfect condition. The morale of the Egyptian forces was consequently crushed and embarrassed.

The short and decisive success of this "Six-Day War" in Israel created an unexpected ripple-effect in portions of our own country. America's military families found themselves feeling jealous. Why could the Viet Nam War not be over in six days? Why was the North Vietnamese enemy so elusive and unrelenting, when our technology, fighter planes, bombs, and other ammunition was so superior in strength? Why was our secret intelligence not as successful as the Israeli's?

Lyndon Johnson – as well as the entire Defense Department – was feeling squeezed. The "Hawks" wanted a decisive military victory, and they wanted it now. The "Doves" wanted immediate withdrawal from any further military actions, win or lose. Johnson was particularly irritated with the Doves, or "Nervous Nellies" as he called them. Their numbers seemed to be growing, and they stood in the way of his vision for success. To have a better sense of all aspects of the war, the President had an elaborate model of South Viet Nam built exactly to scale in the White House, so that his military staff could track every detail of troop locations. He knew that America desperately needed a convincing win such as the Israeli army had accomplished, or else national morale would only slip further away. Yet no solution was forthcoming.

Defense Secretary McNamara decided he needed to get out before this war effort became a colossal failure. He quietly resigned, and accepted a position as President of the World Bank. Before leaving the White House, he privately assured President Johnson that he would not speak publicly of his disillusionment about the war, or his growing sense of futility for America's troops. His reticence fell on deaf ears.

Throughout the country that spring and summer, racial tensions seemed to rise with the increasing temperature and humidity. Patience levels were waning as African Americans expected the enactment of recent Civil Rights legislation instantly to change their social environment. But old habits are not quickly broken.

Random events began to reveal turmoil existing in all corners of the U.S. Armed Black Panthers stormed the Capitol Building in Sacramento, California, demanding to be heard. Stokely Carmichael delivered an emotional speech at Fisk University in Nashville, Tennessee, and instigated a small riot in the process. Ten police officers were injured trying to keep the peace, eight students were hospitalized, and 40 were arrested.

The fad of university students revolting for any and all causes was catching. Jackson State had a four-day riot, which included gunfire between black students and police. One officer was killed, and four others wounded. Retaliation and the venting of hatred were now becoming more and more rampant on campuses.

Local police in any city were outnumbered by the people they were paid to protect. So when any civil rights protest was organized – particularly in the south – the city police or campus police needed additional reinforcements. Both the National Guard and the Army were called on to provide backup support. However, as these protests became more common, a new conflict surfaced. African American soldiers refused to get on to the troop trains when they were being sent to quell such a protest. They reasoned that they had enlisted to fight America's enemies on foreign soil – not to go face-to-face with other African American men who were seeking nothing more than equal rights.

During the final days of the spring semester, students at Cheney State College in Cheney, Pennsylvania, seized the Administration Building and caused the campus to be closed for two days. Founded in 1837, this was an historic campus because it was established as the first all-black college, specifically created to give young black men and women an equal education. The student's cause was unclear, but basically just wanted the assurance that they could be heard. Although 400 students began the sit-in, interest waned rather quickly as they failed to identify a singular purpose. Theirs was an example of protesting merely for protesting sake.

At Columbia University, students took over the Administration Building, cancelled all classes, and for a brief time held the Dean as hostage. The students maintained a "sit-in" for an entire week, until 1000 police were called in to remove them. More than 700 students were arrested. At least 100 students, 4 faculty members, and 12 officers needed medical attention for minor injuries.

In mid-July, police in Newark, New Jersey, beat a Black cab driver, and race riots broke out in the ghetto nearby. Rampant looting took place every evening for six straight days. Small fires were frequently started in the streets. Police killed five men the first night, and the National Guard was called in to provide additional back-up. Twenty more residents of Newark were killed before any sense of calm was restored. As police and National Guard units would quell one disturbance, another would break out just a few blocks away. For some added drama, African American teenagers had found the necessary tools to open most of the city fire hydrants. Consequently there was an extensive amount of water running in the streets every night, which served as an instant playground for the children, but a major nuisance for the police and firemen. If the city of Newark had experienced a major fire any time during that week, there would not have been a sufficient amount of city water to fight it. If nothing else, Newark was fortunate that week in that one regard.

But a far more disastrous riot erupted the following week in Detroit. What made that uprising unique was that most African American residents of Detroit had decent paying jobs thanks to the auto industry, and they owned their own homes, as well as cars. Yet they chose to riot as a demonstration of solidarity with those brothers and sisters less fortunate in cities such as Newark, Atlanta, and L.A.

African Americans began burning their own stores in their own neighborhoods. Massive looting and street fires were common this time, just as in Newark. Detroit firemen documented 1,682 fires with which they had to contend, and more than 400 structures were completely destroyed. It was beyond any possible means of containment.

Detroit's Mayor and the Governor of Michigan respectively pleaded with President Johnson to declare the situation a disaster area that needed federal help. Johnson agreed, and sent in 6,800 National Guardsmen, as well as 3,300 U.S. Army paratroopers. But instead of being limited to billy clubs and tear gas, the police and National Guard were given permission to use gunfire as a means of self-defense. Shooting in the air, shooting at random. After three days of confrontation there were 43 dead bodies in the streets, and 7,000 arrests. More than 1,600 buildings were partially damaged by fire, and two firemen lost their lives in the process. More than 5,000 residents were left homeless. The horror was unspeakable. It was officially recorded as the worst riot ever in the history of Detroit.

The rioters had stones and bricks for weapons, but not pistols. As the body count began to climb, the activists' anger changed to futility. This had not been the best solution. Too many mothers had to identify their young sons at the morgue. And surviving young men realized they had to organize strategically if they were going to have any measurable social changes. Once again, the issue of "civil equality" had been "kicked down the street" for a later date. Only now the stakes were growing higher. The pressure cooker was building, and something far worse seemed to be forming on the horizon.

It was a crisp fall day in Boulder, and David was anxious to finish his classes and head up to the Golden Cue. He had heard that the Cue was hosting a major pool tournament this month, with significant cash prizes. David thought he just might be good enough and lucky enough to win something.

When he got there, the pool hall was relatively quiet so he had an easy chance to talk to the operations manager on duty.

"So, when does this big tournament start that I've been hearing about?" David asked enthusiastically.

"It's right there on the poster," the manager said, pointing to a large sign hanging on the wall. "Entrance fees have to be in by next week."

David was taken a bit by surprise, because he had not heard anything about the $10. fee requirement to be included. "So what kind of pool game will it be?" he continued. "I'm assuming it will be "Straight Call" or some other skill game, right?"

"No," the manager replied as he stored a few racks of balls. "This will be an "8-Ball" tournament. It goes faster that way."

"8-Ball?" David said in disbelief. "Why, that's just 'nigger pool', right?"

The manager wheeled around with a look of shock on his face, and then hurriedly glanced to all four corners of the pool hall before looking back to David. His eyes were squinting with a sense of great intensity.

"Young man," he slowly hissed through gritted teeth, "if Sampson happened to be in this room today, you would be in need of medical attention right now!"

David swallowed hard, because he knew the manager was right. That expression was something he had heard a few times before, and he considered its connotation as a reference to luck or sloppy shots at a pool table instead of pure skill shots. In his heart there was no derogatory racial slur intended. But the words had been spoken, just the same.

Life's great teaching moments often come at the most unexpected times. For David this was one of those memorable focal points of learning. He promised himself that he would NEVER utter the "N-word" again for the rest of his life. Never.

By the fall of this year, two relatively new elements of birth control were beginning to take center stage on the national scene – birth control pills, and abortion.

"The Pill" had been approved by the FDA in 1960. In spite of its initial controversy it gained rapid acceptance, and by 1967 was now officially the #1 form of birth control in America, even though it was still illegal in eight states. More than 7 million women made this product their choice because it was simple, and more importantly, it was effective. A woman could now choose to be sexually active without the risk of pregnancy. That meant an incredible sense of freedom.

An unexpected opponent to the popularity of the pill came from African American activists. They received national media attention as they regularly charged that Planned Parenthood was distributing free birth control pills in the inner cities and minority neighborhoods, and in so doing was committing selective genocide.

This fall the campus nurse's office at the University of Colorado began dispensing the pill to female students, but only on the condition that the student claimed she was having severe menstrual cramps. Within weeks, an unusually high number of women suddenly reported having those severe cramps.

The psychological obsession for total independence and rebellion among young adults certainly contributed to the sexual revolution. The availability of ample quantities of drugs and alcohol played a part. Using amoral celebrities as role models may also have contributed to that trend. But none of those possible variables came close to the pill in terms of its influence on women to enjoy recreational sex with multiple partners. The era of free sex rode on the back of that little pill. It was no longer merely an *opportunity* to have random sex, it was now an *expectation* to do so. The stigma of "secrecy" or "a sullied reputation" for sexually active women was falling away, and young men just considered themselves the beneficiary of that moral shift. It was comedian Steve Martin who would later write in his autobiography that "sex in the late '60's was like shaking hands."

But another form of birth control was also emerging for the termination of an unwanted pregnancy. "Abortion" had been a repulsive concept, with jail time as potential punishment to any secret practitioner. Now the increasingly casual attitudes toward recreational sex were also producing a spike in the number of unexpected pregnancies. Abortion was forced into the conversation.

Because of growing demand, petitions for legal abortion circulated first on the CU campus, and soon throughout the city of Boulder. By the fall of '67, a bill was placed on the Colorado state ballot. To the shock and dismay of the generally conservative state, the bill passed. It was the first state in the Union to do so, and it would be many years before all of the other states would follow. Because of Boulder's collective gathering point for progressive young minds, it had influenced first the State of Colorado, and ultimately the nation. It would not be the last time that the relatively small city of Boulder would have such an impact on the entire country.

Immediately after the election that year, a small clinic opened in Boulder for the sole purpose of providing abortion services. In spite of numerous public protests or occasional death-threats in the ensuing years, the clinic and its staff have remained in business for more than 50 years. In our free-enterprise system, goods and services will always gravitate to where there is a sufficient demand.

The sexual revolution quickly moved beyond the college campus. Enlisted military men had always looked for available women when they were on leave, or on foreign soil. But now a new variable entered into the picture. In its attempts at "equality" for all, the military was beginning to allow women to enlist in the armed forces. Logistically that presented numerous new challenges, such as the need for separate bathrooms and showers, as well as the installation of sanitary napkin machines. But it also created the potential for sex without leaving the base.

Anchorage, Alaska, was one of the first U.S. bases to be confronted with this dilemma. The city itself had very little in the way of entertainment options. By 1967 it still did not have live television programming or direct-dial telephones. Even the daily news was taped at 5 p.m. on Seattle's TV stations, then flown every evening up to Anchorage to air as the 10 p.m. news.

Both the Army and the Air Force established respective bases in Anchorage, and the city's population swelled overnight. The location was ideal for the Defense Department to establish a major U.S. hub, handling both military and governmental traffic needing to get to and from Southeast Asia. Since women weren't going to be sent into live-action situations in Viet Nam, this was a perfect placement for women to serve as traffic controllers, coordinating re-fueling schedules, supply clerks, and hosting high-ranking officers or government officials.

In conjunction with all of the necessary buildings for these bases, the government found additional funds to build a special guest lodge on one of the nearby islands located along the inland passage. It was available only as a very private club for higher ranking officers, and became known as "The Chalet." Playboy Magazine just referred to it as "sin city."

One of the natural outcomes in Anchorage – and any base that included women on their payroll – was the rising occurrence of unwanted pregnancies. There was no option of legal abortion, so those women were "mustered out", and quietly removed from the military.

Every cause has an effect.

Comedy television produced a new and unexpected hero in the anti-war movement. As the fall programming rolled out, NBC took a chance on the comedy team of Dan Rowan and Dick Martin. They were given a weekly one-hour time slot to provide silly sketches, sarcasm and one-liners. The show was called *"Laugh-In."* The humor was to be very fast-paced, clean and silly – and above all, harmless. Viewers got much more than that.

What the writers found was that their best laughs came from edgy jokes in either of two areas: first, the incompetence in the Pentagon and related spoofs about the futility of a war that could possibly go on for 20 years or more; and second, double entendres with strong sexual references. Network censors were suddenly swamped with selective decisions on permissible words, depending on the visual reference. "Your Bippy" was just one example of an unknown body part left to the imagination of the viewer. Within a few weeks, "Sock it to me" had become a new expression familiar to everyone. And within just seven weeks, the program was the #1 show in the country, and remained there for several years running. NBC had a runaway winner that had come out of nowhere.

Numerous acting and entertainment careers were launched out of this comedic mayhem. Goldie Hawn had very few lines, but her ditzy blonde persona won the hearts of young people. It didn't hurt that she was usually dancing in a small bikini, and covered with body paint. Lillie Tomlin had more intelligent humor, particularly in character as "Edith Ann", offering her wisdom on any topic, or as an arrogant phone operator for AT & T. Arte Johnson was the "dirty old man." Henry Gibson offered humorous poetry, often with a political punch. Guest stars lined up, begging to be on the show because of its incredible popularity. Even President Richard Nixon and Rev. Billy Graham made the cut, and respectively signed off on episodes of the show by saying "Goodnight, and Sock it to me."

The underlying common thread which connected all of the inane jokes or slapstick sketches which made the show so popular was its irreverent and rebellious attitude toward everything: government authority of any kind, corporate greed, sexual mores, or the war. Laugh-In was one of the first television shows to make a profound discovery . . . the enormous opportunity of playing specifically to the Baby Boomers was going to change the face of television and entertainment in dramatic measure.

Rock music and journalism experienced a monumental merger in September. Robert Gleason and Jann Werner dreamed of publishing a hybrid mix of newspaper and magazine-style print that could provide behind-the-scenes expose's on the current music stage. They chose the name "ROLLING STONE" based on a popular Blues song by the same title, the British rock band of the same name, and Bob Dylan's hit song, "Like a Rolling Stone."

At 25 cents a copy, the partners hoped to create a vehicle that would allow them to enjoy their passion of following the latest trends in music.

In addition, their writing quickly began to show the ground-breaking attitudes that music was embracing, such as rebellion, revolution, free love, and recreational drugs. The publication's graphic language, inventive photography, and progressive politics found a hungry audience in greater numbers than their highest expectations.

As the circulation and success began to mount in their home office, Gleason and Werner were sometimes criticized for living a lifestyle that their publication openly criticized. Chauffeured limousines. First-class tickets on commercial flights. Chartered private jets. But the magazine itself never got off message. It became America's most noted brand as the messenger of "counter-culture" thinking.

Rolling Stone Magazine has continued to flourish for 50 years by maintaining its radical mindset. They remain the leading voice of "cultural change", and as a result their writers are frequently offered exclusive interviews by musicians or celebrities because of their "no-limits" reporting.

Nicholas Sand established a most unusual business in suburban San Francisco in the fall of '67. His degrees in chemistry and anthropology could have provided a solid career with most pharmaceutical companies. But Nicholas had experienced LSD, and his repeated acid trips led him to decide that he would be the #1 provider of psychedelics, and to strive to get the entire world to "turn on."

He had tested his process for two years with the guru of LSD, Timothy Leary, while together in central New York. LSD was legal at the time, and they openly promoted their new spiritual experience within a community they called "The Original Kleptonian Neo-American Church." Leary had left his position as a Harvard professor to become the "national priest of LSD", seeking to escape the constraints of a utilitarian society and reject the obsession of accumulating and consuming material things. But when the FDA declared the drug to be illegal, Nicholas determined he would go underground to continue his pursuit of providing the perfect recipe to achieve a world of peace and love through drugs.

The counter-culture environment of San Francisco's Haight-Ashbury district seemed to be the most logical location for his enterprise. He set up a commercial space in a warehouse that claimed to be a perfume manufacturing company. That "false front" allowed him the time and space to create a large LSD lab. Over the next two years he produced more than 10,000,000 tiny pills of exceptionally pure LSD that became known as "Orange Sunshine." Distribution was focused on college campuses and hippie communes, as well as the military personnel fighting at the front lines of Viet Nam.

The FBI finally tracked him down, arrested him, and facilitated a quick trial that sentenced him to several years in prison. But while out on bail, Nicholas decided it was time to disappear, and he made a midnight run into Canada. For the next 20 years he hid there under an assumed name, and produced another 30,000,000 units of his infamous LSD pills. When he was finally arrested again, he claimed he had enough inventory to "dose all of Canada two times over."

In spite of living on the run for so long, and ultimately serving more than six years in a U.S. prison, he never changed his perspective. He was adamantly convinced he could help all of humanity reach a higher level of consciousness through the disciplined use of psychedelic drugs. In a constant heightened sensual existence, according to Mr. Sand, one could enjoy a simple sunrise or sunset in a much deeper and fuller way. The FDA and U.S. government disagreed.

He may not have seen his dream come to fruition, but he did help move the entire culture during the late '60's and early '70's to choose drugs over alcohol as the buzz of choice. Getting drunk was now "ho-hum."

College and University administrators were becoming more and more impatient with the trend of student rebellion and uprisings. Catholic schools and other private institutions in particular felt they had more authority than their state-school counterparts to take preventative measures.

Denver University led the way in choosing an aggressive tack that they hoped would assure a disciplined and manageable campus environment. That fall the President announced a new policy of *"In Loco Parentis"* as a greater level of strict discipline, which in essence stated that since the students were away from home, the school would act as their local parent. Presumably the Latin title was intended to make it sound well thought-out, more important, more official, and maybe even based on some historical precedent. But instead, it had the opposite effect.

In predictable fashion, the students were incensed. The campus paper ridiculed the announcement, and challenged students to be willing to join any protest for any issue. Rebellion was their right. The Student Body President announced that he would be an advocate to act in the defense of any student busted for drug usage. He also successfully initiated a new petition to make birth control pills available in all of the girls' dorms.

Unprepared for such a backlash, the school President and Chancellor did not know what had hit them. In reality the students were merely swept up in the "Era" of the time. Oppose the war. Oppose LBJ. Oppose capitalism. Oppose anything connected to the Establishment. There was little or no intellectual rigor given any of the issues – just rebel, and thrill to the freedom of that experience. It was so energizing and empowering to advocate the peaceful overthrow of any American tradition.

Orphans. Adoption. Foster care. Such images of needy children being abandoned by their parents had become quite common during the Great Depression of the '30's. "Orphan Trains" during that era ran twice a year from the east coast, with random stops throughout the mid-west. Parents in New York and surrounding states that found themselves incapable of providing even a minimal amount of food for their children were forced to place their offspring on such a train, kiss them good-bye, and very likely never hear from them again for the rest of their life.

Those trains would make frequent stops through America's farmlands of Illinois, Iowa, Kansas, or Nebraska. Farmers would wait at their local depot, and when the orphan train arrived, they would simply claim one or two of the abandoned children and permanently take them into their home in exchange for providing some labor on their farm. Little or no paperwork was needed. If at all possible, siblings were kept together, but that could not always be assured.

As our country began to thrive once again through the '40's and '50's, the term "orphan" became virtually obsolete. But that sliding trend took a noticeable upturn by 1967. The new pursuit of "free love" was creating an enormous surge in the number of unwanted pregnancies – and ultimately, a corresponding surge in the number of unwanted children.

Sandra was one of those unfortunate young women. As a college student in the Seattle area, she secretly invited her boyfriend to share her dorm room during the '66 Christmas break when most students were home for the holidays. The exhilaration of having unprotected sex once or twice a day for two weeks had its consequences – a few weeks later Sandra missed her period, and realized she might have made a horrible mistake.

Too embarrassed to tell her parents the honest truth, she instead told them she was transferring to the University of Colorado in Boulder. She moved there in the spring, and stayed with two of her classmates from her former high school.

Abortion did not seem like a moral option to her, so she carried the pregnancy to term. Late in that summer of 1967 she entered a Denver hospital and delivered a healthy baby boy. When the nurses learned that Sandra had no intent or capacity to raise the baby herself, they immediately contacted the Lutheran Services Agency. The Denver branch office was facilitating such adoptions every week.

Within ten days, a young couple from Greeley, Colorado, arrived to pick up their new son. The adoption fee was only $1. Sandra would never see her baby boy again. (It would be more than 40 years before U.S. laws would allow adopted children the legal freedom to research their birth-parents and be able to contact them.)

The Lutheran Services Agency had only two requirements of any prospective adoptive parents: first, the couple must have legal proof that they were in fact married; and second, the wife must agree that she would have no job outside of the home, so that she might be an accessible and loving mother 24 hours a day.

Even following the birth, Sandra never told her parents in Seattle what had happened. She never told her former boyfriend that he had fathered a child. She buried her guilt, and swore she would never have unprotected sex from that day forward. Five years later, however, she was unexpectedly pregnant once again. This time she demanded that the father must pay for an abortion. That seemed less unpleasant to her than giving another baby up for adoption.

The freedom and excitement of the sexual revolution also had some painful consequences, and left countless women such as Sandra with emotional scars. For many women those wounds never ever went away.

Hollywood frequently tries to be prescient by creating movies which address issues that have yet to become part of the social mainstream. By breaking new ground these writers and actors can hold significant sway on developing public opinion. Such was the case in mid '67 when a controversial movie hit the big screen, entitled *"Guess Who's Coming To Dinner."*

In the storyline, the daughter of a wealthy Caucasian family surprised her parents by bringing home her fiancé, who happened to be an African American doctor. The script followed the emotional tensions of her progressive white parents, who wanted to be principled and tolerant, but now the reality of this relationship within their own family left them conflicted. The African American parents of the doctor were also skeptical because of certain social problems and opposition that would undoubtedly confront their son. The African American house maid added her own anger to the situation, insisting that races should be separate but equal.

The movie closed with a lengthy and impassioned speech that – after weighing all of the cultural pro's and con's – concluded that "true love" is all that matters. The movie received Academy Awards for Best Screenplay and Best Actress, as well as nominations in eight other categories. It succeeded in speaking into the civil rights debate, and sent a powerful message with intentionality. Freedom and racial equality were moving forward.

The plot for the movie was partially inspired by a real-life story that had been unfolding in Virginia. Richard and Mildred Loving had fallen in love and married a few years earlier. In this case the ethnicities were reversed, where he was white, and she was black. Virginia was one of more than a dozen states that carried laws stating that adultery and fornication by any couple were misdemeanors, but interracial sex was a felony. And in those same states, anti-miscegenation laws protected the assumption that the notion of a white person marrying any other ethnicity was absolutely unthinkable.

The Loving's were arrested, tried, and found "guilty" by the state court of Virginia. Their sentence gave both of them the option of going to prison or moving out of state. For a time, Richard and Mildred agreed to move their family to Washington, D.C. But they dearly missed their extended families, and eventually moved back.

As another court appearance loomed, the issue drew the attention of *LIFE Magazine,* which published pictures and a sympathetic article of the family's dilemma. Bobby Kennedy had also been made aware of the Loving's situation, and directed the ACLU to take their case on a pro bono basis. After receiving another guilty verdict in Virginia, the ACLU then appealed to the Supreme Court, which agreed to hear the case in 1967. In one of the rare UNANIMOUS verdicts from the highest court, Chief Justice Earl Warren wrote in favor of the defendants, stating that "marriage is one of the basic civil rights of any human being." The existing state laws that had prohibited that right were now declared to be racist, and that they had been enacted only to perpetuate white supremacy.

After several years in process, this final court verdict and the movie release coincidentally occurred within a few weeks of each other. As a result, individual states could no longer enforce anti-miscegenation laws. June 12th is still recognized every year as "Loving Day", the official celebration of interracial marriage. Sadly, it would take another 33 years before every state finally removed all of those marriage restrictions from their legal records. Alabama was the last state to join the other 49 in stepping into the 20th Century in this regard.

Like his younger brother "Tommy", Brian was a brilliant young man. He had attended military school for his first 12 years of education, served in the Army for two years, and accumulated a very disciplined and committed mindset to change the world for the better. He was an exceptional tennis player, and quite accomplished at chess as well. His sophisticated appreciation for jazz belied his young age.

His youthful and rigid idealism, however, was filtered through a radical lens that demanded that real change in America could only come through drastic options. He was determined to be in the inner-circle of that needed process for change. The anti-war effort was his logical ticket to do so, because it was national in scope and seemed to be the easiest avenue to engage large numbers of young adults into an unstoppable force.

After numerous warnings, Brian had been kicked out of college because his daily use of a bull horn to recruit adherents and incite campus revolt was considered "unsafe." He then tried hanging around those protesting voices that already had a national presence, and was particularly drawn to Tom Hayden, who was trying to consolidate several camps of the New Left, including the SDS. In November the Viet Cong had released three POW's to Hayden in a strategic attempt to sway more Americans to support the anti-war movement. That small step did not have its desired effect.

But later that same month the peace movement was greatly bolstered by the announcement from Senator Eugene McCarthy that he was running as a Democratic candidate for President, with the singular issue of ending the Viet Nam War. Lyndon Johnson considered McCarthy to be nothing more than a nuisance, wondering why someone from his own party would bother to run against him as the incumbent. Brian – and many other radical idealists – saw it differently, however, and drove to New England to volunteer their help. Now the anti-war movement had a major icon, a credible leader from within the Establishment. It was during those four months in New England that Brian got a taste for genuine change at a national level. Ending the war could be just the beginning. He had no idea exactly how he was going to impact America, but that was his lofty vision.

Ultimately he would do so in ways he had not expected. More and more changes were coming. For Brian and many others, hope ran high that maybe the approaching New Year of 1968 would be the arrival of the Promised Land. . . .

Rolling Stone Magazine cover of John Lennon and Yoko Ono

Mohammad Ali

Dan Rowan & Dick Martin, hosts of 'Laugh In'

Folk singer Joan Baez; Eugene McCarthy

Nicholas Sand

CHAPTER 5

"1968 – UNNECESSARY DEATHS"

"Anybody here seen my old friend, Bobby?
Can you tell me where he's gone?
I thought I saw him walkin' on over the hill
With Abraham, and Martin, and John."

- *Dion (in tribute to Bobby Kennedy, Abraham Lincoln,*
Martin Luther King, Jr., and John Kennedy)

Historians refer to 1968 as the "unhappiest year in American history." *Time* magazine's Lance Morrow described it more ominously when he wrote, "Like a knife blade, this year severed past from future."

Politics was expected to be the dominant story for the entire year. Lyndon Baines Johnson was the incumbent President of the United States, but his popularity was spiraling downward. If he were to be re-elected that fall, he would become only the second President in our nation's history to serve in that office for more than eight years. Early in the campaign cycle everyone considered that outcome to be a given. Yet the growing impatience to end the Viet Nam War caused fellow-Democrat Eugene McCarthy to run against LBJ in the initial presidential primaries that spring.

Initially Johnson did not take his opponent seriously. But when the first Primary votes were counted in New Hampshire, McCarthy came within a percentage point of winning. Sensing a sudden vulnerability in the White House, Bobby Kennedy announced his candidacy for the presidency four days later as well. The war protest movement – in Boulder, and elsewhere

– was ecstatic, and suddenly every activist felt dramatic change could be truly imminent. A heightened sense of urgency came into focus for both political parties. Total peace – or total victory – in Viet Nam had to happen soon.

Walter Cronkite returned from a personal visit to Viet Nam, and announced that he felt the war there was "unwinnable" even if U.S. troops achieved a 300:1 kill ratio. LBJ secretly winced upon hearing that. "If I've lost Cronkite, I've lost America," he confided to his staff. Adding to the growing pessimism that was secretly surfacing in the White House, former Defense Secretary Robert McNamara phoned the President to say that he now questioned America's resolve and purpose even to be in Viet Nam.

LBJ was emotionally crushed. His presidency had started with such promise. He had in fact produced major legislation pertaining to racial equality, voting rights, and the economy, which had solidified his legacy as an excellent politician. But the failures of Viet Nam were defeating him mentally. The failures on the domestic war against poverty were defeating him emotionally. And now the failures in current political polls were overwhelming him psychologically. Within a few weeks, President Johnson held a press conference in which he announced that he would NOT run for re-election. He adamantly added, "If nominated, I will not run. And if elected, I will not serve." His voice was that of a man who was profoundly exhausted and discouraged.

Democrats were stunned. With both political parties making plans for their respective national conventions that summer, the playing field for a new candidate was suddenly wide open. Republicans on the other hand were elated. The odds had abruptly shifted in their favor. Anti-war protesters were emboldened. Certainly a different President could advocate peace instead of a perpetuation of this war. And ironically, the troops in Viet Nam were suddenly numbed and disillusioned. They now felt that their Commander-in-Chief had become a quitter, and had just left them hung out to dry.

America needed something great to happen. And the opportunity was now ripe.

Craig was a classmate of Tom's at Boulder High School, and one of the many "customers" that had purchased a fake Driver's license from him. Craig was still only 17 in his senior year, but enjoyed the sense of excitement and power in being able to use that ID to purchase 3.2 beer at various locations in town.

Most of his friends were skiing on this particular January weekend, so he caught the City bus for fifteen cents, and headed out to the CU campus for a Saturday night on his own. He played a few games of 9-ball at the Golden Cue, but really wasn't enjoying it. At least a dozen of the CU football players were there, and they expected people to lose to them on purpose or risk getting into a fight.

Craig wandered down the street only a half block, and decided to step into Tulagi's for a beer. This was not one of Tulagi's famous "Nickel Beer Nights", but Craig wanted to do something other than just walking around The Hill. His fake ID easily got him past the Bouncer at the front door, and he sat down for what he thought would be a quick drink, and then maybe go take in a movie.

Moments later there was a tap on his shoulder, and a woman's soft voice said, "So, Craig, what are you doing here?"

He quickly turned around, and was surprised to see his High School Science teacher standing there. She was about 27, extremely attractive, single, with short blonde hair. "Uh . . . er . . .," he stammered. "Just havin' a beer, I guess."

He tried to hide his embarrassment, not knowing if he was busted. "Do you come in here often?" she continued. Her smile suggested that she wasn't being hostile, but Craig was still terribly uneasy.

"Oh . . . not too often," he managed to mutter.

"Do you mind if I join you?" she continued, as she slid a chair over from the adjacent table.

"Uh . . . great. . . go ahead," he replied.

They struggled awkwardly through a shallow conversation for the next 10 minutes. With both of their glasses empty, Craig thought it might be time to leave. Instead, his teacher steered the conversation in a different direction. "Should we get another drink?" she asked.

"Yeah, sure," he said. "Let me get us a couple of beers."

"No, no," she answered, shaking her head, "I got these."

Craig was already mystified. But a moment after the beers arrived his sense of confusion jumped to an even higher level. "You know," she quietly posed, "there's been a rumor going around the Teacher's Lounge that a number of students have gotten their hands on some fake ID's." She paused to study his eyes. "Would you know anything about that?"

Craig thought about just making a dash for the front door. But he decided to play his bluff all the way through. "No, what's that about?" he whispered sheepishly, and took a quick sip from his beer.

"Oh, don't worry about it," she said with a sexy grin. "Even if it's true, I think it's completely harmless . . . in fact, I think it's a bit daring."

Craig was suddenly starting to feel a bit more comfortable. They both knew he had lied. With a couple of sips on their beers, their conversation moved from school to sports and hobbies. A couple of times she touched his arm as she was laughing, and once momentarily put her hand on his knee. Craig was familiar with this kind of flirting. He had made out with numerous girls, and had sex three times. *But to have a teacher flirting like this . . . . this is really foreign territory,'* he kept telling himself. After his third beer, Craig glanced at his watch. Almost midnight.

"I'm sorry," he said reluctantly, "but I think I should get going. The city bus schedule is only once an hour, and I should probably catch the next one."

"Oh, that's not a problem," she countered. "I've got my car here. Let me give you a ride."

She paid the tab for both of them, they stepped outside, and he followed her about two blocks down a small side street to her car. It was a '66 Chevy Impala. Nothing too sporty, nothing impressive, but at least it was wheels. After they were settled inside, she started the car, turned on some AM radio music, and turned the heat on "Lo." But rather than shifting the car into gear, she slid across the big bench seat and placed her hand inside his ski jacket.

"I'm not ready for our conversation to end," she whispered as she put her face directly in front of his.

Craig was at a loss for words. "I . . . I . . . . I'm just not sure if this is legal," he finally uttered.

"Oh, c'mon," she quickly responded. "You're not going to tell on me, that I'm your teacher. And I'm not going to tell on you, that you are using a fake ID." She developed a somewhat mischievous grin as she continued. "Seems to me like we're even. I think it's a tie."

It sounded somewhat logical to Craig. As she began kissing his face, he let himself respond naturally. An hour later she dropped him off a half block from his house, just in case anyone was watching. He jogged the rest of the way up the moonlit street, and quietly entered his home through the side door, still proud of the fact that he had now had sex for a fourth time in his life.

In the coming months he stopped into Tulagi's on a regular basis, hoping to run into her again. But it never happened. On that memorable night he had learned one thing . . . the sexual revolution that everyone was talking about was not limited to college students or hippies. And to think he might have been skiing with his friends that weekend.

The U.S. Defense Department tried to stack the statistics coming out of Viet Nam to make sure that the public was confident of eventual victory. After all, Americans did not know that it was possible to lose a war. It was unthinkable. We had vastly superior weaponry and technology. How could any enemy – particularly one so small as North Viet Nam – believe that they could withstand our military might? Surely they would run in hasty retreat. By early 1968 the U.S. had over 450,000 military personnel stationed in Viet Nam.

The village of Ben Tre was the site of a strong confrontation for American troops that January. By the time it was over, every enemy soldier was killed and every grass hut in the village was completely destroyed. One of the U.S. officers commented to an embedded reporter, "It became necessary to destroy the town in order to save it." That particular quote was reprinted in newspapers across America, and became a sarcastic catch-phrase for those that were protesting against the war.

The habitual arrogance and poor judgment of the Pentagon was further uncovered in tragic fashion in late January. The Tet holiday was a national holiday for both North and South Viet Nam, and traditionally was set aside as a one-day truce. But early on that morning of January 31, Viet Cong troops made a highly coordinated and surprise attack on 100 cities or villages throughout South Viet Nam. As part of this Tet Offensive, more than 10,000 North Vietnamese troops captured the South Vietnamese city of Hue. Only a few hundred U.S. Marines were stationed there, yet they were given orders to fight back. Their pleas for air support were deemed unnecessary and thus denied, so the casualty rate was very high.

Initially those few Marines were called cowards for "exaggerating" the situation of being vastly out-numbered. During the next three weeks, U.S. reinforcements were slowly able to re-capture the city of Hue. As the invaders from the north made their way back over the border, they killed civilians that had not supported their attempt at overthrowing the South Vietnamese government. In the aftermath of this isolated battle, more than 10,000 deaths occurred there in the span of only 23 days.

Even the U.S. military's stronghold of Saigon came under fierce attack, and the U.S. Embassy was occupied by North Vietnamese troops for a few hours. Five Americans were killed in their own embassy during that skirmish. The main radio station of Saigon was captured by the Viet Cong for a portion of that first day. Heavy damage was also done to the airport, so that major runways were not operable for more than a week. Americans there were stunned at the audacity that was shown by the Viet Cong in taking the fight from the remote jungles of Viet Nam into the streets of their base city. Saigon had always been considered the safest place in Viet Nam. Three days of fierce fighting ensued, finally going door to door, before control was restored in Saigon. This was no longer merely guerilla warfare. The "little" enemy had just walked up to the "giant" and punched him in the mouth. In spite of extremely heavy casualties, the Viet Cong claimed a moral victory for themselves, and proved they would never give up.

Although the American military leadership refused for many years to recognize or believe the significance of this particular battle, in retrospect this attack at Hue would prove to be the painful turning point in the entire war. For the next six years, any sense of momentum for the U.S. armed forces was temporary and elusive at best. But no one would admit it. There had to be a way to win, or at least to exit with dignity. The question was "How?" Anyone? Anyone?

Demands for equal rights for African Americans had another ugly set-back on February 8 in Orangeburg, South Carolina. Students from South Carolina State's campus held a protest against the blatant practice of segregation in public places. Police cornered a number of those Black students at the local bowling alley, and opened fire. Three students were killed and 27 were wounded. It was another unnecessary tragedy, an occurrence that happened all too often, and barely made the national news.

But the ensuing actions of the local judicial system only magnified the systemic problem that permeated the region. Nine police officers were charged with excessive use of force. After a very brief trial, all nine were acquitted. In the related case, the protest coordinator of that night – although unarmed – was convicted of "inciting to riot", and served seven months in prison.

What a travesty. It's no wonder that Blacks were becoming more and more aggressive in their need to be heard.

It was Patrick Henry who stated "Give me Liberty or give me Death" to our Founding Fathers. African Americans were now becoming that bold in their quest for equality. Just five months later Black militants in Cleveland led a riot that lasted five days. Three of their activists as well as three police officers were killed.

The message was becoming very clear for all Americans . . . Blacks were no longer willing to accept any position as "2nd rate citizens". But their road to true equality was still in the far distance.

A few weeks later President Johnson established the "National Advisory Commission on Civil Disorders" to assess objectively the progress and status of African Americans following his civil rights legislation. The findings were anything but encouraging. Their official report stated that our nation was moving toward two distinct societies – one black and one white – separate but UN-equal. The findings went on to say that poverty and segregation had created a destructive environment within the racial ghetto that was totally unknown to most white Americans. White institutions had created it, white institutions had maintained it, and white society condoned it. This was the greatest source of fuel for the demands for Black nationalism as well as the Black Islam movement.

True equality could not be legislated. Empathetic whites and all blacks began to question if it could ever be attained.

Tom's older brother, Brian, sat staring at the morning newspaper. "I just don't believe this crap," he said as he shook he head. "This Viet Nam war is only getting more and more insane." The front page carried a photo of a South Vietnamese Police Chief using a pistol to execute a Viet Cong officer at point blank range in the middle of a public street. The longer Brian stared at the paper, the more incensed he became.

"Why are people putting up with this?" he muttered. "Why would anyone think that our U.S. troops are doing anything worthwhile over there?"

It gave him and his like-minded friends in the Students for a Democratic Society (SDS) new motivation in their daily protests on the University of Colorado campus. Every morning they set up their tables on the lawn next to the Student Union, providing free literature from various underground organizations. Even his girlfriend came almost every day that spring to help hand out pamphlets, carrying her newborn baby with her. Using bull horns and a cheap portable amplification system, their team members took turns throughout the day yelling slogans of opposition against the war, against the U.S. government, and against almost any authority in general.

The general goals of the SDS had shifted much further to the Left politically in the last three years. It began as a "movement" for battling social injustice and seeking to change the world. But its national leadership was becoming increasingly paranoid and militant within its ranks. Their message shifted as well. No longer was the U.S. government a good government that had simply been misinformed, but now they claimed America was flexing its imperialistic muscle in opposition to a warranted revolution that the Vietnamese people wanted and needed.

In the spring, President Johnson made his announcement that he would not run for re-election. That was like hanging raw meat in a shark tank. Every protest group realized that this was the window needed to implement change. They immediately ratcheted up their intensity with the anticipation that a student-led revolt could actually influence the country and end the war.

Most CU students were ambivalent to the constant broadcast rants of the SDS, but certainly supportive of their freedom to be there. They did not mind when Brian and a few friends chained themselves to the entryway of the FBI office or when they announced they were going to shut down the military draft. That tolerant attitude, however, was not the case with the University's administration. Under the auspices of public safety, they finally had Brian and one of his friends arrested with the charges of "disturbing the peace", "seeking to start a riot", and "plotting a revolution."

Their rationale and sense of urgency on behalf of the University of Colorado was in part based on the fact that in February of that year three university students were killed during a similar protest in South Carolina. In March, Howard University had to suspend operations for five days when hundreds of students organized a sit-in throughout their main campus buildings, protesting the war as well as Howard's ROTC program. And in April, Columbia University had been completely shut down for two days when protesting students had taken over the Administration Buildings. Never had our country seen such widespread chaos across our college campuses. The University of Colorado did not want a repeat performance of some kind on their campus.

By this time many of the civil rights or war protest groups across the country were able to find professors or attorneys that were sympathetic to their cause. Brian's friends arranged for one of those attorneys to come to Boulder to act as his defense before the CU Board of Regents. They were all quite confident that the guarantees of the 1st Amendment would provide an easy victory for Brian against those charges. They were wrong.

While the University applauded free speech for its students, they presented the facts that Brian and his cohorts were not actually students, but "professionals" that were coming on to the campus every day to stir unrest. For the sake of a safe campus environment for all their students, CU quickly brought the hearing to a close, and issued a decision that Brian was permanently banished from ever setting foot again anywhere on CU's campus.

'Screw it', Brian thought, as he gathered his things to leave the hearing. *'I'm still going to be heard — somehow. If the University won't listen to the SDS, then we'll just have to do things differently.'* The CU Regents were somewhat smug in their decision, thinking they had done a good thing — not only for their campus — but for their entire community. They had no way of knowing they had merely awakened a sleeping tiger.

Music is certainly an expression of the soul, and the rebellious attitude of rock & roll became the dominant format of the era because it was a direct reflection of the counter-culture mindset. Both lyrics and chord structure were confrontational as music began to move from melodic to electronic as its core, psychedelic as its label, and from "sing along" to frenzied in its patterns.

Released in late '67, this music style of rebellion went mainstream with the release of a Broadway musical called *"HAIR."* By early '68 it was a smash hit. It personified counter-culture thinking to the max. Between its many songs this production wove a story line of two male hippies participating in illegal drug use, opposition to the Viet Nam war, protesting America's racism and abuse of the environment, and plenty of free sex. The show broke new barriers for its use of profanity, full frontal nudity, irreverence for the American flag, and the inter-racial cast. Unlike so many depressing news stories of the day, however, this musical ended with a very uplifting finale called *"Let the Sun Shine In."* This was a vision of a future utopia. There was hope for mankind if everyone just focused on "love and peace."

The daring and controversial production was an enormous success, playing daily before packed houses for the next four years before going international.

Memphis, Tennessee, has many reasons to be a proud city, but April

4th was not one of them. Late that afternoon Martin Luther King took a break from his mid-day appearances to freshen himself at his hotel before heading to another speaking engagement that evening. As he stepped on to his hotel room's second floor balcony to visit with a few of his associates, the thundering clap of one shot from a high-powered hunting rifle broke the evening air. King collapsed to the balcony floor with a gruesome wound to his cheek and neck.

Pandemonium spread quickly. A call to the police. A call for an ambulance. Yelling instructions to witnesses on the street below. A few people even saw a man running from a rooming house across the street, but were unable to get a physical description.

There was little that King's friends could do. One of them bent over his body and heard him whisper, "Have them play 'Precious Lord, Take My Hand' at my funeral." (This is a plaintive Christian hymn that had been written by an African American evangelist whose wife and infant son were tragically killed in a fire in Chicago.) Those were his final words. By the time the police and ambulance personnel arrived minutes later, he was pronounced dead at the scene.

Police as well as the FBI immediately scrambled to find the killer. Later that evening they found a package dumped close to the assassination site that included a rifle and binoculars. Fingerprints on both items were those of James Earl Ray, an escaped prisoner from Missouri, who had been staying at a rooming house across the street. The rifle had been purchased the previous week under an assumed name. A worldwide manhunt ensued, but it took just over two months before law enforcement could catch up to the killer. Ray was arrested in London's Heathrow Airport as he attempted to board a flight to Africa. He pled "guilty" so as to avoid a death penalty, and was sentenced to 99 years in prison. Although he later escaped from prison once again, he was captured only three days later, and remained in prison until his death.

African Americans were distraught following King's assassination. Riots erupted in 100 cities across the country, causing bloodshed and widespread destruction. For two days the nation seemed to be on fire. More than 21,000 were arrested in those cities, 2,600 were injured, and 39 were killed. In Chicago, Mayor Daley issued an order to "shoot-to-kill" if any "negroes" should begin rioting there. Even some of King's closest friends said that he would have been so disappointed with such an ugly and widespread reaction that followed in the aftermath. King had been the biggest proponent of peaceful civil disobedience. Now Stokely Carmichael openly called for violence – for all black people to get guns. Bobby Kennedy cancelled his campaign appearances that evening in Indianapolis, and instead went into the inner-city to beg the African Americans there to override their sense of hatred and revenge by praying for a heart of peace and forgiveness. For the first time he publicly shared his long-time hatred toward the assassin of his own brother just five years earlier. That unusual candor and empathy generated a miraculous response of cooperation. As a result, Indianapolis was one of the few major cities in America to be spared from the further violence and destruction that ensued over the next few days.

The following week, more than 300,000 attended the memorial service for Dr. Martin Luther King in Atlanta, Georgia. Flags were flown at half-mast in Washington, D.C. for eight days. In the months and years that followed, many cities from coast to coast chose to name a major street within their metropolitan area in his honor. A national holiday was established in his memory to commemorate the legacy of his life's mission for equality for black men and women. The process for true equality would be slow, but he had awakened the conscience of America. King had opened the hearts of adults of any color. Although a few others have tried throughout the years that followed, there has never been another voice of such power and charisma to fill the void left by Martin Luther King in order to carry the baton for human justice and equality. His death was so unnecessary, and so premature.

It was a spectacularly beautiful spring morning in Boulder. Tom and his friends had one month to go before their high school graduation, and virtually zero motivation to go to any more classes. Sitting on the school patio waiting for the opening bell to ring, Dave made a creative suggestion.

"Hey, guys," he muttered, "today is the day that Bobby Kennedy is coming to Denver." He paused for a minute to see if anyone was tracking with him. "If we took off right now, we could get to McNichol's Arena in time to see him make his scheduled appearance. And think of it," he added, "how often do you get to see someone that famous that is running for President?" (McNichol's was an indoor arena that served as home to Denver's professional basketball franchise.)

It took about three seconds for everyone to agree. Dave drove his 1956 Pontiac, which was a big sedan with bench seats. Six guys could fit rather comfortably in a "boat" like that, but on this day they crammed seven into the car.

The drive to Denver was only 30 minutes, but it took another half hour to find a decent parking place. Most of Denver was already in gridlock. Traffic between Stapleton Int'l Airport and the Arena was completely stopped, and Denver residents had lined the major streets in the hope of getting a glimpse of the caravan of black limos that would be carrying Kennedy and his entourage.

By the time Dave, Tom, and their classmates found their way into the arena, the only remaining seats were in the farthest corner of the upper tier. They were lucky to get in at all. An estimated 20,000 people eventually pressed into the 15,000-seat arena, and another 5,000 were forced to remain outside.

Due to a slight flight delay followed by unprecedented traffic congestion in Denver, Bobby Kennedy was more than two hours late in his arrival into the arena. But nobody left. When he finally stepped onto the stage, the crowd erupted with a 15-minute standing ovation. This man was much more than a presidential candidate. This was more than mere celebrity. More than just a rock star. This was the Messiah.

The Kennedy mystique was sweeping the country. He had shifted from "hawk" to "dove" on the Viet Nam conflict, and promptly catapulted himself into the lead in all Democratic Primaries. Contrasted from other politicians, Kennedy had the unusual attitude of "moral outrage." Where McCarthy was a "single-issue candidate" seeking peace, Kennedy was able to embrace the concerns of all of America. As he addressed racial prejudice, rampant poverty, widespread illiteracy, or corruption and graft within the government, he did so with a charisma not unlike his older brother, John. Where most of his peers in public office saw these conditions as somewhat inevitable, he set himself apart by seeing these as unacceptable.

He was in position to be the savior that could end the Viet Nam war. He was the compelling leader that could unite the political divide. He seemed to rise above politics. A 20-minute speech was followed by another standing ovation, and it all seemed to be over much too quickly. Kennedy was off to another city, and the crowd slowly left the arena in a state of euphoria. They had seen the future. Camelot was going to become a reality.

What was most ironic was that Dave and Tom and their classmates – as well as a large percentage of that Denver audience – were actually too young to vote. If you were 18, you were old enough to put on a military uniform and get killed in a rice paddy in Viet Nam under the guise of defending freedom. But one had to be 21 to enter a voting booth and pull a lever. Many of those young adults knew that they might not be able officially to cast a ballot in this election cycle, but they could volunteer to do neighborhood canvassing, phone calls, and other menial tasks. After all, they were going to help change the world. Peace could happen. Anything was possible. And Bobby Kennedy would lead the way.

Four weeks later the grand dream imploded. Bobby Kennedy was dead. He was shot on the evening of June 5th at the Ambassador Hotel in Los Angeles following a victory campaign speech just a few hours after his monumental win in the Democratic California Primary. That night had been the absolute pinnacle of his political career, and he quietly told his wife "that this was the first time I have finally stepped out from under the shadow of my brother." However, a hotel kitchen staff member named Sirhan Sirhan mortally wounded Kennedy while he was being escorted by his security staff toward a rear exit from the hotel.

America was numbed by another assassination only 61 days after the Martin Luther King shooting. The following week, Kennedy's body was transported by train from California back to Washington, D.C. Thousands of Americans lined the railroad tracks at every city along the route to participate in a silent tribute to what might have been. Men saluted, women cried, and children waved flags in solemn respect. Another unnecessary death had been added to the list.

The Democratic Party was now consumed with a sense of futility since the national election was exactly five months away. Idealistic students were angered and disillusioned to an even greater degree. And for everyone – of any color or political persuasion – it now seemed as if the country was beginning to unravel.

The sexual revolution in America received an unexpected boost that summer in the person of Mary Calderone. She had previously held the position as the National Director of Planned Parenthood, but felt that the inner politics of the organization limited her ability to speak her mind fully. She voluntarily stepped down from that role to found a more liberal organization called *"Sex Information & Education Council of the United States"*, or SIECUS.

The guiding mission statement of SIECUS was to "build a movement to make sex about recreation rather than reproduction." To do that, she advocated an extremely liberal program of sex education, starting in Kindergarten. She led the rebellion from a medical vantage point to promote healthy and active sex lives as teens and young adults. In late

1968 the National Council of Women bestowed on Mary Calderone the honorary "Woman of Conscience Award."

Her aggressive stance quickly established herself as a primary target to be vilified by conservative Americans. Rev. Billy Graham, the John Birch Society, and even the White House were just a few of the more notable voices that pleaded with Americans to reject her proposals, and instead hold to a more traditional standard of morality.

Miss Calderone failed to achieve several of her most progressive goals. But friends and foes alike would later realize that she positively impacted our entire country by helping to make sexually transmitted disease (STD's), AIDS, and unwanted pregnancy as common topics for social conversation. Public awareness must first be present before society can enact correction or prevention. In that aspect she may have succeeded far beyond her original objectives.

Avoiding the military draft became an art form. Some tried to exist "off-the-grid", living in seclusion, not paying any taxes, and assuming that the authorities would not spend an extensive amount of time or money looking for them. Many young men simply moved to Canada and sought ways to survive, hoping the war would somehow come to a rapid conclusion while they worked in some form of manual labor to get by. But most guys were not that drastic. They would rather stay closer to home, and look for more creative solutions.

A popular theme was *"If you got the dough, you don't have to go."* A few families were able to bribe the Pentagon or their local draft board as a means to having their son removed from the draft. Anyone that could afford college was motivated to do so, because a full-time student was given a four-year deferment. "Buying time" in that way was worth the effort, hoping the war would be over before the school deferment ran out. Others learned that if they signed up for the National Guard, they would avoid actual military service. The number of young men that claimed "Conscientious Objector" status was six times that of World War II.

Carl was the son of a doctor. Only after he received his induction papers in the mail did he discover how much his Dad really did not want him risking his life in Viet Nam. When the day came to report for his Army physical, Carl's father gave him a small gel capsule of blood. After the preliminary paper work, Carl was given a quick physical. At one point he was handed a small plastic container and asked to go into the restroom to provide a urine sample. Once inside, he bit a corner off the end of the capsule and added the few drops of blood to his urine container before returning it to the nurse. When questioned about the unusual color of his urine, he explained that it was a frequent occurrence due to a high school football injury. Within minutes his file was stamped with a permanent "4-F" exemption due to a serious medical condition of kidney malfunction, and he was sent home – with a sly and thankful grin on his face.

Buck was not so lucky. He was advised to eat and drink heavily for two days prior to his physical – particularly tequila shots. Then the morning of his appointment he was to eat two grains of raw rice. The painful reaction would appear to be that of a small ulcer. Instead, his doctor sensed that something out of the ordinary was up, and just signed a slip of paper that said he had to return in two weeks for another physical. Not only was Buck greatly disappointed, but he went home and vomited for two days as his system tried to recover.

Any full-time university student was given a maximum of eight semesters of a "2-S" classification as their deferment. In that way, as long as that student took a full load of courses and maintained passing grades, they were able to postpone any communication from the draft board for those four years. And if a student declared that he was signed up for a "pre-med" major, he was given an additional two years of deferments. As a result, America suddenly had a plethora of medical students on college and university rosters.

In the early days of the Viet Nam military draft system, someone discovered that if a young man claimed he was a homosexual he could be permanently exempted from the draft as well. That "condition" worked for a short while, but the induction centers quickly learned what was happening, so that fake and over-used excuse was no longer allowed.

One of the most desperate attempts at draft dodging had to be that of Cliff. He had come to the University of Colorado the previous year on a full-ride scholarship to play football. Like many CU students, Cliff happened to come from a very wealthy family. His parents had given him a new Ferrari as a gift for earning the scholarship, and he had confided with a few of his friends at the Golden Cue that his personal Trust Fund was worth over $50,000,000.

But as soon as he got to CU, the prolific "party" atmosphere was too much for him. He often provided all of the booze for many parties, and never turned down an invitation to try various drugs that found their way into the campus. Even though scholarship athletes were often times secretly given answers to their exams, Cliff just quit going to his classes entirely. By his second semester he flunked all of his courses and consequently lost his scholarship. As a result, in the fall of his sophomore year he was not allowed to register as a full-time student, even though he could have paid cash out of his personal checking account. His status was that of a student on "academic probation", and he was allowed to register for a maximum of two courses. And because of that limitation, he was no longer a full-time student, so he lost his school deferment with the draft, and was re-classified as "1-A." Top of the list. The next to be drafted.

Within a few weeks his draft board back in Connecticut called to notify him that he was being inducted into the Army, and needed to be ready to report for his physical the next week. Cliff panicked. Even though he was an excellent athlete, he determined he had to find a way to flunk the physical.

The next evening he walked into the Golden Cue, and quickly got everyone's attention. "Hey . . . who wants to make $100.?" he yelled. The room immediately became deathly quiet. Other than murder, most guys in that pool hall would do anything for such a large sum of money.

Although several pool patrons were quick to say "Yes", it was Samson who walked authoritatively over to Cliff and said, "What do you need, man?"

"I'm serious," Cliff told him. "This will take us less than an hour, but I'll pay you $100."

Samson nodded, the two walked out to Cliff's Ferrari, and they disappeared for the evening. By the next day their story had become legendary – not only in the Golden Cue – but throughout the entire CU campus.

Cliff had driven just a couple of miles into the foothills of the Rocky Mountains, following the two-lane highway of Boulder Canyon which weaved its way up to Nederland. Along that scenic route Boulder County officials had provided numerous creek-side picnic tables and scenic cookout areas for public use. Cliff picked a random picnic site and parked his car. He then removed a sledge hammer from the small trunk space of his Ferrari. A moment later he sat down and extended his left leg on one of the cement picnic benches. Before handing the sledge and a $100 bill to Samson, he took three more gulps from a bottle of Scotch.

"OK," he said to Samson with a grimace, "a deal is a deal. You get one swing, and one swing only. Go for the knee."

Samson hesitated briefly, but knew Cliff was dead serious. The "thud" of a kneecap being crushed is not that loud, but the scream that followed was ear-splitting. The shooting pain even caused Cliff to pass out for a few seconds. Samson quickly helped him hobble back to the car, and Samson drove them both to the Emergency entrance of Boulder Community Hospital.

It took almost six months for Cliff to shed his crutches and the cast on his knee. He would walk with a slight limp for the rest of his life. But his draft board had to give him a "4-F" exemption because of his physical limitation, and for that ultimate outcome Cliff considered the weeks of pain to be a "win." Better to live a long life with a slight limp than to die tomorrow in a rice paddy on the other side of the world.

The call for equal rights for the African American community was no longer limited to the southern states. Professional black athletes and noted black musicians were willing to speak their voices into the national conversation, and provide a rallying point for the morale of all black Americans. James Brown, considered to be the "King of Soul", performed the following song in each of his concerts,

". . . *Say it loud,*
I'm Black, and I'm proud."

Early that summer, several hundred black men and women converged on Washington, D.C., to draw attention to the need for fair pay for their labor. They erected almost 200 tents on the lawn of the Washington Mall that surrounds the Washington Monument. They called their new community "Resurrection City", and stated that they would not leave until the federal government could give them some assurance of new pay levels in their jobs. Hourly wages for garbage collectors, field workers, street cleaners, and railroad workers were specifically cited as being notoriously unfair.

The tent community garnered national news coverage for only a few days since the presidential campaign was in full swing. The Viet Nam war continued to dominate the concerns of most of America. As attention dwindled, some of the Resurrection City stalwarts began to go home, wanting a roof over their head and the use of indoor plumbing once again. It didn't help that the Capitol City had one of its rainiest summers on record, and the grounds around the tents had become a muddy quagmire.

After tolerating the "squatters" for two months, local police abruptly declared that the tents had to be removed, and all persons needed to leave the premises. No arrests were made, and the crowd quickly dissipated. No wage concessions were made by the government. What had started with great optimism instead ended with great discouragement.

Civil rights workers would have to continue to find a better way to sway public opinion.

Any concerns regarding personal nutrition or personal health management received miniscule attention. People simply assumed that any food choice or tobacco choice held little or no negative consequences. Tobacco companies enjoyed the freedom of unlimited advertising in both print and television, and the majority of adults were comfortable to smoke cigarettes. All restaurants and commercial flights allowed their customers to smoke. They did not know – or care – that medical researchers were horrified to see comparative studies which contrasted the tar-coated cross-sections of a lung from a life-long smoker to that of a clean lung of a non-smoker. And no direct connection between tobacco usage and lung cancer had yet been officially established.

Sugar companies worked hard to find new applications where they might insert their product. For the first time, in the summer of 1968 the sugar industry commissioned a research study at the University of California in San Francisco to analyze carefully the effects – if any – from sugar. After extensive experimentation with animals, the findings determined that sugar metabolized differently than that of starches, and produced high levels of enzymes linked to bladder cancer and hardening of the arteries. The initial studies were so conclusive and potentially destructive that the sugar industry frantically halted further research, and prevented any publication of the partial findings.

Science would slowly begin to demonstrate the severe negative effects of both products. The dike had sprung a leak. Tobacco and sugar companies alike hid any evidence of addiction or detrimental health outcomes to protect their profits for as long as possible. And the American public continued to pay the price for that withholding of information.

Late that summer Tom got an unexpected phone call from his older brother, Brian. "Hey, Tommy," his voice cracked on the phone, "I've got an idea. As a gift for your high school graduation, how would you like to go with me and a few friends to Chicago next week?"

Tom was elated, because it was always so cool when a rare opportunity like this came along to hang out with his brother. "Well, great!" he answered. "But why Chicago?"

"Well, it's actually kind of important," Brian replied, as his voice became more serious. "If you have followed the news this summer, you know the Republican Party just had their Convention last week in Miami, and nominated "tricky Dicky" Nixon. Of course, he was the Vice President for eight years under Eisenhower, and then lost when he ran for President against John Kennedy. And so if he got elected this year, everyone knows he would just try to keep everything as status quo in our country."

"Sure, I know that," Tom said with confidence. "But what does that have to do with Chicago?"

"OK, next week is the Democratic Convention, and it's being held there," Brian said. "Every protest group across the country, every radical organization, and every movement for change is trying to get as many as possible to participate. We think we could have more than 250,000 people show up. Hopefully we can have a large enough voice that we could impact the selection of the Democratic candidate. We've got to get a President that is ready to upset the whole apple cart."

"So, what exactly are we going to do?" Tom asked.

"Oh, it's easy," Brian replied. "We just need to make as huge a presence as we can. We'll have a few marches, listen to a few speeches, and in eight days it'll be time to go home. And who knows, you may be lucky enough to get on TV."

The following week Tom climbed into a large Ford LTD station wagon with Brian and three other guys, and they eagerly headed from Boulder to the "windy city." Two surprises awaited them upon their arrival. First, in spite of the intense recruiting efforts by so many radical leaders on so many campuses around the country, the actual turnout was a small fraction of what they had hoped. And secondly, Mayor Richard J. Daley had the city of Chicago "locked and loaded" for any eventuality with several thousand soldiers and National Guardsmen as extra security.

Some organized groups of radicals had accidentally revealed plans ahead of time regarding what might take place in Chicago. Rallies, printed fliers, and newspaper editorials had given the FBI and Chicago itself a written spectrum of their ideas. Bringing expressway traffic to a halt by dropping bags of nails from overpasses. Dumping LSD into the Chicago city water supply. Storming the Democratic Convention Center. Abandoning cars at key intersections in order to shut down normal traffic flow. Although none of those happened, Chicago law enforcement had to be ready for almost anything.

Mayor Daley was proud to lead "the city that worked", and had built a Democratic "machine" that knew how to get things done. He had a framed Bible verse prominently displayed in his office, which read, *"Be Ye doers of the Word, and not hearers only."* For himself, Daley took that directive to mean that a worthwhile "end" could justify almost any "means" to get there. Consequently he was not averse to bending the law if necessary, or turning a blind eye to breaking the law if needed, to accomplish important goals. The local arm of the Mafia – begun by the notorious Al Capone – was entrenched in the local unions, as well as several restaurants, bars, dry cleaners, casualty insurance, and travel agencies for the purposes of laundering money. Rather than trying to eradicate organized crime, Daley tolerated their existence and occasionally used them as a secret partner when desperate times called for desperate measures.

During the previous two years, Daley had bargained with the National Democratic Committee to move the Convention to his city. Daley had previously been instrumental in delivering the Illinois vote during the Kennedy campaign of 1960 by creating duplicate and illegal votes in Cook County. Chicago's organized crime network, The Outfit, was glad to assist in that regard. It was just enough to swing the final outcome and give Kennedy the narrow margin he needed, so the Democrats knew they owed Daley a huge favor. He had pitched them on the concept that the positive media coverage of a great convention in Chicago would move Illinois voters to elect the Democratic candidate once again. Those Electoral votes were crucial. And he gave them his personal assurance that the city would be an exemplary model of orderliness and safety for those seven days that the Democratic Convention was in town.

In preparation, Mayor Daley had ordered double shifts of police duty around the clock, and also requested a large contingent of National Guard soldiers to patrol the streets as a visible show of force. Every police officer was armed with a gun, a billy club, mace, and a helmet. The city set up a strict system requiring permits for anything to take place. They purposely denied any permit that would meet in – or march through – African American neighborhoods on the south side of town to avoid an exponential increase in anger and unrest. Daley even encouraged the Black community leaders to leave town for a week so that they would not be accidentally implicated in any violence that might occur.

Everyone's plans, however, changed on the first day.

A few thousand protesters gathered peacefully at Grant Park that first afternoon and began chanting "PEACE NOW", but soon transitioned to yelling derogatory slurs at those police in full riot gear that had quickly surrounded them. A few stones were thrown at police cars. An over-zealous policeman shot and killed an 18-year old male in the crowd. That was exactly what everyone had hoped would not happen.

Immediately fistfights broke out between some of the protesters and a few of the police. But the intimidating presence of a sea of police on horseback and advancing National Guard troops quickly made the crowd back down. Officers clubbed and punched students with brutal abandon.

Tom Hayden and other key leaders pleaded over the public address system for peaceful actions. But every day the violence escalated. Television cameras rolled as police began indiscriminately injuring protesters. The number of arrests mounted every day as well. Some protesters gained access into the Convention floor, and marched around the perimeter of the main floor waving large "PEACE" signs. A couple of fistfights even broke out between key news media personnel and a few protesters. In spite of careful planning by both sides, the protests, the Convention, and most of downtown Chicago was in chaos.

The powder keg of anger only increased by the 5th day. Speakers riled the crowds by repeatedly claiming that the political process was ignoring the will of the people. In a mock satire of the Convention, protesters nominated a live pig as their candidate of choice. Marchers then began chanting, "Hey, Hey, LBJ, how many men did you kill today?"

Late that evening, after all the marching and speeches had concluded, Brian and his best friend, John, decided to walk the four miles from their downtown rally back to their temporary apartment on the west side of Chicago. A few blocks from downtown, a police officer suddenly started chasing them without provocation. After they had run half a block, John yelled to Brian, "Keep going. I got this. I'll see you back at the apartment."

Brian trusted him fully, and did not cut his stride. But in his mind, for the first time in his life he started asking himself, *'Why am I really doing all this?'* John purposely slowed his pace slightly so that the officer could catch up to him, and then turned to face the officer as he approached. What the policeman did not know was that John had served as a Marine in Viet Nam, and was highly trained in hand-to-hand combat. As the officer swung his billy club, John deflected the first blow, grabbed his other arm, and within three seconds had the officer pinned on the sidewalk lying face down, with his arm twisted behind him in pain.

"You damned pig!" he yelled at the officer. "I did nothing illegal, and you know it!" He quickly removed the officer's pistol and billy club before speaking again. "You know I could hurt you if I wanted, but I'm not going to do that." He took a few seconds to collect his thoughts. "So here is what's going to happen," he continued. "You are going to lay here quietly for two minutes after I leave, and then you are going to find your weapons in the dumpster up at the next corner, and then you are going to quietly go back to the rally where you belong."

With that, John got up and continued running toward his apartment. He did ditch the weapons in the dumpster just as he said, and never saw that officer again. But he did wonder from time to time if that policeman ever told his fellow officers what had happened, or if he ever had to explain to anyone why he had peed in his pants that night.

President Johnson did not attend any of the Democratic Convention that week, which left a bad taste in the mouths of many of the delegates. Mayor Daley and others tried to get Ted Kennedy to run at the last minute. They claimed that the charisma of the Kennedy name was magical enough to retain the White House. A few Democrats also tried to nominate an African American by the name of Julian Bond to be the Vice Presidential candidate as a strategy to bridge the civil rights unrest, but at the last minute Bond had to withdraw because he was not old enough to meet constitutional requirements.

The next day the Democratic Convention announced their delegate vote, and Hubert Humphrey was selected to be the Party candidate for President, with Ed Muskie as his running mate, even though Humphrey had not run in any of the primaries that year. The party felt that since Humphrey was already in the White House as the incumbent Vice President, he would carry the most name recognition with the voting public. This final slate was an enormous disappointment to all the protesters. Rather than showing the courage to change America's course regarding Viet Nam, this made it apparent that the Democratic Party was opting to "play it safe" with a familiar politician that would likely maintain the futility taking place in southeast Asia.

A heightened sense of urgency permeated the marchers that day. More than 10,000 gathered on Michigan Avenue to march through the afternoon and evening. Once again the police began hitting those on the fringes of the mob, creating the biggest clash of the week. Protesters were bullied and bloodied, or physically dragged away by helmeted law enforcement. And once again the TV cameras were there to record the gruesome treatment at the hands of the officers in uniform. Only this time the marchers did not back down. Police rushed the crowd, and tried to disperse them with the use of teargas. More than 500 arrests were made. As they stood their ground the protesters chanted, "THE WORLD IS WATCHING. THE WORLD IS WATCHING."

And it was true – all of America was watching this sad debacle from the safety of their living rooms. The media called it "Gestapo tactics" on the part of the Chicago police even though Mayor Daley claimed that 152 police officers were injured while trying to maintain order.

Everybody lost that week. Public perception saw Mayor Daley as a thug. Chicago was seen as a city using unnecessary and excessive police action against peaceful protesters. The Democratic Party lost its public relations opportunity, as this week unexpectedly became the negative tipping point in the campaign. And the protesters lost their chance to steer the selection process toward a candidate committed to peace. Everybody lost.

In the early fall, Mexico happened to make the evening news in staggering fashion on two separate occasions.

The first such moment took place at the summer Olympics, which were held in Mexico City in October. There was the usual pageantry and superb athleticism that always occurs at such an event. The noble cause of international competition was once again on display via television.

But the most iconic moment of the entire 1968 Olympics did not occur on a scoreboard or a finish line. It did not happen in association with previous world records being shattered. It did not occur in the drama of head-to-head competition. Rather it took place during the medal award ceremony following the men's sprint in the 200 meters event.

Two African American runners finished in first and second place, and naturally were very proud to have won the gold and silver medals respectively. As they stood on the victory stand, the traditional playing of the United States National Anthem began. But rather than saluting America's flag, or singing along with the Anthem as other winning athletes had always done, Tommie Smith and John Carlos shocked the world. Each man bowed his head and raised his right arm into the air with a clenched fist – the recognized militant salute to Black Power.

Most Americans were irate at this apparent sign of disrespect. The concept of athletic competition became secondary, and the issue of America's racism and civil rights suddenly took the forefront on an international stage. African American leaders across the U.S. were quick to defend these athletes and their right to express themselves as they did. An unforgettable statement was made to the world that day, a statement demanding justice and equality in America.

The other major news item from Mexico had come just a few weeks earlier. The novel idea of America's university students protesting en masse had gone international that summer. The new global attitude amongst university students was "if the U.S. students can do this, so can we." Germany and France suddenly had to contend with angry protests from young people in their major cities. In Mexico City, University students chose to copy their American counterparts by organizing a large peaceful march in downtown Mexico City that lasted for three days. The hope was that such a bold spectacle would influence public opinion and policy toward the total overthrow of a social class system as well as capitalism. Thousands gathered in the public square, and the revelry resembled that of a national holiday, with loud chanting and singing.

But the world learned an important and costly lesson that week. Few countries enjoy the true Freedom of Speech that we in America have too often taken for granted.

After three days of protests, the President of Mexico grew impatient and ordered the military to quietly infiltrate this uprising. They were told to wear white gloves or a white handkerchief tied to their left hand so that they would be secretly recognized by each other. On a given signal from the President, the military began to open fire on this student protest. Within just a few minutes, more than 500 young men and women lay dead in the streets. The Mexican police were so ruthless that they followed some of the wounded into the hospitals and killed them there as well.

Every year since then Mexico commemorates this event as the "Night of Sorrows." It was a wake-up call to every protester in any country that even the most peaceful intentions may carry dangerous consequences. Within just a few months, the United States would also learn that it was not immune to the unnecessary tragedy of well-intended protesters giving up their lives for their cause.

Americans thought the national political conventions of that summer had come and gone. But at least three profound and unexpected ramifications followed the drama of the Democratic Convention in Chicago.

The Democrats had to learn a painful lesson by having their poorly managed event televised to all the voters of America. Never again could they afford to have such division or debate of issues on display to the public. The power of media was too great, and had to be managed – or even manipulated if necessary – to help sway an election outcome. From that point forward, party platform issues have been brokered off-camera. Extensive primary elections have been scheduled across the country ahead of time so that the choice of presidential candidate is known well before the convention begins. From that point forward, every national political convention started to become a carefully scripted infomercial, using music, lighting, and celebrities to help dazzle the American public. Every platform minute today is managed by a team of public relations consultants so that undecided voters might be swayed in their direction. The first – and longest lasting – change as a result of that Democratic Convention was the future usage of free media coverage from all the networks to help reach their political party goals.

The second outcome from that week in Chicago was a dramatic continuation of the clash between key protesters and law enforcement in the form of a courtroom trial. Eight of the most visible ringleaders of the protests and marches in Chicago were arrested and charged by the federal government with conspiracy, crossing state lines to incite a riot, and threatening the safety of the community. The individuals included Tom Hayden, Abbie Hoffman, Jerry Rubin, David Dellinger, Rennie Davis, John Froines, and Lee Weiner.

Over the next two years that trial took on the name of "The Chicago 8", and became a watershed spectacle of such variables as individual freedom and civil rights, law enforcement using excessive force, public safety, or federal wiretap laws. Our nation's entire judicial system would shift because of what was going to take place in that Chicago courtroom in 1969 and 1970.

The third outcome also had historical significance, but in a dire scenario. Brian and his friends headed home from Chicago to Boulder with deflated spirits. Everything about that week had been such a disappointment. During some of the quiet hours of that trip while driving on Interstate 80 Brian began to reassess what was or was not getting accomplished. *'A march is not sufficient,'* he thought. *'Mere speeches don't make enough of an impact. Real change is only going to come about by REPLACING systems, not by IMPROVING them with incremental adjustments. Maybe we need to destroy the whole thing and just start over.'*

To attain such a revolution would necessitate the complete destruction of the existing political structure. Bombing strategic buildings or locations would make such a statement to the world. *'This needs to be a complete class system revolution – not simply a youth revolution.'* Brian's attitude lifted as he began to think of other radical leaders that would join him in this approach. Together they would force a change upon America, and together they could change the world.

As he drove, he listened over and over to an 8-track tape of Bob Dylan, called *"Bringing It All Back Home."* The particular song *"Subterranean Homesick Blues"* was mesmerizing to him. Those choppy lyrics of rebellion caught his soul as Dylan sang,

". . . keep a clean nose, watch the "plain clothes",

you don't need a WEATHERMAN to know which way the wind blows. . . ."

That's it,' Brian kept thinking. *'Some of us already know which way the wind is blowing, and we can be the "weathermen" that tell others what is the real truth.'* A smile came across his face as his mind became more determined. *'We'll call the new radical organization "The Weathermen", and America will never be the same.'*

That vision became partially true. The Weathermen would significantly raise the level of fear and tension in America over the next few years. Bombs became their calling-card, seeking to destroy random buildings connected to the government or the military. During a three-year span they averaged over three bombs per day somewhere in the U.S. "Radical" was an understatement. One unusual tenet required of all of their recruits was that no man or woman was allowed to have a monogamous sexual relationship. Every member must be available to every member. That mandate was intended to help reinforce the idea of "radical thinking" in every area of their life. The Weathermen certainly succeeded in those objectives.

Proponents for every other cause felt it was now necessary to emulate both the Civil Rights workers and the anti-war activists by organizing a March or a Sit-in as the most effective way to gain public attention. September gave a momentary spot in the sun to the Women's Rights movement. 150 women made national news by marching down the Boardwalk of Atlantic City, New Jersey, as a public protest in opposition to the Miss America Pageant. This was a very specific target, unlike other women's "bra-burning marches" that generically wanted equal rights and equal pay for women. Declaring such events as The Miss America Pageant to be the objectification and exploitation of women, a small sampling of the media listened as these women called for a cessation of all beauty pageants.

Although the Miss America organization ignored their plaint, and the

Miss Universe Pageant actually outgrew its counterpart in coming years, there were some baby steps that showed that America was ready slowly to shift in terms of women's equality. In November, Shirley Chisholm won an upset victory to become the first African American woman to serve in the U.S. House of Representatives. Campaigning on the slogan *"Unbought and Unbossed"*, she captured the sense of independence and individual freedom that New York voters could support. Her election victory was a day of double celebration for both Civil Rights and Women's Rights workers.

It was a visible "win" for women's rights. Baby steps, yes. But tangible progress none the less.

On the opposite coast, a much different fiasco was taking place at San Francisco State College (later changed to San Francisco State University). In an attempt to strengthen the voice of equality for Black students, an African American professor had urged his students to bring guns on to the campus. Some students objected immediately. The furor only got louder when the President of the University then suspended that professor for threatening the safety and security of the student body. That solved nothing.

Student rallies were swiftly scheduled for a wide spectrum of causes, including civil rights, gun rights, and women's rights. It began to look like an unchaperoned free-for-all. Numerous students walked through the campus with their own bull-horn, yelling their specific demands as they walked. Most classes were cancelled. The unexpected and wide-spread chaos on campus forced the College President to resign.

The school's Board of Regents scrambled to find a safe solution. The decision was to appoint a Japanese professor named S.I. Hayakawa, primarily because he was neither Black nor Caucasian, but also because he had a reputation for being a strict disciplinarian. His first action was to bring military guards on to the campus in an attempt to restore order. It failed miserably.

Students were not about to be pushed aside. Protests, marches, sit-ins, and violence ensued for the next thirty days. The Black Studies Department was destroyed, and would not re-surface for two years. During one of the protests, Hayakawa himself climbed atop a small truck that had been configured with a public address system for the purposes of broadcasting protest messages. He personally pulled out the electrical wires to the loud speakers, which earned him the nickname "Samurai Sam."

Dr. Hayakawa rapidly became a national icon, and his dogmatic and controversial stance for "law and order" on the issues of equal rights or the Viet Nam war – or any protest for any cause – was now legendary. Although he claimed to be a Democrat, and would later serve one term as a Democratic U.S. Senator from California, he became a popular hero for California Governor Ronald Reagan, the staunch Conservative, as well as the GOP establishment, because of his strong stance on enforcing rigid limits among rebelling young people.

Orenthal James "O.J." Simpson became a national household word during the fall semester of '68 because of his spectacular heroics on the college football field. As a running back for USC, he shattered the NCAA record for total yardage gained in a single season. Several of his game-breaking plays remain highlight-reel classics to this day. In December he traveled to New York City with four other college football stars to await the announcement of the Heisman Trophy, which is college football's most coveted individual award. By an overwhelming majority, O.J. Simpson was declared the outstanding player for that year. The world was now at his doorstep. Who could possibly have anticipated his ultimate destiny?

He continued to be the most dominating running back when he transitioned into professional football. The Buffalo Bills suddenly became annual contenders in the NFL with his presence in the backfield. He was the first running back to surpass 2000 rushing yards in a single season, which most players and coaches considered unreachable. (It's also important to note that he accomplished that amazing milestone at a time when there were only 14 games in the NFL regular season.)

O.J. was as much of an electric personality off the field as he was on. His football success combined with his contagious smile made him the most sought after commercial spokesperson of all professional athletes. Ultimately he made far more money as a "pitchman" than he did in his Bills uniform.

The reason he is mentioned here, however, is not because of his legendary football career, but rather because of his ethnicity. O.J. was an African American man whose national stardom began in 1968, and rose high above the country's ongoing conflict of racial inequality and hatred. That racial issue again came crashing to the forefront in late1994 when he was arrested and charged with the murder of his ex-wife and her new boyfriend.

What transpired over the next ten months became the most publicized criminal trial in the entire history of the United States. O.J.'s celebrity status allowed him to hire an "All-Star Team" of lawyers. And by their cunning maneuvering, the charges of murder ultimately took a back seat in that trial to that of racial bigotry. For L.A.'s law enforcement, as well as the rest of the country, that hidden disease of racism had never really gone away. The decades of hard work by Civil Rights advocates, all of the speeches by Martin Luther King and others, all of the marches, all of the legislation that had been enacted, and even the accepted political correctness of "liberty and justice for all" could not overcome what was hidden in the hearts of so many.

As America watched with rapt attention, the heart of ethnic bias was now put on full display in that California courtroom. The State judicial system had to find a judge that was neither Caucasian nor Black, so that there could be no appearance of the slightest prejudice in either direction. Judge Lance Ito, an Asian man, was the "neutral" solution. Nor could the team of prosecutors be exclusively white, or presumed prejudice would again be called into play. Even the possible bias of gender had to be anticipated, so the prosecutors could not be all male or all female. By selecting a black man and white woman, those hurdles were also solved so that the appearance of equality was insured.

Yet the jury box looked like a "stacked deck" in favor of the defendant. More than 200 prospective jurors were questioned in an effort to find twelve neutral individuals. The court explained that this kind of complex trial could last six to twelve months. Most working individuals claimed that such a lengthy time-frame would be too great a hardship on their income and their family budget. The net result was a disproportionate number of unemployed African American men and women were seated on the jury, because they had the time to do so. As part of the L.A. community, they already carried a hidden suspicion of inherent racism within the police and sheriff's departments. When the final twelve jurors were actually selected to begin the trial, it was nine blacks, one Hispanic, and two whites to decide the case. O. J. smiled and whispered to his lead attorney, "If I can't win with this jury, then I might think I actually did it."

What the court could not control was the true attitude of the Detectives who would be put on the witness stand, as well of the true attitudes and biases of the jurors themselves. Both of those variables had more to do with the ultimate verdict than the core question of O.J.'s innocence. Once on the stand, the Detectives denied ever using the term "nigger" in the course of their everyday work. Audiotapes later proved otherwise.

Evidence was also presented which showed that in previous cases the L.A. police and detectives had tampered with evidence in order more easily to assure a "guilty" verdict against African American defendants. As a result their accusations against O.J. became suspect, regardless of how convincing the crime scene evidence in this case might have been.

On the day when the verdict was to be announced, American business came to a literal standstill. People throughout our nation convened around the water cooler to listen on their radios to the live broadcast of the courtroom. A crowd of several thousand also gathered outside the courtroom itself. L.A. riot police on horseback were assigned to the streets as a preemptive measure in anticipation of either outcome in the verdict. As the United States populace held it's collective breath, Judge Ito read the decision of the jurors: "NOT GUILTY."

The immediate roar from the crowd assembled outside of the courtroom was so loud that it spooked the trained riot horses. Many people cheered loudly, and others stared silently in total disbelief. Our nation's system and process of justice had been carried out, but maybe not in the way that people had expected. Several African American women on the jury later acknowledged that their minds were firmly made up from the first day of the trial, because "we take care of our own." To them, justice was served that day for the countless previous incidents of mistreatment or unjust verdicts against Black people. Justice was served that day for the deep pain carried by those Black people throughout America that had been looked upon as sub-human by anyone with a segregationist attitude. Justice was served that day for the decades of inhumane abuse from white people. To all of them, justice was served that day because a wealthy Black man got away with murder.

Justice, however, was not served that day for the family of Simpson's ex-wife. In a civil trial that soon followed, O.J. was pronounced "GUILTY", and ordered to pay $33.5 million to the grieving family. He never did.

Despite the mountainous efforts otherwise, intense discrimination continues to exist to this day in the hearts of many white Americans against Black Americans. Equally intense reverse discrimination exists in the hearts of many Blacks against whites. What this trial proved – more than any other trial since Abraham Lincoln was alive – is the unfortunate truth that the cancer of racism still eats away at the heart of every major city in the U.S., and runs very deep for so many. Sadly, the mere act of passing mandatory integration legislation cannot change that, and our country continues to suffer as a result. There appears to be only one logical solution to this lingering stain on our nation. As philosopher Dr. Norman Geisler has posited, only interracial marriage on a grand scale for a few generations would eventually erase any ethnic separations, and achieve the "melting pot" of mutual acceptance. Nothing short of that seems as likely to succeed.

The highly-contested presidential race mercifully came to an end on November 5 with the national election. Richard Nixon had campaigned on the message of a "return to Law and Order" for America, which appealed to the general public as a slap against the incessant protesting by young adults. Nixon strategists counted on the fact that most protesters were too young to vote, and that most of the voting Establishment just wanted an end to the campus revolts.

Nixon also talked frequently about "honorable peace in Viet Nam", but clearly had no specific plan how to do so. May of this year had been the bloodiest month of the entire war. In October the Army and the Marines had just sent 24,000 troops back to Viet Nam for INVOLUNTARY 2nd tours of duty. That was a new precedent, and the quagmire seemed to be getting worse and worse. Maybe Walter Cronkite's ominous prediction was right.

On that election day it was late into the night before an official outcome could be declared. Nixon was announced as the winner over Hubert Humphrey by the narrowest of margins. It was one of those rare campaigns where the victor did not even come close to receiving 50% of the popular vote, and barely got the necessary 50% of the Electoral votes. The reason for that phenomenon was that Alabama's Governor George Wallace ran as a Third Party Candidate. Wallace had not offered a strong position on the issues of the Viet Nam war or the U.S. economy, but instead concentrated his entire campaign focus on a "return to segregation." He adamantly opposed the mandatory busing of black students into predominantly white schools. His anger primarily resonated with those in the South that had also grown tired of the Civil Rights Movement. He knew it was highly unlikely that he could win outright, but he also knew that if he won a few states, he might prevent a majority winner, which would force the election decision into the House of Representatives, where he could broker a deal for his choice for President. His vitriol only magnified the splintering of American voters.

To the chagrin of both major parties, Wallace's message was strong enough to capture more than 13% of the popular vote nationally, and actually to win the majority of votes in five states in the general election. Louisiana, Arkansas, Mississippi, Alabama, and Georgia cast their collective 45 Electoral votes for Wallace. That degree of success for an Independent third party candidate would never again be equaled.

The election outcome was a gigantic disappointment to the anti-war movement and the student population, and left them with a feeling of deep remorse and disillusionment toward the entire political system. On a national scale the American public had just turned its collective back on them. The war was now destined to continue to drag on. John Mitchell was appointed the U.S. Attorney General the following week, to be a rigid enforcer of established laws and thereby forcibly reduce or punish civil unrest anywhere in the country. Although seemingly impossible, the clash of opposing world-views would only get worse in the coming months before it would get better.

Viet Nam was already considered by many to be the most shameful war in American history. And it was 1968 that witnessed the two most shameful chapters of that entire 10-year war.

The first of those two events surfaced at the Long Binh Detention Center in Viet Nam where the issues of civil rights and equality unexpectedly over-lapped with the controversy of the war itself. U.S. black soldiers rioted against their fellow white soldiers, provoked by frequent derogatory name-calling or mistreatment. One white soldier was physically beaten to death, one military administrative building was burned to the ground, and several security guards were injured.

What ultimately amplified the morale problems was that the officers in charge initially tried to hide the incident. In an effort to put on a good face, a "public relations" statement was released that "whites and blacks proudly serve the U.S. together." Any soldier, however, knew that was categorically untrue.

The second event was far more unsettling. Numerous variables were already in the mix that may have contributed to this tragic ordeal. For example, military training says that one must always obey ANY command from a superior officer. Without that, you have a recipe for mayhem and mutiny. Another factor in this particular military setting of Viet Nam was the elimination by the news media of any statistics for "civilian deaths", which was simply changed to "enemy killed". Since it was often unclear who the real enemy was, the general rule-of-thumb became "If it's Vietnamese, and if it's dead, then it's Viet Cong." Ground troops tried to become calloused to the shooting of any Vietnamese person, rationalizing that it was either a VC soldier, or – at the very least – a VC informant.

On a sunlit morning late that year, Lt. Hugh Thompson and two of his crewmen were flying a Huey helicopter back and forth along the river delta, waiting for any calls for retrievals if Army units on the ground might need evacuation assistance. As they flew over a small community known as My Lai, they witnessed something horrific. Several hundred Vietnamese men, women, and children were working in the rice paddies below. Approaching them through the tall grass from the east was Company Charlie, a unit of just over 100 U.S. soldiers.

At the given command from their leader, Lt. William Calley, the ground troops began to slaughter these unarmed farmers, using rapid gunfire, grenades, and bayonets. From their helicopter above, Thompson and his crew witnessed actions that deeply scarred their minds, such as . . .

- a young boy, maybe 4 years old, was standing in a dazed state of shock, already wounded in one arm, and holding his torn flesh as blood oozed between his fingers. As a U.S. soldier approached him, their eyes met for a moment. The soldier then shouldered his weapon and sprayed the boy with several bullets.
- a young woman was running away, holding what appeared to be a small package. Another soldier shot her through the back, and she crumpled to the ground. He carefully rolled her lifeless body over, to see if she had been carrying a bomb. Instead he discovered it was her newborn baby, with half of its head now blown off.
- more than 50 of the rice workers were herded into a large ditch, where they were told to kneel down. The soldiers then proceeded to mow them all down with automatic fire, in a gangland fashion similar to Al Capone and the Valentine's Day massacre.
- dozens of the rice workers surrendered, and were marched into a meadow, and told to sit down and be quiet. After 20 minutes, the soldiers grew impatient and slaughtered them all in a hailstorm of bullets.
- soldiers walked into nearby grass huts and executed entire Vietnamese families while they were having breakfast.

Two news reporters were also traveling with Company Charlie that week, and stood in numbed disbelief as this debacle continued. They observed gang-raping of several teenage women, murders at pointblank range, hands being chopped off, tongues cut out, some adult men were scalped, shooting all of the livestock, and finally burning all of the huts in the adjacent village. This was no longer warfare, soldier against soldier. This was inhumane butchery.

Lt. Thompson landed his helicopter in the midst of this chaos, next to a small number of wounded women and children, and he and his two crewmates began offering First Aid. As a few ground soldiers approached, he expected them to assist him in administering general First Aid to those that were only wounded. Instead, he watched ten more women and children killed execution style.

While Lt. Thompson was yelling at these men to stop, Lt. William Calley arrived at the scene, and instructed his men to continue. Lt. Thompson's rare courage and integrity jolted a few of the soldiers out of their crazed rampage.

"Get out of our way," Calley barked at Thompson, before looking at his men. "Men, we've got a mission to do. Now let's keep moving!"

"Sir," one of his men replied, "this isn't a mission. This needs to stop."

Calley held a pistol to the Private's head. "Are you disobeying an order?" he barked.

Thompson interrupted again. "Hold it! This is nothing but mass murder, Lieutenant. Now somebody help me tend to these wounded!"

In the following minutes, more than 200 lives were spared because of what Lt. Thompson chose to do. As the gunfire subsided, a few other Vietnamese crawled to safety in the trees that bordered their rice fields. But the damage was done. In just less than three hours, an entire company had collectively gone on an adrenalin-charged and insanity-driven rain of bloodshed, fueled by fear, pent up anger, and the futility of not knowing for certain who their enemy might be.

The lives of 504 unarmed men, women, and children ended that morning in the rice fields of My Lai. The ramifications of what actually took place would not be fully reconciled or sorted out for many years to come.

Excessive amounts of public relations "spin" from the Pentagon had been unable to generate any new support for the war. The best objectives for each of the "Bob Hope Tours" and the carefully worded news releases were at the very least meant to break even and hopefully bolster the morale of those persons that already maintained a positive outlook on the war effort, i.e. those that held the mindset of "OUR COUNTRY – RIGHT OR WRONG." Yet every month those numbers of supporters were slowly dwindling. Now, as the sketchy rumors of My Lai began to creep into circulation throughout the U.S., the remaining war support waned at a greater speed. America had already lost this war – but didn't know it yet. . . .

Mayor Richard J. Daley

Senator S.I. Hayakawa

Senator Robert Kennedy

Dr. Martin Luther King

Viet Nam protest

Black Power Protest by U.S. athletes at Olympics

Killing Viet Cong informant in Saigon

CHAPTER 6

"1969 – SPIRALING DOWN"

"You say you want a revolution,
Well, you know we all want to change the world.
You tell me that it's evolution,
Well, you know we all want to change the world.
But when you talk about destruction
Don't you know that you can count me out.
Don't you know its gonna' be alright, alright . . . ."

- the Beatles

In January, Mark and his fellow soldiers arrived in Viet Nam for their 12 months of active duty. They were physically fit and surging with adrenalin as they stepped on to foreign soil. But their basic training had not prepared them for the atrocious conditions that awaited them. U.S. television coverage was able to capture the images of the blood, suffering, and destruction that was happening every day. War – as seen through the eyes of a television news camera – was no longer noble. But three critical things were missing in those daily reports. First, U.S. television could not capture the nauseating stench of death under the hot Asian sun. Every week Mark and his fellow troops found bloated, rotting North Vietnamese bodies left on the jungle's hillsides or floating down a river, gruesome reminders of a recent confrontation with a U.S. fighter plane or ground troops. Mark had field-dressed several elk and deer in his short lifetime, and knew the pungent smell of animal intestines or a punctured stomach wall. That seemed like nothing compared to a human that had been dead for two or three weeks.

Those gut-wrenching smells were the first jolt that told Mark this was a different world from boot-camp. The second shock was the inhumane treatment of Vietnamese people on the part of his officers. Since the rule of thumb was that no one could be trusted, Vietnamese men and women were "presumed guilty until proven innocent." And the biggest jab in that regard was when he discovered a large cardboard box near the mess hall that looked like it contained dried apricots. On closer examination he realized it was hundreds of human ears that had been cut off enemy soldiers. Any sense of humanity or civility had to be left on the tarmac where they arrived, and hopefully could be picked up again a year later when it was time to return home.

A third shock left Mark and his closest friends questioning the psychological effects of this ground war. More than 1/3 of all U.S. troops already stationed there were regularly using LSD, opium or heroin. It was an escape mechanism for young men trying to cope with the trauma of dead or wounded comrades that were being retrieved every week. Finding a source was easy. Manufactured in the hills of nearby Cambodia, hard drug products were systematically moved into every Vietnamese village near a U.S. Army outpost. Any Vietnamese waitress in a bar could quickly locate whatever was needed if she was paid an extra tip. To Mark, it all combined to make Viet Nam seem like a "hell-hole." He promised himself – if at all possible – that he would stick to beer, and avoid any addictive drugs.

The culture of South Viet Nam was now in complete upheaval. Prior to any U.S. military presence in Viet Nam, that country had been carried by an agricultural economy. More than 80% of its citizens had lived in small villages that dotted the countryside, and they labored every day of the year in their fields. But the war was quick to destroy much of their rice crops, their bridges, their rural roads, and the distribution channels for their basic supplies.

By 1969 the vast majority of Vietnamese citizens were forced to move into the major cities for survival. The city of Saigon tripled in size in less than four years. Sprawling bamboo ghettos sprang up at the edges of these cities, offering no sanitation, while providing only limited shelter along with rampant exposure to numerous diseases. Teenage girls had two options for work – as a bar waitress or as a prostitute. The pay was about the same. Girls were turning tricks for a carton of cigarettes, or for the soldier's C-rations for that day. Either of those "payments" was then taken home to be shared with her family in an effort to eke out an existence.

Corruption permeated the supply depots that were located in the port cities and airports. Vietnamese Generals as well as government officials were quick to line their own pockets with a little extra cash as they watched their beloved country become a living hell for so many others. At least 20% of all goods that came into the country disappeared out the back door and into the black market, or more than $1,000,000,000. each year. Food stuff, paper goods, liquor, civilian clothing, and even some military supplies were illegally seeping into the back streets for barter. One opportunistic young man was arrested for trying to sell a U.S. helicopter back to the U.S. Army.

Mark and his comrades quickly learned that their efforts there made little logical sense. It was unclear WHO the enemy really was. It was equally unclear WHERE the enemy really was. To maintain a high level of visibility, U.S. fighter planes made daily sorties to drop bombs on designated palm trees and jungle coordinates, whether there had been any report of enemy fire there or not. Such bombing often took a heavy toll on innocent civilians. Gunners on helicopter runs were told to fire at any man or woman below them that was seen running, because that implied their guilt. And as a result such American carelessness and the unnecessary casualties of Vietnamese civilians became the greatest recruiting tool for the enemy. This was not a conventional war, and America somehow seemed to be finding brilliant ways to defeat itself.

Mark couldn't wait to finish his tour there and get back to the quiet foothills of Colorado. *"Just keep your head down and pray you get through one day at a time."* That seemed to become his daily mantra. With every body bag lowered into a coffin for shipment back to the U.S., all of this fighting made less and less sense.

The growing trends of sexual freedom, opposition to authority, as well as complete and unrestrained individualism, now spilled over into professional sports. Prior to this year, all professional athletes were required to wear sport coats and ties when traveling as a team, and were expected to conduct themselves as gentlemen according to society's highest standards. That clean-cut, "all for the team" image was forever changed by two players in two different major professional sports during 1969.

"Broadway Joe" Namath had been the most highly sought after college football player in history. To the consternation of football purists, Joe Namath chose to shun the more established National Football League and instead signed with the New York Jets of the upstart American Football League. The ownership within this new league considered it an historic coup that just might save their fledgling dream of an expansion league for professional football. Namath's new team easily won their conference championship that season, and approached Super Bowl III with an unexpected swagger. The AFL was considered a "junior league", and had lost badly to the NFL team in Super Bowls I and II. Although the Las Vegas odds-makers placed the Jets as 19-point underdogs, Namath himself guaranteed a win without compromise for Jets fans. That kind of trash talking and braggadocio had never been seen at this level.

The most noted betting handicapper in Vegas for such sporting events was Jimmy "the Greek" Snyder. He chose to wager his entire net worth of more than $1,000,000. against the Jets on this "lop-sided mismatch", claiming there was no way that these "minor league" Jets could win. As a result of this mistaken prediction, after the game he was destitute and ended up living in the terminal of O'Hare Airport for more than two weeks, accepting handouts from sympathetic passengers that were going to or from their flights.

What made Namath's persona even more shocking was that he limited his football practice time during the week prior to the big game, and instead, for several nights was seen frequenting all the bars and nightclubs of Miami, each night with a different hooker on his arm. He flaunted all the existing standards of professionalism, and made a point of partying to excess. As a young man in his early 20's, Namath wanted to taste all that the world had to offer, and did not hesitate to let the public know it.

If he and his teammates had lost on that cloudy and drizzly January 12th, normality may have returned to the NFL. But the Jets handily defeated the Baltimore Colts that afternoon, and the sport of professional football was radically and permanently changed. In retrospect Super Bowl III is unquestionably seen as the most important football game in history, and the most pivotal for several reasons.

Because Namath delivered on his promise of a guaranteed win, the AFL was suddenly accepted as equal with the NFL. That single game forced the two leagues to accept a merger, and to realign their respective teams to make up the various blended conferences. The Super Bowl subsequently became the most watched event on television in the following years. As individuals, professional athletes had now become celebrities and sex symbols. Salaries began to sky-rocket to match those of movie and television stars. Players found new freedom in how they expressed themselves, including hair length, clothing styles, and aggressively being a part of the "social scene." Pro athletes would not miss out on the freedoms that other "twenty-somethings" were enjoying, thanks in large part to the self-focused trend-setting of Joe Namath.

Major league baseball also experienced a seismic shift in this year because of a completely different kind of rebellion against authority. Curt Flood had been an All-Star center-fielder for many seasons, primarily with the St. Louis Cardinals. He had a strong passion for helping anyone who was treated unfairly, and was one of the few professional athletes to publicly march against segregation with Dr. Martin Luther King.

At the time, all baseball players were bound to their team under the "reserve clause." It gave team owners the sole discretion over any player trades that might occur. Curt Flood changed that forever.

Even though he was considered a well-paid professional athlete, a sense of being treated unjustly as "sterile property" consumed him in 1969. The ownership of the Cardinals found it necessary to trade him and two of his teammates so that they might bring in several younger players in an effort to rebuild for the future. In a stunning reaction, Curt Flood chose to refuse the trade, and personally chose to sue Major League Baseball. He claimed that he was used as nothing more than a "slave", and that he had no voice in where he played. He knew that this action potentially carried the individual risk of him never being allowed to play ball again. But his moral compass said this was a very good thing for his teammates and the future of baseball.

The case ultimately went to the Supreme Court, where he narrowly lost. As his lawyer had warned, it prematurely ruined his career. Baseball owners black-listed him, and Curt Flood never played major league baseball again. He also frequently received anonymous hate-mail and death threats for "trying to destroy the sport of baseball."

Ultimately, however, his court case had a much different outcome, even though Curt Flood was never able to benefit personally from the changes that he brought about. The Supreme Court allowed for possible "free agency" for individual players, but only through collective bargaining. Those steps were soon reached, and free agency became the most significant change to the sport of professional baseball since its inception 130 years earlier. (Within a few years this concept of free agency was adopted by the NFL and NBA as well.) Players' salaries as well as stadium attendance increased dramatically once players had the freedom to re-negotiate their own salaries or let themselves be traded to a higher bidder.

Curt Flood forever changed baseball because he was willing to rebel against the owner's monopoly to promote what he considered the "greater good." His opposition provided significant benefits for all Major League baseball players who followed him. Two decades later he was given the NAACP Jackie Robinson Award for contributions to black athletes. Over time his heroic stand made hundreds of millions of dollars for other athletes, yet he himself died a very poor man.

Rebellion for the sake of monumental change often carries consequences of monumental proportions.

Washington, D.C. was buzzing throughout the month of January in preparation for the Presidential Inauguration on the 20th. Numerous gala parties were scheduled in traditional fashion. Once again America would proudly display to the world her unique ability to facilitate the peaceful transfer of power. Following a marching band and a chorale's rendition of the National Anthem, Richard Milhouse Nixon placed his hand on the Bible and was sworn in as the 34th President of the United States. No mention was made of the fact that he had lost the presidential race to John Kennedy in 1960, and had left Washington with a snarl as he said, "You won't have Richard Nixon to kick around anymore." This day signified one of the greatest political turnarounds in all of election history.

Nixon gave a bold inaugural address, inviting all Americans to share his optimism in facing the daunting challenges of excessive inflation, worrisome unemployment, extreme campus unrest, and a war in Southeast Asia that needed to end with some sense of national dignity. Americans would soon learn that he clearly had the political savvy to maneuver through the maze of Capitol Hill, but it was his personal character that would ultimately lead to an historic implosion.

The platform appearances and formal inaugural celebrations seemed to be routine for Washington, D.C. But just a few blocks away, the story was quite different. Thousands of protesters had gathered for a three-day "counter inauguration." Braving freezing rain and below-average temperatures, the crowd hoped to make a national statement of the need for comprehensive change. But there was little unity as to where that change should begin.

Attempting to lead the charge was the National Mobilization Committee to End the War in Viet Nam (MOBE). This group was trying to become the self-appointed head of a consortium of many smaller groups that appeared to have a similar purpose – to demand an immediate end to the war. The question was how radical a group must be in order to have its voice heard. Their appeal had gone out to any and all groups on the Right, the Left, Liberals, radicals, and supporters of any niche, if only to generate a greater turnout.

The strategy failed. A number of radical groups, including the Students for a Democratic Society (SDS) chose to ignore the invitation from MOBE, and not even show up for this melded protest. Those groups that did arrive wanted equal time for their own chosen purposes. Some speakers ranted about an unjust war. Others demanded equal rights for women, including representatives from the "Women's International Terrorist Conspiracy from Hell", or WITCH. Another speaker pleaded with his audience to boycott grapes until migrant workers had a fair contract. One female speaker was booed off the stage because she would not remove her T-shirt and expose her breasts. The diverse issues may have splintered the crowd, but their one common thread that connected each to the other was that of intense anger.

MOBE had established a clear intent to be politically confrontational, but not physical or violent. And based on that premise they had received a legal permit at the last minute from Washington, D.C. authorities to hold their outdoor rally. That goal failed as well.

A portion of the crowd ventured from their muddy hub near the Washington Monument to march toward the White House while yelling anti-Nixon slogans. Police on horseback tried to accompany them to make sure they did not venture past their assigned area. Firecrackers were thrown from the crowd, which caused the horses unexpectedly to bolt and panic. The excitement left piles of fresh horse manure in the street. Taking advantage of the situation, the marchers picked up handfuls of this steaming excrement and flung it at the police as well as the limousine of Vice President Spiro Agnew and other guests as they arrived for an inaugural party. Eggs and tomatoes were thrown at other random targets. A Molotov cocktail was hurled through a window of the national headquarters for the Selective Service, causing extensive damage.

Another protest group brought a live pig in a travel cage, claiming this was their preferred candidate for President, and asked for media coverage as they held their "in-HOG-uration ceremony." The pig accidentally got loose, and required several police officers to help re-capture it. That was a

90-minute adventure that was more crazy than it was dangerous.

Skirmishes then broke out as police began clubbing random protesters, and in retaliation a sizeable number of other marchers pelted the police with rocks. Officers made 119 arrests, but no one was hospitalized. There was little consensus among the various groups that were represented at this counter-inauguration, but there was one major accomplishment as an outcome to their efforts – the national media coverage gave the anti-war movement a much needed shot-in-the-arm. As a result, America would see much larger and more focused protests coming in the next few months.

Boulder – and particularly the University of Colorado – was quickly becoming a bastion for radical thinking and cultural upheaval. The city of Boulder was much more liberal than the rest of Colorado, and the University campus was more liberal than the neighborhoods which surrounded it. This small community would ultimately become the originating epicenter for massive change in America on such major issues as legalized abortion, legalized marijuana, or same-sex marriage. The city was becoming a composite of any and all progressive elements in America. If there were a cause for change anywhere in the U.S., Boulder likely had some of its adherents. The wave of protests became so diverse and so frequent that they often lost their individual ability to generate any sense of distinction or emphasis.

But in March a new boundary was crossed that could only be described as a "protest against free speech." Tom's mother had been a college friend with S.I. Hayakawa while at the University of Hawaii. Acting on behalf of the University of Colorado, she was asked personally to invite him to come and speak at CU. Hayakawa's national notoriety had grown in his first year as the new President at the University of San Francisco, where he concentrated on strict law enforcement to protect his campus. Rightly or wrongly, his perceived reputation among students and radicals was that of a person willing to sacrifice the freedoms of speech and public expression for the sake of his desired level of control.

When the official announcement was made that Dr. Hayakawa was coming to CU for a speech, a sense of pandemonium blew through every radical group in Boulder. The Black Panthers assumed they would simply boycott the event. The SDS planned to picket the auditorium the day of the speech, but also expected they would not actually attend. Others demanded that CU retract their invitation, and cancel the event entirely. Eventually, several protest groups collectively decided that they would make a greater statement of solidarity if they all attended the speech, but then in unison walked out during the opening minute of the address.

When the evening arrived, the 2500-seat auditorium was dangerously packed with a standing-room-only audience. Anticipating the possibility of violence in the crowd, CIA agents and plain-clothes police officers were secretly sprinkled throughout the building. Only about 90 blacks were present, but chose to sit in the front three rows so that their planned exit in the early moments of the program could be more dramatic. As the crowd impatiently awaited the beginning of Hayakawa's presentation, there were numerous mob chants against the war, or the police, or injustice in general. When a University professor finally stepped to the podium to introduce the guest speaker, he was immediately shouted down with choruses of "Boo's", cursing, and the stomping of feet.

When the noise abated slightly, the professor began. "Good evening, and welcome to the free marketplace of ideas." Immediately the crowd roared again with jeers, swearing, and taunts. The professor paused, but then attempted to complete his introduction of S.I. Hayakawa over the ranting of the crowd.

Few in the auditorium could hear anything of the actual introduction. Mass cheers of "Off the Pigs!" and "The revolution has come!" were yelled as Hayakawa approached the mike. He stood silently and took in the taunting. As he opened his mouth to speak, dozens of paper airplanes, a beer bottle, and a folding chair were thrown onto the stage. Rather than starting his prepared speech, Hayakawa started his own rhythmic chant. "Rats off campus, Rats off campus," he said with a wry smile. That was met with more agitated yelling.

In a feeble attempt to quiet the crowd, he stepped to the side of the podium and – while facing the African American contingent – began doing a strange jig. As he maintained eye contact with them, he returned to the mike and said, "You're good dancers. You liked that, didn't you?"

A dozen more folding chairs came sailing up on stage as he tried to continue. Hayakawa urged the crowd to make a logical choice . . . to walk out, or wait their turn for using the microphone. As he then proceeded with a few extemporaneous comments, he shared his thoughts of how the early Nazi's rose to power by refusing to hear other ideas, and when out of ideas, they resorted to burning things and destroying things.

At that, some of the militants began climbing onto the stage. Campus Police rushed from behind the curtains to prevent any direct confrontation, and escorted Hayakawa to a side room for safety. An announcement was made that there would be no further speech until calm was restored in the auditorium. A mass walk-out of more than 400 attendees exited the venue, yelling and cursing as they left. The rest of the crowd waited over an hour to see if he would resume his presentation.

Shortly after 10 p.m., Hayakawa returned to the podium. The crowd had calmed somewhat, and chose to listen for a brief time, to hear what he had to say. To their surprise, he began by talking about his deep empathy for Blacks and the mistreatment they had received throughout American history. He shared his own traumatic experience of being a young boy in a Japanese family living in San Francisco that was sent to an internment camp in eastern California during WWII. He knew the deep anger of being the recipient of racial prejudices. He knew the temptation of lashing back at oppressors. But he also learned that any response must be lawful in its process. He then praised academic freedom and the privileges that it afforded to a person. Then somewhat abruptly, he bowed slightly and left the stage, after speaking less than seven minutes.

Feeling cheated, the crowd once again rose in a tumultuous roar, yelling and throwing items onto the stage. It would only get weirder.

John Buttny had been standing in the back of the auditorium, taking in the entire event. John had served as a Marine in Viet Nam and, following his return to the states, had become one of the best-known voices in Boulder against the war. (He was the protester that had the physical confrontation with the Chicago police officer during the Democratic Nat'l Convention the previous year.) He was a primary leader in the local chapter of the SDS, had been arrested several times for attempting to incite a riot on CU's campus, and was now on probation. One of the CIA agents at the rear exit recognized John, and asked him to go on stage quickly to try to calm the crowd. The agent felt that John carried the needed credibility with the radical community, and might be the best possible solution for restoring and maintaining an orderly environment in the auditorium while asking people to leave peacefully.

John said he was willing to try to help. He made his way to the front, hopped up onto the stage, and took the microphone to begin asking people to calm down and leave the building in an orderly manner. Instead, the plan backfired. Undercover police hidden back-stage did not know that the CIA agent had made this request, and thought John was trying to create an impromptu protest of his own. They quickly tackled him and had him arrested without hearing his explanation.

The brief show of force caused the crowd to chant slurs against the "pigs" once again, but they slowly left the building when is was apparent there were a high number of law enforcement personnel there. The evening ended without further disruption.

But in the aftermath that followed during the next few days, several unexpected factors took place. The "Associated Students of the University of Colorado" submitted a written demand for S. I. Hayakawa to issue a formal apology for his racial insults and pre-meditated baiting of students. New University policies were hurriedly put into place to restrict who might be invited in the future to appear on campus. The CU administration officially disassociated with the SDS organization, stating that it would never again be allowed to have a presence of any kind on the University grounds. And lastly, a bomb went off in the University bookstore, blowing out one wall and several windows. There was never a proven correlation to the Hayakawa event, but the coincidence was compelling.

In retrospect, there were many unfortunate losers from this week. But the biggest loser was the foundational privilege of free speech.

Growing opposition to the Viet Nam War held a major place in the news in March. From "across the pond" John Lennon and his new bride, Yoko Ono, honeymooned in Amsterdam. They chose to stage a "Bed-In" for seven days as a protest to the war. Every day the news media was invited into their honeymoon suite to interview them while they remained in bed together, covered only by a single sheet. The shock value of that setting caused the news coverage to explode, and young adults became news "junkies" for a few days. Lennon's influence in America was unequaled at the time, even though he was not even in the country.

Also in March, some of the ugly details regarding the war crimes of the My Lai massacre began to trickle into the American conversation. The two journalists who had witnessed that day of bloodshed first released their photos to the St. Louis and Cleveland newspapers, and then to *LIFE Magazine*. Most subscribers tried to refuse to believe the graphic horror of what they read. But too often any Viet Nam veteran now returning to the U.S. was already being called a "baby killer."

Sgt. Ron Ridenhour had now finished his tour of duty in Nam, and was out of the military. As a civilian, he wrote letters of his eye-witness account as a passenger on Lt. Thompson's helicopter, and mailed those letters to several Congressmen, Senators, the Secretary of Defense, and the White House. Even worse than the detailed record of the initial acts of murder, his notes now claimed an organized and sinister cover-up attempt on the part of the U.S. Army, including deliberate lies from several senior officers. A final assertion that grabbed his reader's attention was the possibility that these horrific actions were the most extensive war crimes in U.S. military history.

Further Army investigation began to acknowledge that something ugly and evil had in fact happened. The question of the integrity of Lt. Hugh Thompson again surfaced at the forefront of the inquiry, and his testimony became the turning point in the hearings held by a panel of Washington, D.C. legislators and military brass. While the anti-war constituents saw Thompson as an honest hero, for the time being his fellow military personnel considered him nothing more than a traitor, a "rat", and a disgrace to the uniform.

President Richard Nixon had technically inherited this My Lai problem, because it had actually occurred during LBJ's final months in office. But Nixon was willing to do almost anything in an attempt to save face for our nation's military. He was determined to avoid failure in the court of public opinion, and privately ordered "dirty tricks" if necessary to discredit Lt. Thompson and other witnesses in any way possible. He did not want Americans to think that our own soldiers could have stooped to the animalistic levels of some of our worst enemies by exercising the wholesale slaughter of unarmed civilians at point blank range. His public message repeatedly stressed that this was merely an isolated incident, but that overall our Army's objectives and performance were very good. Nixon's hidden penchant for lies and cover-up not only delayed justice in this situation, but those same moral flaws would re-surface again, and ultimately undermine his entire presidency only four years later.

One very large and unexpected hurdle emerged during these hearings on the possibility of war crimes. By mid-year, 75 of the 104 men that were in Company Charlie when it had carried out these gruesome acts near My Lai were now out of the Army completely. As regular civilians once again they were thus immune to any military jurisdiction, immune to any U.S. judicial bench since those alleged crimes had not taken place on U.S. soil, and they were immune to any Vietnamese court since they no longer lived in Viet Nam and there was no extradition treaty between those two nations. These men logically presumed that they were totally in the clear.

Yet Americans were somewhat in pained disbelief when a dozen ground troops were officially charged with a range of crimes such as assault, rape, and mass-murder, including Lt William Calley, the leader of the platoon, as well as his company commander, Captain Ernest Medina. And four additional officers of higher rank were also charged with dereliction of duty, failure to report a war crime, or the cover-up of a crime.

A military trial was set for the following year, to weigh the gravity of multiple war crimes. This was in fact a tragic day for the reputation of our entire Defense Department.

April 4th was the first anniversary of the assassination of Martin Luther King. This date witnessed one of the most unusual "marriages" of two causes – the Civil Rights Movement and the Jewish congregations within New York City. Rabbi Woskow invited supporters of both communities to a ceremony that he called the "Freedom Seder" gathering. Just over 800 accepted his invitation, including blacks and white, Jews and Christians, rabbis and ministers.

The Rabbi was able to inter-weave elements from the current plight of Blacks in modern America to the story of the liberation of the ancient Hebrews in Egypt. As he spoke, a large poster was prominently displayed behind him that read "JEWS FOR URBAN JUSTICE." He told of how the nation of Israel in 1350 B.C. had been held as slaves for more than 350 years in the land of the Nile, the land of the Pyramids. "The Exodus" finally marked their departure from slavery in that foreign country, and their transition into their own land that God had promised to them. Liberty and justice had finally taken place. Since then the Passover Seder had commemorated that event every spring for more than 3,300 years.

A new bond was established that night, as leaders of the black community and the Jewish community realized that both groups had suffered great atrocities at the hands of an oppressor. Liberation, freedom, and equality had become the shared standard for all of humanity. Woskow read excerpts from the writings of Martin Luther King and Mahatma Ghandi, calling on all of mankind to love each other as fellow citizens of earth. At the conclusion, whites and blacks solemnly stood and locked arms as they sang *"We Shall Overcome."*

That evening, the urgency of "freedom and equality" took on new meaning for everyone present. Jews had known what it was to be down-trodden, to be treated as sub-human beings. Thanks to this variation on the Jewish tradition, Civil rights leaders suddenly realized they had a new ally in their pursuit of equality.

In the spring of '69 Hollywood released a movie that carried the sexual revolution into new territory. Affairs – particularly among men and women within the entertainment field – had been commonplace for decades. But the general tenor had always been that such sexual dalliances must necessarily be discreet, and became valid grounds for divorce if a person was caught.

"Bob & Carol & Ted & Alice" took a different slant. Leading the cultural wave and its new-found acceptance of sexual variety before or within a marriage, the script followed two married couples who first acknowledge their individual infidelities, then slowly begin to condone it and even welcome it. When one husband confesses his temptation to have an affair with an office co-worker, his friend advises him, "As long as you already have the guilt, don't pass up the opportunity."

By the end of the story, the two couples take a Las Vegas vacation together and end up in one bed as a foursome. Audiences flocked to see it again and again. The movie received four Academy Award nominations, and was one of the most profitable Hollywood releases of the year. The powerful influence of the media had again provided a message that the public wanted to hear.

The City of Boulder Police Department may have found one of the most creative ways to build some rapport with the rebellion-minded college students on the local campus. A few cops approached some of the leaders of the fraternity houses, and challenged the young men to a "flag football game." The University administration had already approved the proposal, as long as additional officers were there exclusively to provide security if needed. For the students, the visual image of being able legally to oppose law enforcement had an immediate appeal, and the match was set for late May, just two weeks before graduation.

Posters announcing the event began to appear throughout the campus, as well as on the walls of The Golden Cue and other business establishments nearby. It was dubbed as the "1st Annual Hairy Bacon Bowl" for special reason. "Hairy" denoted the students, since most had long hair as well as fuzzy attempts at facial hair. "Bacon" was just a take-off from the derogatory reference to police as "pigs."

On the day of the game, more than 3,000 students walked into Folsom

Field (the campus football stadium) to take in the free entertainment. Both sides had "cheerleaders", which were men attired in sweaters and mini-skirts and very bad wigs. Most of the student football players were bare-footed, some in bell-bottomed jeans. Two extra officers also provided the multi-functions of referee, linesman, back judge, and timekeeper.

As the game got underway, there were several organized cheers from the student section that made crude references about the police. But soon everyone just settled in and enjoyed the fun. Although it was not a shut-out, the students won rather handily. Some might have thought that the police had chosen to "take a dive", but no one knew for sure. When the whistle blew indicating that time had expired, there were handshakes all around.

Maybe some of these pigs aren't so bad after all. At least that is what most students thought by the time they left. The police definitely gained some needed respect in the process. It would pay major dividends over the next few years. And the "Hairy Bacon Bowl" continued annually through the spring of 1973.

Mother's Day should be a time for family gatherings. Flowers and gift cards for Mom. Treat her to dinner at a nice restaurant. Try to spoil her for a day. Instead, Mother's Day this May was a near disaster of biblical proportions for the entire Denver-Boulder corridor.

The U.S. government had built a laboratory just south of Boulder under the strictest secrecy. The Rocky Flats Nuclear Weapons Plant (just known as "Rocky Flats") was deemed a necessity at the height of the Cold War. The Department of Defense needed a necessity at the height of the Cold War. The Department of Defense needed warheads. The 1300 acre site was chosen because of the attractive climate and excellent work force in the immediate area. The entire property was bordered by 9-foot barbed wire fences, and patrolled by armed guards.

By May of 1969, more than 3,500 scientists and engineers filed through those security access points every day to work in the lab. Plutonium is so dangerous that line workers had to wear full-body suits, and only handle the raw material with led-lined gloves through a glove box. One gram of plutonium could be lethal for 1,000,000 people, and the lab had more than 7,000 pounds of it on site. At the end of every shift each day the workers were checked for radioactivity on their clothes and hair.

With a minimal workforce on that Sunday afternoon, no one noticed when a plutonium chip in building 771 sparked and started a fire. Safety alarms had been disconnected, so the fire went undetected as the ventilation system quickly fanned the flame throughout the entire assembly area. Toxic black smoke was belching from the exhaust stacks before any employees could suit up in fire fighting gear. An apocalyptic crisis was unfolding.

Water was considered the worst possible option for fighting a plutonium fire. Typical water pressure from a fire hose could move the raw material and cause a nuclear chain reaction. Sand or oil were most effective in dousing a small plutonium spark. But this fire had already advanced so far that engineers quickly decided that water was the only option.

Although the would-be firemen worked feverishly, it was more than 10 hours before the inferno was under control. Miraculously the ceiling did not melt, or northeastern Colorado would have been exposed to radiation levels far greater than Hiroshima. An unknown quantity of plutonium particles and other toxins were released into the atmosphere through the smokestack, and dispersed over Boulder, Broomfield, and north Denver. But an unthinkable disaster had narrowly been averted.

In spite of full safety suits, a few employees received dangerous levels of radiation exposure that day. Two men had to go through double shower scrubs, where all the body hair as well as the outer layer of their skin was carefully rubbed off so as not to draw blood. Yet one of these men was still so "hot" on the radiation test that he was permanently transferred to the security gate job, and never allowed into the lab again to avoid any possible additional exposure.

The next day the Defense Department released a small news item to the press that landed on page 28 of the *Denver Post*. It claimed that no one was harmed, and there was no need for any on-going concern of possible danger.

How arrogant and calloused. Even though countless American lives were threatened, the government once again chose secrecy over transparency. Deception over honesty. Sadly, it was another line item on a list of lies that was growing...and growing...and growing.

On both the high school and college campuses across the country, this year presented the blatant opportunity for sexual jokes having to do with the "Class of '69." Some teens may not have fully understood the sexual definition of the "69 position", but they enjoyed re-telling any joke with a "69" punch line.

Wendy was a member of the Class of '69, an attractive young high school student, and a classmate of Tom's younger sister. She dated frequently throughout her years at Boulder High, and like most students enjoyed making out. But her choices went a little further.

Wendy had made a firm determination for herself that she would not get pregnant, as two of her classmates had done. For her, that rationale became a rigid commitment on her part to personally eliminate any such risk of pregnancy by abstaining from having sex. However, she felt conflicted while making out and petting, because she knew guys would be very aroused sexually. Her solution was that she would perform oral sex on her date before the evening was done.

By the time graduation occurred late in the spring of '69, Wendy had gone down on more than 30 of the boys in her senior class. But she took pride in the fact that she was not pregnant.

As one High School Counselor observed, sexual mores had made a shocking shift in just three years. In '66 it seemed that only the cheerleaders were the girls that were sexually active. By '69, she estimated that 75% of the students were there. The sexual revolution had virtually removed any moral compass of guilt or shame for most young men and women. It was now a simple matter of individualistic freedom. Most chose to be "serial monogamists" in their relationships, while a few leapfrogged from "hickies to hookups." In that short window of three years, the mindset had jumped from "liberty" as personal freedom within an accepted moral code to "license" as a necessary Antinomian self, able to reject and even openly oppose any established morality.

The Beatles had sung about "Revolution", and it was now evident that a cultural revolution was in fact rapidly moving throughout all sectors of the country. And not just rock & roll music was documenting that shift. Even the staid and somewhat stoic producers of New York's Broadway musical industry incorporated the changing mindset into their stories. A light-hearted comedy entitled *"Thoroughly Modern Millie"* came to Broadway that year, and the lyrics accurately reflected the times. The stage play's theme song carried this musical statement:

"In olden days a sight of stocking
Was known as something shocking,
Now – Heaven knows – anything goes."

As the decade of the '60's was drawing to a close, that was not an overstatement. Anything goes.

Dr. David Reuben fueled the sexual revolution by publishing his book, *"Everything You Ever Wanted to Know About Sex."* In graphic detail he provided a sex manual that sold more than 100,000,000 copies, and became the #1 best seller in 51 nations. Reuben helped to create a comfort level in discussing any detail of sex in matter-of-fact terms, which promoted the liberated acceptance of any and all sex activity outside of a monogamous heterosexual marriage.

The choir of voices making public demands for sexual freedom added a significant new member that summer. Gays and lesbians had been the object of many cruel jokes, but little had been done to try to understand them. In the summer of 1969 a 19-year-old man from St. Louis became the first recorded death caused by AIDS, but the news media and the medical world took little notice of that event, in large part because they did not truly understand the severity of its cause.

The media did, however, begin to take notice of the issue of gay rights beginning on June 28th. Like numerous other cities, New York had a law that if a bar knowingly served drinks to a gay person, they could have their liquor license cancelled. To increase their arrest totals, plainclothes police would flirt with gay men in bars until the unsuspecting victims could be charged with "solicitation by a homosexual." In retaliation for such entrapment and unfair treatment, gay men created "The Mattachine Society" for the purpose of developing a charter for gay rights. The only question was how and when to take those demands public.

New York City was home to a bar called "The Stonewall Inn", located in Greenwich Village. Although it was operating without a liquor license, it had become the most popular nightly gathering place for gays and lesbians. Thus it was also a frequent gathering place for police that wanted to make an easy arrest. New York police officers would oftentimes harass such establishments to enforce three laws: lack of a valid liquor license, solicitation of homosexual acts since they were illegal, and any person not wearing at least three articles of gender-appropriate clothing could be arrested. All three statutes made the Stonewall Inn an easy target.

That particular summer evening, nine officers entered the bar and arrested the employees for selling liquor without a license. They also roughed up a number of patrons for the fun of it. But this time the crowd did not retreat. The customers started throwing beer bottles at the policemen, and the officers finally had to barricade themselves inside the bar while they called for backup. More than 400 patrons rioted in the street, and lit the bar on fire while the officers were still inside.

Although no officers were killed, the riots continued every evening for the next five nights, with an ever increasing number marching in the street each night, demanding equality, acceptance, and respect. A new segment of radical activism was birthed that week, patterning itself after the Civil Rights leadership. A new Gay Rights Movement had begun.

It would be many years, however, before mainstream America could support those demands that had been initiated that summer with the "Stonewall Riots." It would be exactly 30 years until the National Park Service would choose to place the Stonewall Inn on the National Register of Historic Places. And it would be an additional 17 years after that until President Barack Obama designated the site as a National Monument.

President John F. Kennedy had been assassinated while serving in the White House. Bobby Kennedy had been assassinated just five years later while campaigning to win the White House. Thus the weight of the Kennedy's political influence now rested on the shoulders of their youngest brother, Teddy, to perpetuate the legacy of the family name. Many Americans believed that after a few more years of experience in the U.S. Senate, he would be ready in 1972 to fulfill the dream of having a Kennedy once again in the Oval Office. The "Kennedy mystique" had never gone away.

Those dreams were shattered on the evening of July 18, 1969. Following a late night party near Martha's Vineyard, Ted Kennedy was driving 25-year-old Mary Jo Kopechne, one of his former campaign aids, to a private beach on Chappaquiddick Island. Kennedy swerved off of a small bridge, crashed through the guard rail, and drove the car into the water channel below.

In the darkness of his submerged car, Kennedy was somehow able to free himself and swim to the surface. His younger passenger was not so fortunate. Kennedy dove down a couple of times in a futile attempt to try to find the car. He finally swam to shore and hitched a ride to his hotel. There he showered and changed clothes around 3a.m., then purposely had a brief face-to-face conversation with one of the hotel staff. As a married man as well as a public figure, he desperately wanted to protect his image. His initial plan was to create a carefully crafted alibi of an eye-witness seeing him at the hotel, then later claim that Mary Jo was the driver and sole occupant in the car that had met such a tragic end.

But a phone call to one of his closest advisors convinced him otherwise. Ted was reminded that Mary Jo had left her purse and car keys at the party. It was very apparent to everyone why she left with the Senator, and that she expected to return shortly. Ten hours after the accident, Ted Kennedy finally called the authorities. Extensive search efforts that following morning eventually retrieved the car as well as Mary Jo's body.

A private funeral service was held for Mary Jo a few days later. Senator Kennedy attended, wearing a fake neck-brace in an effort to garner some emotional pity from the public. Although the Kennedy family's insurance company paid $141,000 to her parents, Kennedy himself never apologized to them.

In a classic example of "money buying justice", Kennedy pled guilty to the reduced charge of "leaving the scene of an accident." He was given a two-month suspended sentence, and had his driver's license revoked for 12 months. Although he remained in public office, his integrity, reputation, and career were forever destroyed. Any dreams and aspirations he may have had for the Presidency – as well as the life of that beautiful young woman – were both killed at Chappaquiddick. A Kennedy would not be going back to the White House.

July 21st was an historic date for all of humanity. Astronaut Neil Armstrong was scheduled to be the first human to walk on the surface of the moon. It renewed the conviction of mainstream America that – in spite of the cultural turmoil surrounding the Viet Nam War and Civil Rights protests – this was still the greatest country in the world. The government desperately needed this success, to move its citizens to look "up", and even for a few moments forget about the war in Viet Nam or the civil rights battles at home.

Both Mark and Tom wanted to follow the story closely, but the stark contrast in how they experienced that momentous event could not have been more blatant. Tom hosted a late-night party for a dozen friends in Boulder, with ample beer and marijuana on hand. Everyone was quite stoned by the time they gathered around the new color-TV to see Armstrong carefully step from the lunar module on to the moon's dusty surface.

Mark, on the other hand, was on the other side of the world, finishing his Army "gourmet breakfast" of powdered eggs and weak coffee, before heading out for another day on patrol around the rice paddies of South Viet Nam. Along with several other Privates, he listened to the live news coverage as it crackled on their only camp radio. For him it was a momentary respite from the madness.

Americans had no idea of the many "behind-the-scenes" scenarios that the White House had to anticipate for national events such as this. Because of the risky nature of the space program, astronaut Frank Borman had warned the White House staff that success on this moon mission was not an absolute certainty. In spite of years of calculations and preparations, tragedy might possibly occur. Speech writers for the President had already secretly scripted the copy for a somber message to the nation if the lunar lander failed to take off, and as a consequence our astronauts would be stranded and left to die slowly on the moon. Thankfully that speech never needed to be delivered.

"One small step for Man – One giant leap for Mankind." The mayhem and pains of life took a brief pause for all Americans that evening as Neil Armstrong took his first step onto the moon's surface and uttered those famous words. Citizens of every political persuasion were united once again, if only for a brief window of time, with a sense of national pride. Anger and dissention could wait until tomorrow.

A gruesome story out of L.A. hit the news wires the first full week of July. An unassuming older couple had been brutally murdered, stabbed multiple times, and their throats slit. Robbery did not appear to be the motive, since there was no safe in the house and no valuables appeared to be missing. The act of murder itself was not uncommon for any major city, but one thing made this crime particularly cold-hearted and strange – the killers had used the victim's blood to write "Political Piggy" in large letters on the living room wall. Detectives were baffled.

One month later the killers struck again. Entering the home of Hollywood movie producer Roman Polanski, they brutally stabbed the five occupants to death, including Polanski's young girlfriend, actress Sharon Tate, who happened to be eight months pregnant. This time one of the killers used the victim's blood to write "PIG" on the front door.

The following night the killers chose another house at random, and finding a back door unlocked, quietly slipped into the home of a supermarket executive and his wife. They first bound their victims, then stabbed them more than 40 times each. This time human blood was used to write "Death to Pigs" and "Helter Skelter" on the living room walls. One of the murderers even allowed time to take a shower before they left.

This particular crime spree created a new level of fear on a national level. Network news made this a daily story as police searched for clues. Many Hollywood celebrities and other wealthy people from the greater L.A. area went into temporary hiding, not wanting to risk being the next random victim. Frank Sinatra, for example, barricaded himself in his Palm Springs estate. What began to unfold in the coming weeks became the very personification of evil.

Charles Manson had dreams of becoming a star as the lead musician with a rock & roll band, even with the hopes that he would someday be more successful than the Beatles. He spent extensive time with Brian Wilson, one of the Beach Boys, in Wilson's private recording studio, working on several of his own compositions. What Wilson did not know was that earlier in the year Manson had already murdered another drug dealer after being personally threatened.

Manson had also started a commune that he called "The Family", which was built on the promise of unlimited sex and drugs. The growing rebellion of teenage runaways combined with the sexual revolution provided a sufficient number of willing partners. This family was comprised of 32 adults and 12 young children. Manson and his followers sold enough drugs or stole enough cash from time to time in order to provide room and board for everyone while living in a rural farmhouse and complex outside of L.A. As the leader of this cult, Manson bragged of having sex with various partners from within the family before lunch and again before dinner every day. He frequently assigned specific couples to have sex with each other, or groups of eight to twelve to have group sex.

These followers willingly complied with his kinky wishes because they saw Manson as a prophet or the new "Messiah." His message of mind control was that the world was soon going to collapse in a cultural crash and be taken over by African Americans, with only a select few Caucasians able to participate in its implementation. His instructions for his "family" members to murder at random were strategically intended to implicate African Americans as the murderers, and thereby create public fear which would accelerate the coming chaos and crash of society that he envisioned under the weight of a "race" war.

Charles Manson was arrested the next month on suspicion of car theft, although the charges had to be dropped because of insufficient evidence. Several clear fingerprints at one of the previous murder scenes, however, led law enforcement detectives to arrest one of the women in the Manson "family." She immediately plea-bargained for immunity, claiming that she knew extensive details on these crimes, but that she herself did not actually participate in the murders.

Manson and the other members of the family were all arrested, and the trial was scheduled for early in the following year. Even though the murdering spree had ended, fear throughout America was now escalated for different reasons. Any murder is certainly a tragedy. But in this horrific situation, the American public's greatest dismay was their complete and utter inability to understand why this had happened. No understandable motive was present. No clear or consistent target. How could someone like Manson have such mind control over other young people so that they would obediently murder someone else? How could young and innocent women from wholesome family upbringings participate in such bizarre or evil activities and yet show no remorse? What role did drugs play in this series of gruesome murders? And if drugs were a critical element, could every other drug-using young person in the country be susceptible to doing something similar?

Charles Manson single-handedly heightened the nation's level of fear and suspicion against the drug community as a whole, as well as suspicion for every young person that simply wanted to dress as a hippie. Manson's arrest photo – and the term 'helter skelter' – became synonymous with the epitome of evil, representative of so many misled young minds crazed by drugs, and of young adults desperately searching for their own expressions of choice without any constraints whatsoever. America was now finding itself segregated not just by skin color, but also by the choice of clothes or length of hair displayed by any of those young people who were simply striving to be "free" in finding their own self.

The most iconic moment of this entire decade of rebellion and cultural upheaval was not a protest march against the Viet Nam War, nor was it a sit-in as a peaceful form of opposition to racism and segregation. Rather, it was a music concert simply known as the Woodstock Festival. For 3 ½ days in mid-August, the emerging music world convened in upstate New York for a monumental gathering of historic proportions.

Original plans optimistically hoped for 50,000 to attend an outdoor concert on a grassy hillside of a 600-acre dairy farm near Woodstock and Bethel, New York. Two months of physical preparation took place in erecting a large stage and sound system, designated parking areas for thousands of cars and buses, as well as food stands and port-o-lets. An admission price of $5 per person would be charged as people arrived at the entrance "gate." At first the expectations seemed overly grandiose, but ultimately those plans were grossly inadequate.

The vision of non-stop rock & roll music for three days, mixed with ample amounts of sex and drugs, captured the hearts of hippies, peaceniks, and college students from coast to coast. Without the benefit of any social media the idea had gained word-of-mouth momentum for more than a year, and by August 15th over 400,000 young people arrived on the scene. Traffic jams from every direction reached the point of a total standstill, gridlock for miles on every approaching highway, so that thousands of cars were left abandoned at the sides of the road and passengers walked the last mile or two to find a seat in the meadow. The waves of people arriving on foot were more than the security team or ticket takers could possibly handle, and very quickly everyone just had to be allowed to come in for free. (As a result of no ticket sales, financial disaster was the natural outcome, and organizers were left with more than $1,000,000 in unpaid bills. They eventually made most of that back later, however, by selling the rights to the original sound track.)

The clogged roadways created a "domino effect" of logistical problems. Musicians scheduled to perform were unable to gain access as planned, and had to be flown in by helicopter. Food delivery trucks could not get through the maze of miles of abandoned cars, so the same helicopters were used to deliver emergency palates of boxed food items. Food stands which had been set up ahead of time now raised their prices from 25 cents to $1 for a burger or hotdog. Two of those food stands were subsequently burned down by attendees who accused the vendors of being too capitalistic.

There was only one port-o-let for every 850 people. A significant sanitation problem ensued as more and more people were forced to relieve themselves among the trees nearby. More than half of the time over the course of those four days there was a light rain falling, so that the field became a muddy "hog wallow." Vast numbers of men and women opted to swim naked in the adjacent stream as a way to remove the mud from themselves. At night people crowded together to sleep in VW vans or buses wherever possible, but the majority had to huddle underneath their blankets and sleep outdoors.

The concert itself was a stunning list of some of the greatest rock & roll or folk music stars. Memorable segments included Jimi Hendrix playing the national anthem on his electric guitar, or Crosby, Stills, Nash, and Young singing one song for more than 12 minutes. Musician's pay ranged from $2500 to *"The Grateful Dead"* to $7500 to *"Jefferson Airplane"* and $10,000 to

"Credence Clearwater Revival." Numerous other bands had been invited, but chose to skip it, thinking it would be a poor use of their time. For the rest of their careers, *"the Doors"*, Joni Mitchell, *"The Byrds"*, Jethro Tull, and *"Led Zeppelin"* all regretted that they had declined the request to being there.

John Lennon also failed to get there, although he sincerely tried. He had promised the organizers that he would be there to perform a set of his newest solo songs, but in the week prior to the event, U.S. Customs officials refused to let him back into the United States. That directive had come straight from President Nixon, who instructed all government agencies that Lennon should not get back into the U.S. because of his outspoken opposition to the Viet Nam War. Nixon was bent on covertly quieting any and all voices that stood against his Viet Nam position, and Lennon was at the top of his list.

TV personality Roy Rogers had been invited to close the entire event by singing his show's popular theme song, *"Happy Trails To You."* However he also had declined the invitation.

Thankfully, medical demands at Woodstock were at a minimum. Not one fist-fight or act of violence was reported during the entire four days. One woman gave birth to a healthy baby in the middle of that crowd. One man over-dosed on a random mixture of drugs and died before anyone could get him to a hospital. Another man was accidently killed when he crawled under a small pile of straw to sleep, and a farm tractor inadvertently ran over him.

News magazines tried to capture the enormity of this event with multi-page photo spreads. But pictures cannot capture smells. Pictures cannot capture the inner sense of total freedom and exhilaration as hundreds of men and women milled around after having shed their clothes. And pictures cannot fully capture the euphoria of thousands of people being high for most of the time they were there. The singular name "Woodstock" would forever be associated with the "ultimate capstone" in the era of the pursuit of sex, drugs, and rock & roll.

Joni Mitchell reflected the longings of the Woodstock crowd that so desperately wanted world peace, sexual fulfillment, and total contentment in life when she wrote *"Woodstock"* a few months later. The lyrics seemed to yearn for a better day as she sang . . .

". . . by the time we got to Woodstock
we were half a million strong,
and everywhere there was song and celebration.
And I dreamed I saw the bombers

riding shotgun in the sky,
and they were turning into butterflies
above our nation.
We are stardust, we are golden,
we are billion-year-old carbon
And we've got to get ourselves back to the Garden."

Brian had left his parents' home in Boulder that spring with mixed reviews. His father wanted to be proud of everything his first-born son might do, but struggled with their differing world-views. Brian did not try to hide his radical ideals from his father. He genuinely believed that a total over-throw of the U.S. government was necessary, and that current events suggested now was the opportune time. He was well-connected in the radical movement, and with help from Mark Rudd and Bernadine Dorn had already started the early community of the "Students for a Democratic Society" (SDS). He was convinced that a clandestine revolutionary organization could now accomplish that objective of completely destroying the existing government, with the ultimate goal of a new Anti-imperialist, Communist state based on the ideals of Marxism and Leninism.

As his parents disappeared from sight in his rear-view mirror, he wondered if he would ever see them again. He was headed east to meet with Bill Ayers, John Jacobs, and a few other leaders within the SDS who indicated their agreed assessment that an even more radical approach now needed to be taken. Together they drafted a position paper that called for a fighting force of white people to be allied with the Black Liberation Movement in a combined mission to destroy U.S. imperialism and establish a classless world. They would reach out to the oppressed workers of the world who created wealth for the elite, and begin a revolution that would sweep across America and on to every nation on the planet.

Recruitment would be concentrated on disillusioned high school and college students, since these would be the most likely audience to embrace radical opposition to any authority figure, including the school administration, police, employers, and parents. To underscore the pervasive attitude of overthrowing all existing standards and mores, the position paper even specified that bi-sexual experimentation was encouraged. The Weathermen had grown impatient with the limited results achieved by other radical groups after years of non-violent resistance, and now endorsed much more aggressive tactics. Kidnappings or assassinations, however, would not be on their menu.

The one major point of disagreement within the Weathermen was the degree of violence that they would seek. Jacobs demanded violence of any kind, with little regard for human life. Make the country cower in fear, if necessary. Bloodshed was a logical consequence of any "war." Brian, on the other hand, championed the idea that their bombs could target specific buildings or institutions that represented the capitalistic system, but fair advance warning could be given to allow people time to avoid the area. His personal definition of integrity meant opposing certain political ideologies but still having a high degree of respect for human life. A compromise was reached that the only humans that would be targeted would be military personnel or police officers, since those were the two groups that were defending the very system that needed to be overthrown.

In June Brian and the other new leaders of the newly-formed Weathermen headed to Chicago to attend the SDS Convention, and demand the take over the entire network, including its mailing list of 100,000 members. Their announced slogan was to "bring the war home" by creating such a militant upheaval that the U.S. would be forced to forego any continuation in Viet Nam in order to focus by necessity on protecting their homeland.

The Chicago conference was irreparably fractured. Most SDS members wanted to continue as originally planned. But several openly announced their withdrawal from the SDS, and asked to be considered new members of the Weathermen. It was anything but unanimous, yet it certainly became apparent which camp had the momentum.

The following month, 30 members of the Weathermen leadership council secretly flew to Cuba to meet with key representatives from the North Vietnamese government. This greatly bolstered the North Vietnamese commitment to total victory, because they could now sense that America would be unable to continue to sustain the needed manpower and national energy for the war by having such a divided country. The Weathermen agreed to an arrangement of armed political action within the U.S. if the North Vietnamese would provide them with training and tactics in guerilla warfare, as well as some funding and explosives.

Americans had no idea what was in store for them.

Chicago found itself in the national news again that fall, in the direct aftermath of the Democratic National Convention that it had hosted the previous year. The "Chicago 8" court trial began in an effort to bring to justice the major ringleaders of the anti-war protests and marches that had taken place. All eyes were now trained on Judge Julius Hoffman, to see how he would conduct this case.

From the opening gavel, it was apparent that the judge had already determined the outcome. Which objections were overruled and which were not, or which photos were admitted as evidence and which were not. It all spelled "G-U-I-L-T-Y." The defendants used the courtroom as a platform to rant against President Nixon, the war, and racism. Bobby Seale, a Black Panther and one of the eight defendants, became so irate that he began screaming obscenities until the judge had him gagged and tied down to his chair.

Along with the original charges of conspiracy to cross state lines with intent to incite a riot, by the end of the trial the defendants and their attorneys were also found guilty of more than 170 counts of contempt of court. Sentencing a few months later ranged from two to five years, and fines of $5000. However, none of them actually served any extensive time because a Court of Appeals shortly thereafter overturned the criminal convictions as well as most of the contempt charges.

The bizarre antics surrounding the trial became a new national rallying point for all protesters of the war, as well as any protests against the "rigged Establishment." Only 30 days after the trial had begun, Chicago was once again besieged by thousands of angry activists.

Brian and the other leaders of the Weathermen saw this as their first opportunity to make a new statement for revolution. Along with so many hitchhikers and vans full of like-minded young people, Brian again arrived in Chicago determined to make "change" happen.

The "Days of Rage" lasted for four days, with hundreds of reports of broken store windows, rocks thrown at police cars, and streets blocked by public gatherings without an appropriate permit. No deaths were reported, but dozens of protesters and 28 policemen received minor injuries. Although many of the marchers wore football helmets or motorcycle helmets, they were no match for the 1000 police on hand. Six Weathermen were shot and wounded. On three occasions Chicago police cars drove into a mob, scattering bodies as they went. As a test, Brian set off his first "pipe bomb" in a city park. No one was injured, and actual damage was minimal. But he began to see a vision of what might be if they used bombs strategically.

By the end of the four days, more than 160 of the rioters had been arrested, including most of the SDS and Weathermen leadership being held in jail. The Weathermen had to pay $243,000 in bail to gain the release of their comrades. The City of Chicago had no idea that those funds originated with the North Vietnamese.

To insure control, the National Guard was once again required to help the local police reestablish a sense of normality in Chicago. But Brian and the rest of the Weathermen leadership were growing in their confidence that any and all means were at their disposal. America would soon learn to fear the name 'Weathermen.' And bombs would become their routine "calling card."

Daily news seemed to be locked into three categories, and three only: first, the deteriorating war effort in Viet Nam; secondly, constant clashes surrounding African Americans with their demands for equal rights; and thirdly, the economy being in full retreat due to the ravages of inflation. It was difficult for any other news story or issue to find a justifiable place at the newsroom assignment desk. Yet in the fall of this year, "equal rights for women" was able to crack the invisible shield for assigned news coverage.

In September, Yale and Princeton chose to break the "gender barrier" and enroll female students for the first time. (U.S. military academies would not do so for another seven years. And Harvard would not follow for another eight years.) But the academic door was pushed ajar in a visible step toward true gender equality.

Leadership in the women's movement also demanded changes in the public workplace. Most corporations would not allow a woman to retain her job while pregnant. Nor would commercial airlines allow a stewardess to be married. And in most states, women were not allowed to serve on a courtroom jury.

In the same month, Sheila Michaels insisted on being introduced as "Ms. Michaels" – not "Miss" and not "Mrs." – when appearing on a popular New York radio station. That new label was instantly embraced by women in the listening audience. It represented a refreshing symbol of independence regardless of marital status. Within three years Gloria Steinem established a highly successful women's magazine using that simple title "Ms.", making the term mainstream.

Because such a large segment of the American female population were already housewives, and most of those were content with the status quo, the women's issues did not hold equal weight in comparison to the other crises facing the country. Many married women were uncertain if this movement was really about "equality", or was it really about "hatred of men." Gaining any deeper traction for this issue was slow and difficult. But the culture of "change" for women had a new foothold in the U.S., and was slowly spreading into every other segment of society as well. Although advances for women were moving at a snail's pace, there were advances nonetheless, and women were the latest beneficiaries from the generic and progressing shift for change.

Confrontations over civil rights had been birthed in the Southern states. But as African Americans across the country became emboldened to show their support for the rights of their southern brothers and sisters, it often revealed the hidden racism that existed in many pockets of the U.S. In October of this year, that hatred was exposed on the college football field.

The University of Wyoming had developed an exceptional football program, and this year was ranked #12 in the country. The team included fourteen African American players, eight of whom were on the starting squad. The Cowboys had not forgotten the excessive racial taunting they had received the previous year when they played Brigham Young University, which had no black players on their entire football roster. As the re-match approached this year, the black players discussed amongst themselves how they might make a statement for racial equality, and a show of solidarity with their African American comrades everywhere. Their simple request to their coaching staff was that they be allowed to wear a black armband over the sleeve of their uniforms for the BYU game.

But the request backfired badly. The Wyoming coaching staff – who were all white – responded by declaring that all fourteen black players were immediately and permanently cut from the team. The coaches' racial intolerance was masked with a rationalization that they didn't want dissention or trouble-makers in the locker room. The "Black 14" were not allowed to join their teammates on the sidelines, and were not allowed back into the football training areas. Since they had been on football scholarships, they were forced to drop out of school. They had been expelled for merely "asking permission to do something that would be meaningful for them."

Although Wyoming won the game against BYU the following day, they lost their final four games that season. They won only one game the following season, and the football program spiraled down for twelve years. The Wyoming Cowboys never again achieved a "Top Ten ranking." Like-minded racists in the Wyoming fan base had been quick to support the head coach for that decision in the near-term, but as soon as the team started losing again the following year, those same fans demanded that the entire coaching staff be fired.

At the very least it was fitting justice. But the "Black 14" were never reinstated. Their football playing days were over.

In an attempt to nudge public opinion on the Viet Nam War in a more favorable direction, President Nixon announced that 25,000 troops would be returning to the U.S. by September. The news bulletin seemed trivial, and it didn't work. Any news story coming out of Viet Nam that summer seemed to be bad news. Another devastating news release revealed that the President had secretly ordered the unauthorized bombing of Cambodia in an attempt to destroy supply depots for the North Vietnamese. Nixon was so incensed that this information was made public that he gave secret instructions to some of his operations team to place phone taps on 17 specific news reporters in hopes of finding out which persons on the White House staff might be leaking such detrimental details to the press.

"Public Relations" became another attempt at trying to win over the support of the American voter. In spite of increased government efforts to boost the morale of the military by sending comedian and movie star Bob Hope and a few other celebrities to entertain the troops, the American public's image of the war was plummeting downward. Never before had so many people in America made a public protest on any singular issue. Added to the poor trend of the battle itself, the pending trial for the My Lai massacre was now producing incontrovertible evidence of gruesome actions on the part of several U.S. soldiers. And the apparent attempted cover-up that followed by the Pentagon was just as serious as the crime itself.

On September 4th, 114 Marines were killed in a single day in heavy fighting near Da Nang. Even the most adamant proponents of the war were beginning to question our nation's strategy for victory.

That fall, network television executives cancelled "The Smothers Brothers Comedy Hour." It had nothing to do with poor ratings. In fact, this had been one of the most popular variety shows on the air. But the network leadership was angered by the fact that the show continually inserted skits or jokes that put down the war effort. When it became impractical to censor every Viet Nam punch-line or every mocking reference regarding President Nixon, they decided to axe the entire show. Sadly, the growing death toll from the war now included a great piece of comedy and entertainment.

In October more than a dozen major cities in the U.S. shared a synchronized day of anti-war protests. A total of over 1,500,000 persons peacefully marched through their respective communities, calling for a national strike against the war, and creating a new paradigm of national opposition. President Nixon went on network television in a frantic effort to rally renewed support for the troops, asking the "silent majority" to make themselves known.

Vice President Spiro Agnew also held a press conference, in which he called any such opposition to America's leadership as "nattering nabobs of negativism." It was a nice sound-bite, but those criticisms fell on deaf ears. His disdain for all protesters quickly elevated his stature among the Right, and bumper stickers appeared overnight across the country which said "SPIRO IS MY HERO."

Just two weeks later, in direct defiance to Nixon's appeal, a peaceful demonstration was held on the lawn of the Washington Monument because it was a location that could actually be seen from the offices inside the White House. More than 400,000 men and women showed up – a new record attendance for any single event on the National Mall – carrying signs of protest against the war, and silently praying. It was an over-whelming sight for the President and his staff. They all secretly realized that things were now at a point of desperation.

From across "the pond", John Lennon added his influence once again to the growing voice of opposition. He had been the recipient of the "Medal for the Order of the British Empire" (MBE), one of the highest honors that any British citizen could receive. This medal was traditionally bestowed by the Queen of England herself onto a person who had made significant contributions in the arts or sciences. Lennon held a press conference in London at which he announced his decision to return the Medal to the Prime Minister because he could not willingly accept any recognition from a government that was allied with the United States and its war effort in Viet Nam. Such international pressure might begin to accelerate an end to an unjust war, or so he hoped.

U.S. Army recruiters were no longer able to meet their needed quotas of new recruits, so on December 1st a new draft "lottery" system was instituted. An extensive drawing was held at the Selective Service headquarters, and numbers from 1 to 365 were randomly assigned to the various dates throughout the calendar year. Every eligible male was then given a corresponding lottery number linked to his date of birth.

This solution did equalize the playing field in a sense. Each local draft board could go as deep as necessary into the lottery's numerical sequence every month to make sure there were sufficient enlistees. Rather than enticing potential recruits voluntarily to sign up by offering monthly cash and educational benefits, the new system achieved the needed numbers of bodies by fiat. This new method, however, for generating the necessary number of recruits created an unexpected and problematic environment. Now almost every young man that was drafted was there completely against his will. General morale of the military immediately dropped to a new low, so that training officers now had a new set of issues to overcome. More and more soldiers made up their minds that if they were sent into live action, they would opt to disobey orders. And if fired upon, they would throw down their guns. In so doing, the Defense Department was now setting itself up for a more certain pending failure due to the growing numbers of an enemy within.

Suicide and its associated grief visited the home of Lois and Art twice within the span of three months. In July, their despondent 33-year-old son-in-law, John, put a bullet through his brain. In early October, less than 90 days later, their youngest daughter, Diane, leaped to her death from the 6th-floor window of her West Hollywood apartment.

Typical news media coverage might have given this a quick passing glance at best. But this was no typical family. Art happened to be the most popular and beloved celebrity on America's daytime television. *"The Art Linkletter Show"* seemed to build a personal bond with its millions of faithful viewers. Consequently parents across the country felt a shared sense of personal loss with this family.

During the previous year Diane had been experimenting with an hallucinogenic synthetic drug known as lysergic acid diethylamide, or LSD. On more than one occasion she told her parents and friends that she had had a "bum trip" from that drug. In spite of pleas to the contrary from her parents, Diane frequently continued to seek an escape through LSD.

Within hours after her tragic death – and before the official autopsy was released – the grieving Art Linkletter held a national press conference. He stated that this case was not a suicide, but rather was "murder" at the hands of those that manufactured and sold LSD. He pledged that he and his wife would become a public voice against the permissiveness and drug abuse that was now so pervasive in the U.S. Parents again found comfort in his words. The vast majority of Americans were able to accept that storyline.

The autopsy, however, offered a different explanation. No indication of LSD was found in Diane's bloodstream, and personal friends confirmed it had been more than 12 hours since she had taken any acid. Her official Death Certificate listed only "suicide" as the cause of death.

The general public ignored that conclusion. Drugs were rapidly becoming the universal scapegoat for any and all of America's social problems. Parents and older adults found a sense of "reason" and "order" in their worldview if the rebellious behavior of young adults could collectively be attributed to drug usage. Parents didn't know what else to do. The government could only declare such drugs to be illegal. And young adults didn't care. They were free, and hell-bent on enjoying any experience – in booze, sex, drugs, or ideology – that this new society had to offer.

Because America had enjoyed more than 15 years of peace from '48 – '64, the domestic economy had flourished in grand fashion. The national vision was that if everyone could EARN enough money, all problems in life could be resolved. The affluence of the American middle class was far greater than any country in the world. The country had certainly succeeded in earning vast sums of money.

That principle became suspect, however, when the USSR beat America in the race of getting a man into outer space in the early '60's. Now a new vision for our country said that if everyone could LEARN new skills and new information, a vastly expanded education system could solve all of our needs. Grade-school curriculum was revamped, and new colleges sprouted like dandelions to handle the population wave of young baby-boomers as they approached high school graduation.

But twenty-somethings were not convinced that either option provided worthwhile or lasting meaning. Experimentation into any kind of life-style was much more attractive, and certainly more exhilarating. LSD was not an illegal substance in the early '60's. However laws changed rapidly when it was apparent that young people were using various drugs for recreational purposes. By the end of the decade, *"The Grateful Dead"* became the band most associated with the drug rebellion, and LSD was their drug of choice. Their message was that life was at its best when one was pursuing brotherhood, love, and plenty of LSD. Their rallying cry was "never trust anyone over 30." The only rule was that there were no rules.

Completely carefree. That was an idyllic dream that everyone was chasing, but no one could fully capture to their complete satisfaction. The counter-culture tried desperately to invent a new world by seeking total freedom and authenticity, unable to define why it always came up lacking. As the '60's came to a close the disillusioned dream-chasers rejected "EARN" and "LEARN" as a vision for the masses, and considered instead a new solution in "BURN." Maybe it was time to destroy everything in our governmental and societal structure, and start over from the very foundation.

The ultimate dream was that of unending peace, unending love, and a world of no rules or no responsibilities. That was the image that Bob Dylan ached for when he penned the song,

"... *I wish in vain that we could sit in that room again,*
A thousand dollars at the drop of a hat.
I'd give it all if our lives could be like that."

Earn. Learn. Burn. Vastly contrasting approaches, but none seemed to satisfy the growing chaos. The solution to the elusive dream would not come any time soon.

Chicago could not seem to get a break, and continually found ways to "shoot itself in the foot". The Cubs had one of the most talented teams in all of major league baseball in the late '60's, yet could not quite make it to the World Series. The Bears consistently had a series of the most gifted running backs in all of professional football including Gale Sayers and Walter Payton, but as yet kept finding ways to miss the playoffs. And worst of all, the Chicago police force seemed to have a knack for repeatedly making poor decisions in a moment of crisis.

The mishandling of the Democratic National Convention and its related protests had left another giant black eye on the city. Events surrounding the Chicago 8 Trial, and the subsequent "Days of Rage" had again made the police look like nothing more than reactionary thugs. Accusations of unwarranted police brutality against blacks on the South Side of the city surfaced with alarming regularity.

So no one seemed too surprised in early December when The Chicago Sun-Times carried a gruesome story on its front page regarding questionable police actions once again. Acting on a tip from a member of the organized crime syndicate, police surrounded an old brownstone house on the south side of the city, confident that it contained the local ringleaders of the Black Panther Party. Public discourse regarding the Panther's angry demands for equality as well as reparations for past injustices had long ago been exhausted, and now law enforcement had exceeded its level of tolerance for what it considered a threat to community safety. Around 4 a.m. police quietly entered the house and found two black men asleep in adjacent bedrooms. They were not roused from their sleep, nor were they warned. On a coordinated signal, two shots were fired at point blank range into each man's head. Their bloodied and lifeless bodies were left for neighbors to find the next morning.

No arrests were ever made, no charges were ever filed, and no one officially claimed responsibility. Rumors were purposely leaked by some police officers that it might have been a drug deal that had gone bad, and chose to let the case grow cold. But the African American community knew what had actually happened. Black Panthers were still human beings. The shooting only served to widen the degree of hatred and distrust between the African American community and local law enforcement. It was just another tragic example of racial hatred and misuse of power being taken to an unnecessary extreme.

So much of America still had so far to go in understanding the inclusivity that rested in what the Founding Fathers had originally drafted in a world-shaking document *". . . ALL men are created equal, and are endowed by their Creator with certain unalienable rights, and among these are Life, Liberty, and the Pursuit of Happiness."*

The decade of the '60s had begun with peace, prosperity, and such promise for all Americans. It ended at the opposite end of the spectrum.

America was now fractured from several directions. The valuation of the U.S. dollar was in a free-fall. The morale of our fighting men in Southeast Asia was cascading down a rocky slope. Back home, the contrasting perspectives of the Viet Nam War created an ever-increasing gaping schism for any constructive discourse. The demands from all minorities for equal rights from many sectors had brought tempers to an ugly boiling point. Young adults were aggressively pursuing personal freedoms through unfettered sex, experimentation with mind-expanding drugs, and consuming new music that reflected those attitudes of rebellion and individualism. All of those conflicts were on display in northwest California on December 6th as a dramatic and pathetic culmination to a decade that was now in complete upheaval.

The rain-soaked meadows of Woodstock in upstate New York had hardly dried out before a sequel concert was planned for the West Coast. The newly discovered potential for financial and marketing gain from such a large outdoor concert was too great to ignore. The Rolling Stones had established themselves as the 2nd greatest rock & roll band of all time, trailing only the Beatles. They were currently on an international tour, and enjoying significant success. But a growing complaint was gaining traction, which said that their ticket prices were much too high. The Stones wanted to quell that rumor, and hurriedly planned a *"WOODSTOCK WEST"* concert. The design was to have another massive outdoor concert that would be free of charge, and include numerous rock bands in an all-day event, culminated by the Stones playing as the grand finale. A one-day "clone" of the original Woodstock event would be a big "win" for everyone. Local rock radio aggressively promoted the concert in exchange for a few back-stage passes. The attendance goal was to surpass the 400,000 that had witnessed the New York Woodstock just four months earlier. But in their haste to arrange such an event, everything went perfectly wrong.

Despite the short notice, due to the persuasive influence of the Rolling Stones, it was easy for their concert promoters to get an impressive list of major bands that were willing to join them for the event. Even though there was no revenue from ticket sales, the musicians all knew they would more than make it up through increased record sales and shared movie rights from the filming of the all-day concert.

But finding a suitable venue became a nightmare. The main stadium in San Francisco was not available because of an NFL game that was scheduled there the next day. Other locations could not or would not provide a permit on such short turnaround time. With only two days to go, the owner of the Altamont Speedway agreed to open his facility. It had sufficient acreage, seating capacity, and parking. That was the good news. What it did not have was adequate port-o-let facilities for such a large crowd, nor a suitable elevated stage that would be necessary for a concert such as this. That was the bad news.

A temporary stage was hurriedly built on the racetrack, facing the grandstands. But because it was not elevated, there was not a natural barrier to prevent concert-goers from potentially trying to rush on to the stage. The solution was to hire the Hells Angels to provide security for the entire event. That was the first giant step toward potential trouble. The second step was that the security contract fee offered to the Hells Angels was $500. worth of beer, more than enough for them to be drinking steadily throughout the entire day. The third step was when 300,000 raucous young people arrived for the concert that morning, most of them high on drugs before they got there.

As the concert progressed under the California sun, fights broke out several times in the crowd. By mid-afternoon all of the Hells Angels seated on the perimeter of the stage were drunk, and seemed uninterested as people became more restless and agitated. That changed quickly when several attendees decided to try to get on to the stage. Hells Angels members quickly beat them back with sawed off pool cues and bike chains. Two attendees were finally successful in getting onto the stage and interrupting *"Jefferson Airplane"* in the middle of one of their songs. Uncertain if the band was encouraging this misbehavior, two of the Angels wrestled the young men to the ground, while another Angel accidentally punched the Jefferson Airplane's bass player so hard he fell to the stage unconscious.

As the afternoon progressed, scores of those in attendance were injured, and a few hospitalized. Numerous cars were stolen and then later abandoned. Extensive property damage to the bleachers was reported, as well as several structures on the raceway grounds.

Late in the day portions of the crowd began chanting taunts against some of the bands. *"The Grateful Dead"* were scheduled to follow *"Crosby, Stills, Nash & Young"* as the final band before the Rolling Stones came on for the finale. The Dead had been accustomed to rowdy audiences wherever they played, but this seemed vastly different. Given the increasing violence in the crowd, and the unpredictable nature of the Hells Angels, they decided to leave without playing any of their set. They moved quickly to their awaiting helicopter and disappeared in evening sky.

The Rolling Stones were halfway through their closing portion of the concert when another 18-year-old man made a couple of attempts at getting on to the stage. After being rebuffed twice by Hells Angels members, he drew a pistol from his jacket pocket and approached the stage once more. Another Angels member happened to see the pistol, quickly drew his own switchblade knife, and stabbed the young man to death. Actual video of the killing was caught on camera by the crew that was filming the entire concert.

The Rolling Stones assumed this short disruption was just another fist-fight, and continued playing their songs. Police later arrested the Hells Angel member, and charged him with murder. He was found innocent of those charges by acting in self-defense, since the video clearly showed the young man approaching the stage with a pistol in his hand. An autopsy determined that the concert-goer was high on methamphetamine.

Three other people died at that concert. A 21-year-old man drowned when he tried to cool down in an irrigation canal adjacent to the raceway, but was too drunk or too stoned to swim. Another couple was killed by a hit-and-run driver that evening as they tried to leave the concert by walking across an unlit parking lot.

The entire day was a tragic contrast to the original Woodstock phenomena. What had been a four-day gathering of "peace and love" in upstate New York had now degenerated into a day of "mayhem and anger" in northern California. Rolling Stone Magazine reported extensively on the concert, and summarized the event as "the product of diabolical egotism, hype, ineptitude, and at its base, a fundamental lack of concern for humanity."

(In an ironic epilogue to this debacle, the Hells Angels were extremely upset by the lack of support from Mick Jagger, lead singer of the Rolling Stones, in the months that followed. They secretly conspired to kill him at his home on Long Island as a final statement of revenge. They chartered a small boat and planned to sneak on to his property from the shore side rather than trying to circumvent the sophisticated security gate at the street entrance to his home. But the plot failed when their boat partially sank in a violent summer lightning storm. Thankfully, all the passengers were rescued.)

Woodstock West seemed to be a fitting end point to a decade now consumed by anger, uncontrolled self-interests and confusion. From every corner of the country, young and old alike, liberal and conservative – everyone knew that the status quo could not continue. America was on the edge. Change in several areas of our society desperately needed to occur. The question was *'Change – But in what direction?'*, and *'Would the coming new decade of the '70's be able to do so?'*

What Americans did not realize was that the bottom had not quite arrived. Politically, economically, and socially – as a nation, they were about to be shaken to their very soul . . .

Woodstock throng

Senator Ed Kennedy

Joe Namath

President Richard M. Nixon

The Rolling Stones

CHAPTER 7

"1970 - PARTY TIME"

*". . . and the eagle flies with the dove,
and if you can't be with the one you love,
well, then, love the one you're with."*

Stephen Stills

By early 1970 Anita Pallenberg had become the ultimate "poster girl" for living the unfettered life of sex, drugs, and rock & roll. In the mid-60's she had attended a Rolling Stones concert in Rome, where she sweet-talked a security guard into letting her go back-stage to wait for the band members at their dressing room door. There were always "groupies" hanging around back-stage at such concerts, hoping to hook up with a rock star. With very little convincing necessary, guitarist Brian Jones agreed to take her home for the night. They became lovers, and she began secretly to travel with the band.

Pallenberg soon introduced Jones to LSD, which also brought violence and abuse into their relationship. She quickly found herself more attracted to Keith Richards, the band's bass player, and seduced him in the back seat of his chauffeured limo. She then promptly dumped Jones in order to pursue a lengthy affair with Richards instead. Over the ensuing 12 years she and Richards had three children together. They also shared a grand love for hard drugs, and their excessive indulgences became legendary.

Travelling with the Stones gave Anita frequent opportunities to rub shoulders with many other celebrities or persons of influence in the entertainment world. Labeling herself as a "model", she was able to find numerous offers for minor roles in movies, including *"Barbarella"* with Jane Fonda, and a sex farce called *"Candy."*

But the epitome of her borderless lifestyle occurred this year when she was given the female lead in a movie called *"Performance."* Her male counterpart in that movie happened to be Mick Jagger, lead singer for the Stones. This pair of lead actors went off script during the filming of a love scene, and actually had sex together on the set while cameras were rolling. She later told a magazine reporter, "Whenever I liked something, I really got into it. And I really liked the entire band. How better to get into the band than to *BE* with all of them, you know?"

Keith Richards became so incensed at the news he threatened to break up the Stones. Rehearsals were cancelled for a few weeks until he could regain a degree of stability. Soon thereafter, the relationship was restored so that he and Pallenberg were able to resume their risky life of excess together, and deepened their addictions in unison. But after more than a decade of such destructive escapades, including numerous drug busts and rehab centers, they quietly parted ways.

The general Establishment – both Democrats and Republicans alike – had grown impatient and disgusted with the prevalence of drug usage and rebellion amongst young adults. When the Beatles announced that they were permanently disbanding as a musical group, many parents felt a moment of relief, and expressed hope that their kids could return to listening to live music without any screaming or jumping around in some crazed fashion.

The cultural separation between youth and adults – or between cultural rebellion vs. cultural tradition – became an easy target of ridicule for either side of the spectrum. In early February a businessman named Jeff McDonald savagely murdered his wife and kids, but then told police that "drugged out hippies" had committed the gruesome crime. That decoy was an accusation that most middle-of-the-road Americans wanted to hear, and it took months before the police were able to discover the tragic truth.

In late February all hippies, activists, and rebellious young people were greatly bolstered by the news that came out of Chicago. To the chagrin of Mayor Richard Daley and his militant police force, all of the defendants in the "Chicago 8" trial were declared "Not Guilty" on the charges of conspiring to start a riot. The verdict provided a new source of fuel for the idealism of protesting as a legitimate – and necessary – means of producing change in the American system. That outcome only proved to widen the schism between the generations. This time the brash face of anti-establishmentarianism and protest had won.

That same spring, another court trial on the West Coast created a nation-wide sensation. Charles Manson and his "family members" were tried for first-degree murder. When Manson entered the courtroom for the first time, jurors were shocked to see that he had used a butcher knife to carve a large "X" in the middle of his forehead. (He later extended it into the shape of a Swastika.) His fierce glare became posterized as an image of demonic evil. Judge Olden was so fearful of this man that he later admitted he carried a pistol under his robe throughout the trial.

At first Manson demanded to defend himself. During his preliminary defense he would frequently wander on tangents regarding the coming Apocalypse, the evils of the American establishment, and the necessity of drugs to experience the fullness of life intended by our Creator. After too much irrelevant testimony, the Judge finally declared that he could no longer defend himself, but had to use a state-appointed attorney.

Several other members of the Manson family camped outside the courtroom throughout the ordeal. Eventually they were arrested and charged with "contempt of court" and "trying to prevent a witness from testifying." They were given jail sentences that ranged from three to thirty days.

The judge was not so lenient with the others. At the conclusion of the murder trial, all four persons in the "family" – including Manson – were found guilty, and each was given the Death Penalty as the sentence for their participation in these heinous acts. Shortly thereafter, however, California eliminated the Death Penalty from its judicial code within their state, and all four sentences had to be commuted to Life in prison.

The other three family members served more than 20 years of their terms, and eventually were released on parole. They tried quietly to re-enter society as law-abiding citizens, finding jobs and spouses, getting married, and raising families of their own. One Manson family member even became a pastor for a Christian church. Charles Manson, however, never saw the outside of a prison again. He was denied parole on 12 different occasions, and died in his solitary cell 47 years later.

The horror of their brief reign of terror was over – or so Americans thought. But Manson's influence of hatred and random evil was not fully erased. Just five years later, the name "Manson" would surface once again when one of his followers made national news in another act of inexplicable violence. Manson's message would haunt America yet again.

Virtually all citizens of the U.S. had become bored with most of what was taking place within the NASA space program. Rocket launches that had been given hours upon hours of live TV coverage just seven years ago now simply received a brief mention on the evening news. Yes, it had been fascinating to see a man walk on the moon last year, but even that historic accomplishment was quickly considered "routine." Reality here on planet earth was moving too fast to dwell on such things as space travel.

In April, however, NASA put the entire world on "Pause" once again. Apollo 13 was scheduled to send three men to the moon for another moon-walk and a new set of experiments. The liftoff and first few hours of the flight went exactly as expected. Engineers at the control center in Houston were tracking their monitors with moderate interest when the first indication came in that something was seriously wrong.

A small "O-ring" had failed, causing an explosion in an oxygen tank located on the landing module that accompanied the space capsule. This in turn severely damaged the oxygen supply as well as the control capabilities of the entire craft. The full mission itself was immediately aborted, but the monumental challenge remained as to whether or not it was even possible to bring the three astronauts back to earth alive. The NASA engineers' new assignment was the equivalent of frantically re-designing and re-assembling a new plane while it was still in flight.

For the next four days, America held its collective breath. News teams scrambled for something positive to broadcast, because the finite timeline made things look very grim. President Nixon even went on national television to ask the American people to pray for the astronauts and their families. (In such a moment of crisis, no one from the ACLU waved an objection that this might be a breach of the axiom of "separation of church and state.")

The successful return of Astronauts James Lovell, John Swigert, and Fred Haise after six harrowing days in space is still considered the space program's finest hour. If there can be such a thing as a "successful failure", this would be at the top of the list. It showed the world once again that

American technology and ingenuity could solve almost anything.

Within a few years NASA lost its government funding, and any further space exploration was turned over to private interests. Maybe it was time to redirect those brilliant minds and billions in tax dollars to solving domestic issues instead.

The Weathermen had decided it was now time to "make some serious noise." In early February, the west-coast cell of the Weathermen chose to ambush the Berkeley police station. They placed two bombs in the officers' parking lot, scheduled to go off during a shift change around midnight. More than 25 policemen were at their cars when the first bomb went off. As stunned officers came running from the municipal building to help, the second bomb was detonated. More than 30 large windows were shattered, several police cars severely damaged, and six officers required medical attention. But no one was killed.

Two weeks later Bill Ayers and the Detroit chapter of the Weathermen placed two bombs outside the police station of that city. Both bombs were discovered before they could be detonated, and no damage was done.

The following week, just a few days after the successful outcome for the defendants of the Chicago 8 Trial, the Weathermen on the east coast decided to focus on a different court battle back in New York. They targeted the home of New York Supreme Court Justice John Murtagh, who was presiding over a case involving twenty-one members of the Black Panther Party.

After painting "FREE THE PANTHER 21" and "VIET CONG HAVE WON" in large letters on the sidewalk, the Weathermen exploded three Molotov cocktails in front of the judge's house. Thanks to the preparation and guidance of Brian, the local Weathermen agreed to place an anonymous phone call to the police moments ahead of time, so that no residents in the neighborhood would be injured. They were lucky this time. Only a few windows were shattered, and a car in the garage was partially burned.

Two weeks later, on March 6, people were not so fortunate. The New York cell of the Weathermen decided to assemble and plant a large bomb at a military dance that was about to be held at the U.S. Army Base in Fort Dix, New Jersey. Mass casualties were expected, but because military uniforms were present, it was considered a legitimate target.

The Weathermen temporarily occupied a four-story brown stone home in a quiet neighborhood of Greenwich Village, coincidentally next door to Hollywood actor Dustin Hoffman. The owners of the house were on an extended Caribbean vacation, and agreed to let their daughter and a few of her friends house-sit for them while they were away, not knowing their daughter had secretly joined the Weathermen cell.

Days were spent in constructing a bomb made of dynamite and roofing nails that could have devastating capability. With little bomb-making experience, however, and no safety mechanism, this bomb exploded pre-maturely in the basement of the house. The entire building imploded on itself in a resounding roar. Three of Brian's best friends within the Weathermen network were killed instantly, including two men and a woman. Two other female Weathermen members that were home at the time, including the homeowner's daughter, were able to climb out of the ruble with minor scratches, although most of their clothing was missing. The ex-wife of Henry Fonda happened to be living across the street, came outside to see the devastation, and offered the two women a change of clothes to cover themselves minimally. The young ladies gladly accepted the necessary clothing, and then made a hurried excuse to leave through the back door before the police could arrive.

Early investigation assumed that this explosion must be attributed to some leaking gas line, or a faulty propane storage tank. But in the days that followed as construction machinery removed the piles of bricks, plaster debris and splintered ruble, workers found clusters of detonation caps. The FBI suddenly realized that this was an accidental bomb explosion, and immediately roped off the property as a crime scene. It was impossible to find any useful fingerprints, but the FBI knew they were studying something that would have been so much worse if it had reached its intended target.

The Weathermen had much to learn about explosives, and this disaster was their wake-up call. Over the next three years the FBI recorded more than 1100 bombings somewhere across the U.S., attributed to the Weathermen and their followers. A staggering average of more than three bombs per day. It now had truly become a war on American soil.

By the spring of this year, the "fad" of college student protests had touched almost every campus in America. For some students, their participation in any such group opposition was a fun alternative to attending classes, or a light-hearted diversion from the drudgery of studying. The particular issue of the day could be incidental as long as it provided an entertaining – or even suspenseful – change to the routines of campus life.

For a select few, however, their passion was most sincere, and they genuinely believed this was the needed course for a better tomorrow. They were convinced that their united voices would somehow change what needed to be changed, that their yelling into bullhorns and throwing rocks into Administration office windows would produce constructive results, and that large sit-ins which prevented anyone else from having access to a classroom building might somehow give birth to a more perfect world.

Cal Berkeley chose to cancel the final two months of their spring term due to excessive student unrest. All students were given a guaranteed "B" for any class in which they had pre-registered. Nick was given an unexpected offer from two of his professors . . . he could accept the automatic "B" in those classes, or he could flip a coin. If he won the coin flip, he would receive an "A", but if he lost the coin flip, he would get a "C." Nick liked the offer, but walked away with a "C" in Statistics as well as Intro to Psychology. At least some of the professors had found a small way to insert a little intrigue or entertainment in the midst of the campus chaos. Little did they know that campus strife was about to reach a new low.

Expectations were high on May 4th as students at Kent State University in Kent, Ohio, rallied together in an attempt to make another statement against the continuation of the War. It was not the first time that Kent State students had done so. There had been several campus rallies in the recent past. A few memorable speeches. A march around the circumference of the campus. And at every such event the campus chapter of the ROTC was there on the sidelines to provide a small but visible measure of stability and safety.

Today would be drastically different. In order to maximize campus participation, the main student agitators had spent a week in advance announcing that they were going to march on to the entryway of the University President's House to demand that he officially disband the University's ROTC program because of its direct connection to the military industrial complex. That objective was intended to be a small but tangible step – an accomplishment that would say to the rest of the country that Kent State was doing its part to stop the "war machine." Having learned of their heightened protest plans ahead of time, the University President secretly called the Governor of Ohio and requested that he authorize some National Guard troops to be on campus that day for added security. The

Governor willingly complied.

Thus on that balmy Monday morning as students made their way to the rendezvous point at the center of the University grounds, they were unexpectedly greeted by not just a few fellow-students in ROTC uniforms, but 100 National Guard troops standing in formation, in full military uniform, wearing riot helmets, and carrying heavy rifles. Student leaders were incensed. This represented a new and more tangible object for their anger. Today these National Guard members would have to be the first recipients of their group rage, before they moved on to the University President's House.

It didn't take much to transition the student body into a fevered pitch against their uninvited guests. A couple of yelling rants into a mediocre microphone, a couple of group chants such as "NO MORE WAR!! NO MORE WAR!!" Within minutes the students had taken on a frenzied mob mentality. First it was just cursing, directed toward the Guard. Vile name-calling at the top of their lungs from hundreds of students. Verbal taunting as a few even dared to walk between the rows of young men in uniform. Screaming directly into their faces as if they were inert statues that could not move. It was almost entertaining for some students.

When troops lobbed a few smoke bombs or teargas into the mob, the students quickly threw those items back into the middle of the military formation. Then the jeering escalated into rock-throwing. Although the troops had helmets with full face guards, they were not immune to occasional painful blows to their arms and legs. Their limited military training began to kick in, mentally telling them that they were facing an enemy that threatened their safety and even their lives. For some of the Guard, the crazed look of the yelling students seemed no different than an imaginary enemy on the battlefield.

After more than twenty minutes of the verbal onslaught and hurling of rocks, one of the uniformed "statues" slowly broke formation, lowered himself to one knee, and raised his rifle until the sights zeroed in on the loudest mocker. As he squeezed the trigger, the loud report of gunfire echoed from building to building across the campus. Another member of the Guard quickly fired his gun from a standing position. At least sixty more shots rang out in almost deafening succession in less than one minute.

For a moment the yelling abruptly stopped. An eerie silence hovered for a few seconds as everyone tried to assess what had just occurred. Eye-witnesses said that many of the students assumed that the National Guard was only capable of shooting blanks, like training exercises for "playing soldier." After all, these were just unarmed students that they were facing, right?

But the silence that had replaced the cursing and verbal taunting was now being broken by random shrieks of fear and dismay. Then frantic screams of disbelief. Most students scattered in a panicked sprint, running back to their dorm, or any nearby classroom building that might provide temporary shelter. A small contingent remained, completely numbed by what they were seeing.

A few bodies were lying motionless in the grass. Several more were squirming in agony, badly wounded but still conscious. Friends were trying to offer help, in spite of little or no actual First Aid training. At least five coeds fainted and two vomited from the chaos combined with the sight of so much human blood and suffering.

The planned protest for that day was abruptly over in a matter of a few minutes. A photographer for the campus newspaper captured the iconic photos, quite different from what he had expected to print in the coming weekend edition. Four Kent State students had been killed at point-blank range with high-powered rifles, and nine more severely wounded. One was permanently paralyzed. National media and network television concentrated on the story for several days. Was the response of the National Guard justified? Why was our country in such deep turmoil? Where was the general student population of America headed?

There were no sufficient answers. Young American men in uniform had just killed young American students.

As a national tribute to the tragic drama in Kent, Ohio, during the following weeks numerous colleges allowed their graduating seniors the option of wearing the traditional cap and gown, or for the same price they could wear an armband with the "Peace / Dove" symbol as a silent protest. It at least gave an "out" for those students that were so conflicted in wanting their undergraduate degree, but also wanting to make some kind of statement of rebellious solidarity.

Exactly one month following the Kent State shootings, the graduating seniors of Mercyhurst College, a small Catholic school in central Pennsylvania, took things a step further and radically changed their graduation ceremony in honor of the Kent State victims. There were only a few brief and solemn speeches given as a memorial remembrance. Little was said in the way of congratulations to the departing graduates. And instead of the traditional celebratory music for the processional and recessional marches, the graduating students selected a recording of

Buffalo Springfield's single greatest hit. All those in caps and gowns that day solemnly entered and departed their Mercyhurst auditorium to the familiar words,

"Somethin' happenin' here,
what it is ain't exactly clear.
There's a man with a gun over there,
a-tellin' me I got to beware.
He's sayin' 'STOP! Hey, what's that sound?
Everybody look what's goin' round."

Yes, all of America was troubled. And yes, all of our country was mourning in oh so many ways.

In the days and weeks that followed, numerous other college campuses across the country began to express their empathy and hostility toward the Kent State shootings in a variety of styles. A total of 448 institutions of higher education had to close their campuses for several days because of the massive student unrest. The President and Chancellor of the University of Denver went into hiding, so that he would not have to contend with the agitated student body. It was a classic example of administrative leaders with no real clue of how to do their jobs effectively. *"In Loco Parentis"* was not working at all, and the grieving students demanded to be heard.

DU Students were asking that the entire institution be closed for two days as a solemn memorial. Because of the administration's "non-response", the students erected a "tent city" on the front lawn of the Administration Building. Students set up dozens of tents, and executed their own moratorium from classes for two days. It was a peaceful exercise, but after 48 hours the police and National Guard moved them out without incident.

On May 8, less than one week after the Kent State shootings, more than 1000 students in New York City marched on their City Hall in a multi-purpose effort to protest their general unhappiness with American society – vocalizing a collection of demands including the elimination of the National Guard because of their mishandling of the Kent State protest, an end to the Viet Nam war, an end to inequality for blacks, an end to the unfair treatment of women, and so on.

Although their group chanting did not generate a response from Mayor John Lindsay or anyone else at City Hall that day, it did provoke a response from an unexpected audience. Unionized construction crews happened to be working on city street repairs adjacent to the protest site. Helmeted workers spontaneously shut off their machinery and surrounded the students. Like much of blue-collar America, they had grown tired of "spoiled college brats with no job" that seemed to be complaining about – or opposed to – just about everything, but not contributing to society in any tangible way. This was now the construction worker's perfect chance to make a statement of a different kind.

Armed with a few hand tools or their bare fists, the work crew began physically beating the helpless protesters. A few students ran into the municipal building in a desperate search for shelter. Most scattered in any direction they could find, hoping to blend in with the crowd that was watching. No one was killed in the skirmish, but more than twenty students had to seek medical attention for such things as broken arms or multiple lacerations requiring stitches. Conservatives and traditionalists across America claimed this day as a rare and over-due day of victory for "the voice of reason."

The following week, however, protesters in Jackson, Mississippi, were not that fortunate. On May 14, students at Jackson State University decided it was their turn to have their voices heard. Previous marches in Mississippi had concentrated on civil rights and the legal right for black men and women to vote. The march on this date chose to focus exclusively on opposition to the war.

By now it was quite easy to get a crowd to show up for any purpose. A disproportionate number of people in the greater Jackson community were unemployed and thus had time on their hands, so any cause was a sufficient reason to get out and join a movement for the sake of change. At least 200 local residents joined more than 300 university students as they marched across the campus and headed down the main street of Jackson.

A human wall of City Police in riot gear met the marchers at a major intersection, and used their bull horns to demand that the marchers stop, disperse, and go home peacefully. On this day the mob would not relent, and started physically pushing against the police riot shields. A few empty beer bottles were flung into the cluster of officers. Then a volley of rocks followed, and a few small pieces of old cement from sections of the deteriorated sidewalk.

A deputy on horseback struggled to keep his mount under control as the crowd continued to surge in all directions. He fired his pistol into the air twice in an attempt to warn marchers to stay away from his horse. Other officers down the line heard the gunfire, and were uncertain if it had come from a fellow officer or from someone in the mob. Several additional pistols were immediately unholstered, and multiple shots rang out. Some policemen purposely aimed into the air, some purposely aimed into the crowd.

The sense of rage became magnified as the unarmed marchers quickly weighed their options . . . either try to rush and kill all the police, or back away and choose to protest another day. They chose the latter. As the front line receded, they saw that two university students were lying dead in the middle of the street. Twelve more were wounded and in need of emergency medical care. Somehow the unthinkable horror of Kent State had repeated itself within less than two weeks. No longer were American lives only being sacrificed on the battlefields of Viet Nam. Now the war was claiming the lives of young men and women here in the States. The polarization of America was only getting worse. Something would have to give.

June 22nd was a red-letter moment on the calendar for all young Americans. To date, a common component of protests against the war was the absurdity in logic that a young man could be conscripted into military service for his country at the age of 18, could be forced to wear the uniform, could even kill the enemy, yet that same young man was unable to enter into a voting booth and pull a lever as a vote for or against the nation's Commander-in-Chief or any other elected officials until he had reached the age of 21.

With the full support of both Houses of Congress, President Nixon signed into law the official bill that lowered the voting age limitation from 21 to 18. Of all the things that Richard Nixon did during his years in the White House, this may have been the only presidential decision that garnered Tom's avid agreement. He was suddenly old enough to exercise his franchise as a citizen and cast a ballot. Mark, on the other hand, was still walking through the jungles of Viet Nam on this day, and did not hear anything about the new law until he completed his tour of duty and returned to the U.S. later in that same year. He really didn't care at that point, because he was already 21. But young people now felt empowered with a new and legitimate avenue to voice their views.

The Paris Peace talks got underway in the summer. The notion of authorized representatives from North Viet Nam, South Viet Nam, and the

United States holding a face-to-face discussion on PEACE created a surge of anticipation that the war might end soon. The worthy attempt, however, soon became a mind-boggling symbol of futile political bureaucracy.

It took 34 days to determine exactly where they would meet. It then took more than six additional weeks to agree on the specific size and shape of the conference table that would be the center-piece of their meeting room. Such prolonged "posturing" produced a wave of cynicism from everyone but the most adamant supporters of the war. Ambassador Averell Harriman had a distinguished career of serving the U.S., and was named as America's representative to this summit.

Once discussions finally got underway, it quickly became apparent that all sides were doing nothing more than repeating their respective long-standing positions as "sound-bites." Even the news media became disenchanted with the exercise, and quit trying to provide daily reports that had any merit.

Sadly, neither side seemed to have any sense of desperation for ending the war. Every week the death toll in Viet Nam continued to mount. But a negotiated peace would remain elusive for several more years.

In early June Randy and his classmates graduated from high school in suburban Minneapolis. As innocent and clean-cut young men, he and his best friend decided that they would hitchhike to California in search of some memorable adventures. Shortly after heading west on I-94, one of their first rides changed their thinking. The driver suggested that they consider Boulder, Colorado, as an alternative to California because that was the most "happening" place in the country. Since the naïve high school graduates had no specific game plan, Boulder quickly became their new destination.

Their next ride was a semi truck that got them to Cheyenne, and from there, a VW van with four young women took them all the way into downtown Boulder. Less than 24 hours after leaving their Minnesota home, they found themselves staring at the rock formation known as the Flatirons and the adjacent foothills that loomed as a protective barrier between the city limits of Boulder and the Continental Divide just 18 miles away. While they certainly loved all the lakes that peppered the Minnesota landscape, they had never seen such a beautiful setting for a city. Their adventure was starting out in grand fashion.

With backpacks in hand, and enough cash for a month, they asked the first passerby for directions to a comfortable place for lunch. Fate, as it turned out, had plopped them less than a block from an unusual sandwich shop called "Magnolia's Thunder Thighs." It was a major gathering place for hippies, college students, and transients.

The two new arrivals cautiously made their way through the eclectic collection of restaurant tables, picnic tables, and benches that cluttered the restaurant. Randy immediately realized that he had the shortest hair of anyone in the crowded eating area. But everyone seemed quite friendly, and his nervousness quickly disappeared once he was chowing down a greasy hamburger, some fries, and a Pepsi.

After lunch they studied the "NOTICE BOARD", which included a variety of thumb-tacked listings for everything from apartment vacancies to rides needed somewhere else to miscellaneous items for sale. While they were writing down a couple of phone numbers from the "Housing" column, a petite young patron at the next table struck up a conversation. Her long straight hair, floor-length paisley dress, sandals, round "granny-glasses", and an over-sized "peace symbol" as a necklace made her look like the poster model for the "perfect hippie."

"You guys new here?" she said with a contagious smile.

"Yeah," Randy stammered, "we just got here. We don't even have a place to stay yet."

Her grin widened, almost as if housing was unimportant. "Well," she finally added, "there's always places where someone can crash for a few nights. You'll find something." The three of them chatted for a few minutes. She was about to walk away, but then turned and continued. "Hey, since you're new here, why don't you come to my friend's party tomorrow night. It's just three blocks from here, and you can meet some nice people."

Randy was elated. Meet some people. Maybe get some free food. What could be better? He hurriedly wrote down the address. "Hey, thanks a lot!" he added, as she excused herself and left.

The following evening Randy and his friend arrived at the party with a youthful sense of anticipation. The hosts were a young married couple who had inherited this modest sized house from her grandmother, and enjoyed having lots of friends frequently hang out at their place, with plenty of candles, bead-curtains, and Bob Dylan music. And most importantly, plenty of marijuana was on hand.

Randy never did find the young lady that had invited them, but instead found himself in a lengthy conversation with Sandi, the owner. She was a beautiful brunette, probably about 25, and her loose bell-bottomed jeans could not disguise her great figure. After sharing a joint and a couple of beers, she abruptly changed the conversation.

"Hey, I want to show you something really cool that's in our back yard," she said.

As they left the dim lights of the back patio toward the far corner of the yard, Randy was able to make out the faint silhouette of a large tepee, at least 12 feet high, and 8 feet in diameter at the base. Sandi lifted the entrance flap, and they stepped into virtual darkness.

"This is great," Randy said, as he ran his fingers along the canvas siding, "it's almost like –". He stopped in mid-sentence as he suddenly felt Sandi's hands wrap around his waist. "Hey, what the – " he stammered.

"It's fine," she whispered, "this tepee is my special place," as she began undoing his belt buckle.

"But . . . you're married!" he argued. Randy tried to offer this as an objection, yet not wanting to protest too strongly.

"Yes, that's true," she responded, as she gently pulled him to the ground, "but there are no rules when I'm in my tepee."

Very few people can ever say that they lost their virginity in a Native American tepee. But Randy could. It was only his second day in Boulder, and his adventure was going incredibly well.

For some, sex was nothing more than a simple act of self-gratification. At 18 Randy suddenly found this to be true. In the coming weeks he discovered so many young women willing to make love with anyone, without any expectation of commitment. Stephen Stills' song lyric to "love the one you're with" was not a fantasy around here. And drugs of all sorts were always available. Daily networking at "Magnolia's" could produce anything Randy needed. For a while he thought he had found heaven on earth. It was all too easy. Too perfect.

But Randy changed his opinion just five months later when his best friend and traveling companion suddenly died from an overdose of heroin. That innocent 18-year-old man just was not ready to handle a life with absolutely no parameters. Randy had to call his own parents, as well as his friend's parents back in Minneapolis, with the tragic news. It was the lowest point of his life. He felt like hell had swallowed him whole. In his state of shock, Randy joined a "Jesus people" commune located near the University of Colorado campus. There was such a contrasting sense of genuine community there. It seemed a lot safer to Randy to get high on Jesus than repeatedly to put one's life at risk. The new environment within this commune undoubtedly saved his life. Too bad he had to lose his best friend in order to get there.

There's a new Marshall in town. Literally.

Following a careful search process, on August 1st, the township of Nederland hired a new Marshall. The mountain community on the west edge of Boulder County wanted a no-nonsense law enforcement leader that could protect their little mountain town from the ever-growing problems spilling out of Boulder. Too many hippies. Too much drugs. Too much petty crime.

Renner Forbes seemed to have everything the townspeople were looking for in a man to lead their law enforcement. He was an experienced officer with strong references. He preferred small town living to that of a major city. And just as important, he was a huge man with an inordinate muscular build – looking somewhat like a professional wrestler – whose mere presence could intimidate anyone that tried to get sideways with the law.

Forbes had a steep challenge to meet from the moment he arrived in town. His predecessor had burned out emotionally, and abruptly resigned when the stress of this responsibility finally over-whelmed him. More than 2,000 hippies were living in a large meadow known as "Dream Canyon" just two miles north of town, with excessive trafficking of drugs. There were weekly calls regarding other hippies breaking into mountain cabins and living there until the owner discovered the unwanted squatters and needed to kick them out. There were frequent abusers of the system that would intentionally get arrested on some minor charge so that they could use the brief jail time to get a free meal or two, and maybe a good night's rest in a warm room before being sent back on the street.

So many of these young adults had no ID, and only went by a chosen nickname. "Sunshine", "Weedman", and "Coast" were a few of the more notorious characters that the Marshall got to know right away. Guy Gaughon had taken the name "Deputy Dawg", and seemed to enjoy taunting law enforcement at every opportunity by wearing a fake police badge and holstering a toy pistol on his hip.

The Marshall tried to exercise patience at first, and took a little time to identify what priorities should be handled in what order. But he was short on tolerance for anyone he perceived to be slothful, and soon began to take the law into his own hands. Boulder County had no idea what was about to take place.

In late August Tom and his roommates had an amused laugh as they read the front page of the local newspaper. Women of New York City had gathered on Fifth Avenue to call a strike for women's equality. Their mode of operation and strategy was not to organize a protest march, not to hold a "sit-in", and not to bomb a building. They had a new approach. To assure maximum media coverage for their cause, the women removed their bras and lit them on fire. Such "bra-burning" became a crowd-pleasing trend, if for no other reason than men gathered around, hoping to see a quick flash of exposed breasts somewhere. Every cause felt the need for some form of protest in order to garner substantive attention and publicity. These efforts of the Women's Movement were most unique.

The following week a new voice of dissent appeared on September 6th when hijackers took control of four commercial jets on the same day. Their message was not a call for the cessation of fighting in Viet Nam, nor for equal rights for African Americans, nor for the equality of women. But their chosen means had an alarming similarity to the riots and the bombings by "operating outside the norm", and raised the level of tension throughout America and beyond.

Here were young men and women that were willing to break the law in an attempt to change the law. Here were young men and women that were willing to threaten the lives of innocent by-standers in order to be heard. Here were young men and women that were fearless in their commitment to radical idealism, willing to risk their own lives if necessary.

The national sense of urgency just went up another notch or two. America certainly wanted safety and better control for all of these situations, but – more importantly – they just wanted answers to "Why?" For mainstream America all of these protests just seemed so counter-productive.

By the middle of 1970 the drug community had developed a unique language unto themselves. "Heavies" were the dealers who could move large quantities of a variety of drugs as needed. "Haves" were the middle-men, who usually had a supply on hand, but at the very least could acquire needed drugs for friends on short notice. The risks were high at either level, but a constant temptation for many because of the volume of money that could be made. Both the "Heavies" and the "Haves" always had women circling around, willing to trade sexual favors for small amounts of their favorite habit of choice.

Boulder and Aspen had become the two major Colorado destinations for large quantities of drugs. Major shipments would arrive from Mexico or Europe, often using women as curriers. Another tactic was to buy a new VW truck from Germany, already loaded with specific drugs, and have it delivered directly to Colorado. Because of Aspen's excellent landing strip for the jet-set crowd, larger shipments could arrive very easily by private plane. Vans or small trucks would pick up their loads there before making the four-hour drive into Boulder. Aspen police officers carefully managed the drug traffic in their city, always allowing for a "commission payment" to themselves. Frequently Aspen police would even buy drugs for their personal use while still in uniform.

Boulder police, on the other hand, were clean. There never was a report of any corruption, in spite of the significant temptation to do so. That alone was an indication of their respect for their Police Chief Vendel. The officers gave little effort to curtail individual drug usage, acknowledging that every student was going to experiment a bit, but made it clear they did not want major "heavies" to set up shop in town.

Trusted friends found it easy to provide an assortment of drugs for each other, but always in limited quantities of only $5 to $20 at a time. LSD was not addictive, and provided an incredible "trip" experience for just $5 to $10, but was inconsistent in its availability. Marijuana, mescaline and peyote were easier to find, and cocaine was doable, but much more expensive, and much more addictive. And heroin was for the crazies that felt they were indestructible. The customer base was almost limitless. So many young people from all over the U.S. were arriving in Boulder because of its reputation for a lifestyle of unbounded gratification in every way. Most of these young arrivals were lonely and needing to feel a part of a "community." Often times those persons would be willing to share their drugs for free in an effort to find a new friend. Sadly, most had no family foundation or moral compass of their own, and were quick to destroy themselves with the more addictive choices.

What amazed law enforcement was the sense of complete "trust" that users had when it came to any drug transaction. A person could have sold rat poison or Dran-o, and no one would have known until it was too late. But most deals were straight forward and honest. There was always the occasional death in town due to some type of drug over-dose. Several of Mark's good friends became such victims of terribly poor self-management.

And just as often, there was the occasional death because someone refused to pay – or was unable to pay – their drug bill to a major dealer.

For a brief time, Mark's best friend, Wayne, organized a marijuana farm in a few of the secluded meadows hidden in the ponderosa pine forest between Nederland and Boulder. He hired hippies to carry guns and ride on horseback to patrol the grounds, in exchange for free weed. But the added hassle did not seem worth it. The associated risk of drawing too much attention to himself made him suspend that idea after one growing season.

That risk of selling or using large quantities of drugs was everywhere. In September the rock & roll world was stunned to learn that Jimi Hendrix had died from an accidental over-dose, ending his meteoric music career at the young age of 27. Considered one of the geniuses in electric guitar musicianship, he broke new ground in style and sound. He was famous for playing his guitar with his teeth during the middle of his show. And when he made a guest appearance on Johnny Carson's *"Tonight Show"*, his loud amps blew out the entire NBC sound system so that he and his band had to quit in the middle of their song. His sudden death was a brief but sobering reminder that drug usage had its ultimate risks.

Just two weeks later, another iconic musician was gone. Janis Joplin – coincidentally also only 27 years old – died of a drug over-dose just as Hendrix had done. Suspicion was, however, that hers was not an accident. She had just returned from her 10-year high school reunion, and was distraught that her sudden material success could not buy her happiness or respect from her former classmates. For any such person, if personal drug use became an attempted escape from depression, it created a dangerous combination.

Too many other rock musicians had close calls with drugs because they had such large sums of money as disposable income. *"Dan Hicks and the Hot Licks"* were scheduled to play at Tulagi's in Boulder that fall. Just minutes before the scheduled show was to start, Hicks was found passed out up in a tree on CU's campus, completely disoriented from a bad acid trip. At other Boulder concerts a member of the Grateful Dead as well as another member of the Rolling Stones crew respectively had to be treated at Boulder Community Hospital for temporary heart-stoppage from too much cocaine.

Buying. Selling. Using. There were associated risks with any element of the drug world, yet demand increased anyway. It had become an assumed part of being completely independent, of being completely free.

Some of the most visible or radical protesters were not always students. A California University faculty member surfaced in the national news in this regard in the summer of 1970.

Angela Davis made a name for herself as an extreme activist for multiple causes. As an African American woman who had grown up in the south, she had witnessed first-hand the ugliest examples of racism when three of her grade school friends were murdered by the Ku Klux Klan. As an adult she became an outspoken advocate for civil rights, women's rights, rights for prisoners, and new rights for the poor. She sought to position herself as a counter-culture advocate in every avenue possible. Employed as a faculty member at UCLA, she had an attentive and supportive audience for her opinions.

Her tenacity got her into legal trouble that summer when the University fired her for trying to recruit other faculty and students to join her in an all-black branch of the Communist Party. (It was later discovered that her doctorate degree was issued from a University in East Berlin, Germany.) Although the University of California had fired her, she sued the State of California and was reinstated in her job. She may have won that situation, but her legal problems were only beginning.

In August, Davis secretly purchased several firearms that were to be used in a daring attempt to take over the courtroom of Marin County, California. Three black men were on trial there, including her lover. But the planned breakout failed miserably. Once in the courtroom, the defendants brandished their weapons and took three jurors and the judge as hostages as they attempted their escape. Police surrounded the parking lot and began shooting. The judge and all three defendants were killed, and two of the jurors were wounded in the mayhem. When the weapons were ultimately traced to her, Davis was charged with conspiracy and sentenced to 20 years in California's penitentiary.

Her supporters claimed that she was unjustly tried, that the courts were exercising a racial bias against her, and that her real "crime" was simply that of speaking out against America and capitalism. John Lennon and Yoko Ono contributed financially to her defense efforts. Bob Dylan wrote a supportive song about her case. The Rolling Stones also dedicated a song to her on their next album release. Posters were mass-produced which read "FREE ANGELA DAVIS." That portrait with her massive Afro hairdo became a popular item hanging on the walls in university dorm rooms and inner-city apartments across the country.

For the time being, Angela Davis was seen as an enemy of the state. After being incarcerated for sixteen months, she was released on bail. For many students – and even some faculty members – lawfulness was now merely a personal option.

Boulder had more than its share of teen-age runaways. It was relatively easy for these juveniles to hide in the hippie communes, steal a few groceries when they had to, but mostly pan-handle for food or money on the street corners. Colorado University Professor Horace Holmes decided something needed to be done.

The professor created a few "attention homes", hosting four to eight juveniles at a time, in an effort to get them off of the street. The facilities concentrated on youth ages 12 to 15 that were already wards of the court, and offered help with homework and meals as long as they cooperated with the rules of the house. It became a cutting edge program by producing "treatment instead of punishment", and gained national recognition by providing a new strategy for confronting crime as well as juvenile delinquency.

Once again Boulder had established a practical model that would be copied across the country. Boystown USA quickly adopted this approach, and began to operate as a "family." As a result they permanently closed their dormitory, and saw improvement in scholastic results by implementing this idea of a more personal environment for every youngster.

Many older Americans just shook their heads in judgment at young people that were making decisions that were foreign to them. Horace Holmes chose a different tack, and showed that creativity and problem solving were possible, even with rebellious young people.

The war in Southeast Asia continued to produce such conflicting information. U.S. troops were now advancing through neighboring Cambodia, in search of Viet Cong. The very notion of spreading this conflict to other countries in this way perpetuated the fear of an ugly war that appeared to be going completely in the wrong direction.

The Defense Department released a bulletin in the early fall which stated that the U.S. had gone an entire week without a single casualty in Viet Nam. This was the first time that accomplishment had happened in over five years. That singular fact could also have been interpreted as a morbid thought because of what that meant for all the other weeks, but the Pentagon was grasping for uplifting information or statistics that might be spun for morale purposes.

General Westmoreland continued to preach his war philosophy of "kill-ratio." With rare exception, every military skirmish recorded a death toll greater than 10: 1 of Viet Cong vs. American troops. The four-star-general interpreted that repeated statistic as certain victory in the making. Ho Chi Minh was telling his North Vietnamese military leaders something completely different. "Yes, the Americans will kill many of us," he said. "And we will kill some of them. But eventually they will grow tired of such death, and they will go home. And all of Viet Nam will be united with us once again."

Americans were less and less convinced that our military had any legitimate purpose in Viet Nam, and such a mindset of uncertainty was reinforced that same month by the Supreme Court. The Court voted NOT to hear a case from Massachusetts in which a civilian was demanding the legal right to refuse military service in an undeclared war such as this. By leaving that decision to the individual states, the Court only amplified the growing sense of impatience and confusion because of so many varying perspectives that could co-exist.

Kevin returned to Boulder in September, having served two tours of duty in Viet Nam, having twice received a Medal of Honor for his heroic efforts. Just a month before being shipped home, he had dragged two wounded comrades to safety under heavy enemy fire even though he himself was also wounded. Yet when he got home, he was anything but a hero. He was shocked at the cold treatment he received from those young people that were opposed to the war. While transferring trains in the Chicago train station, someone tried to spit on his uniform. By the time he got home to Colorado, he decided not to tell anyone about his Medals. He hid his uniform and both Medals of Honor in an empty tool box under his bed. In the onslaught of so many voices speaking out against the war, he began to feel ashamed for having obeyed orders.

Valley Forge, Pennsylvania, hosted an anti-war rally that same September, motivated by the presence of a few celebrities. John Kerry had served in Viet Nam, and was another recipient of a Medal of Honor. He had now become a strong voice against the war, claiming that he had since thrown his Medal into a river because he believed there was no longer any honor in this war. Hollywood movie stars Jane Fonda and Donald

Sutherland also joined him on the platform, and added their voice to the increasing demand for the U.S. to immediately withdraw from Viet Nam regardless of the label of victory or defeat.

Many American citizens may have been listening, but the White House not only continued to ignore their pleas, but also began preparing in secret to double-down on their rigid insistence of winning.

Mark received his honorable discharge from the U.S. Army that fall, and within 72 hours after leaving Viet Nam was back home in Boulder County. He was one of the lucky ones. No physical wounds, and his mental scars were manageable. No drug addictions, and no thoughts of suicide. He wasn't bitter, nor was he inclined to speak out against the war. He just wanted to get on with his life as quietly as possible.

He was shocked at how the community in general had changed since he had left less than three years ago. Hippies seemed to be everywhere. Hippies were now living in large communes in nearby Roosevelt National Forest, because any National Forest is public land that is free and open for citizens of the U.S. to use and enjoy. More than 2,000 hippies were living in the Sprang Meadow or the Caughlin Meadow, which became known as the "Summersville" settlement. They called themselves the "STP family", named after a specific drug of choice, and were notorious for naked parties with group sex, and drugs available to anyone who wanted to join them.

When he was in Boulder, he observed that hippies were always begging for help, and becoming more aggressive in doing so. Having migrated primarily from California, these "long-hairs" were accustomed to receiving free food when they begged. Hippies were always loitering at the city's only shopping center, or congregating all day in the city parks. There were always a few that had to be going in and out of the local jail. And everywhere they went, they were denouncing capitalism and ridiculing the war effort.

A number of Boulder residents had become so frustrated with the influx of these law-breaking transients that they formed their own vigilante network. They urged local citizens to carry a pistol, and to enforce local laws whenever necessary. Mark tried to be neutral, figuring everyone could co-exist as long as they lived within the law. But his home-town had changed drastically since he left. Walking down a Boulder street one afternoon, Mark happened to be following two hippies that had flowing hair down to the lower part of their back. He thought it might be a couple of attractive women, but was stunned a moment later to see that they were both men.

Within two weeks after his return, Mark got his job back at the Nederland gas station. The owner warned him that the hippies were frequent customers, and were often times difficult to handle. Some would try to steal gas, or shoplift some of the candy bars by the cash register. Others wanted to sell drugs in exchange for a fill up of gas. And on rare occasions some of the women had been known to offer sexual favors in exchange for a tank of gas or even a few quarts of oil.

Mark was convinced he could never be tempted by such an offer, for a few reasons. First of all, their free-loading and "begging" lifestyle repulsed him. He really didn't like anyone that appeared lazy. And secondly, they all seemed so filthy dirty to him. Their cars, vans, or school buses were a cluttered mess, their clothes were badly worn, their hands and face were usually dirty, and because they always walked around in sandals or no shoes at all, their feet were pathetic to look at.

Less than a month after working at the gas station, however, temptation and opportunity intersected for Mark on a sunny fall afternoon. He happened to come out of the gas station's supply closet in the back room just in time to see a VW van covered with painted "peace symbols" as it pulled up to the gas pump. A young woman of striking beauty got out of the driver's seat and entered the customer counter area. She had long blonde hair, a tight T-shirt with no bra, and a colorful skirt. And even more impressive was that she was so clean. Her face and hands were perfect, her clothes looked new, and her hair even smelled nice. Mark was a bit in awe.

"How 'ya doin'?" Mark asked as his standard greeting.

"I'm good," she replied, as she tapped her fingers nervously on the counter top for a moment, and then continued. "Is there . . . is there anything I could do for you in exchange for a tank of gas?"

Mark tried not to stare at her T-shirt, but could not help it, and stammered for an answer. "Uh . . . what does that mean?" he finally blurted out.

She smiled, and seemed to gain a little confidence. "Well, . . . I can do some wonderful things with my mouth."

Mark actually winced. The situation was just too much for him to pass up. In spite of his pre-conceived biases, he gave a nod of his head and motioned for her to follow him into the back room. A blow job next to the supply closet, a fill-up of the VW gas tank, and she was back on the road in eight minutes flat.

And – much to his disappointment – Mark never saw her again. But the era of "free love" now had a completely different meaning for him.

A small twist of irony occurred that November in the mid-term elections as two governors took office on opposite sides of the country and on opposite sides of the political aisle. Ronald Reagan, the newest super-star of the Republican Party, was re-elected Governor of California, campaigning once again for America's need for less government and a return to traditional values of right and wrong. Although the state of California typically had a strong leaning for the Democratic platform in national elections, the voters crossed the aisle in choosing a man that might bring them back to a moral high ground. How ironic.

On the other coast, Georgia voters selected a small-town peanut farmer and out-spoken evangelical Christian named Jimmy Carter to be their Governor. The ultra-conservative southern states predominantly voted for Republican candidates, but this year those same voters crossed the aisle to elect a Democrat that was committed to equal rights and integrity. Ironic once again.

Within just a few years, both men would be sequentially elevated to the highest office of the land, campaigning on their same strengths. Reagan remained the champion of smaller government and more traditional values, while Carter stood as a man of integrity at a time when Washington, D.C. appeared to have little or none. Again, more than ironic.

There was one last twist. At the time of these 1970 elections, Ronald Reagan was an early supporter of a woman's legal right to choose an abortion. Because he rallied his followers to believe in a free market system with less government intervention, this was another example of the need for personal freedom without government interference or limitations. Jimmy Carter, on the other hand, believed that an abortion was in direct conflict with the very sanctity of life itself, and thus claimed it should not be a legal option for a woman. As these men rapidly rose through the ranks of their respective political parties, both found it necessary to reverse their stance on abortion in order to be in line with their party's platform. Totally ironic.

A popular dream for millions of college guys was to start a rock & roll band. Howard and his friends in the men's dorm were just more persistent than others. As students at the University of Colorado, they were creative enough to look for a distinctive "hook" – something that would set them apart from so many young musicians that produced such similar sounding tunes at a very high volume.

After experimenting with a few ideas, they chose to go "retro", with greased-back hair and a fresh re-mix of fun '50's tunes. Their name would be *"Flash Cadillac."* The goal was not just to depend on energizing "oldies" dance music, but also to let their personalities make it "crazy fun." Howard was just the guy.

Tulagi's was still the national record-holder for the number of beers served in a day by any bar in the U.S. But they wanted to have a competitive edge over the other two bars adjacent to the campus that also catered to the CU students. Lots of live music and dancing was their strategy to get there.

Howard's timing was perfect, and persuaded Tulagi's owners with the notion that on their slowest nights of the week his start-up band could still get students into the bar to enjoy dancing. It was worth a shot. So Flash Cadillac had their first gig, playing Monday nights for four weeks. With plenty of cheap black-and-white handbills plastered all over campus to promote their live performances, by the second week Tulagi's was packed out, and Flash Cadillac never looked back.

One of Howard's inventions that quickly became a crowd favorite was the "Wild Elephant Dance." All of the male patrons had to pull their front pants pockets inside-out, which represented the elephant "ears." Then they had to unzip their fly or unbutton their pants and fully expose their "trunk" for the entire song. Trunks of various sizes were flopping around to the cheers of the crowd. The revelry was insane, and Tulagi's had its next winner. The owner extended the band's contract, and gave them Tuesday nights as well. The wild elephant dance had put them on the map.

Howard then took their success a step further by instituting a "Twist" dance contest unlike anything that creator Chubby Checker could have ever imagined. During that particular set of music, competing couples were invited to take turns showing their best Twist dance moves, and the Flash Cadillac band members would subjectively act as judges to eliminate them one at a time. As the number of contestants narrowed to the final few, Howard announced that the principle of "show-skin-to-win" was in play, meaning that more bare skin might positively influence the judges. It could have been intended as a joke on his part – no one will ever know for sure. Within moments, one of the last five couples stripped completely naked and continued their twist dancing. The crowd went berserk with applause, and the band had no choice but to crown them the immediate winners for the night. Their "crown" was a toilet seat that had been ripped out of the men's restroom, and gleefully hung around the young man's neck.

The following week, when the Twist contest was reduced to five final couples, and the "skin-to-win" factor was announced, all five couples immediately got naked. What made the task of judging even more difficult for the band was that there was more than one erection in the room. Lots of bouncing boobs will do that. It all became the talk of the campus for several days.

By the time the next Monday evening concert arrived, there was a waiting line to get into Tulagi's. The "Wild Elephant Dance" had its usual participation, with a predictable amount of laughter. And when the Twist contest finally surfaced an hour into the band's music set, more than 50 couples started the contest already in the nude. Flash Cadillac could not believe the phenomenon they had created.

To the band's great disappointment, rumors of their new-found success reached the Boulder Police Department within about three weeks. Officers immediately shut the place down, enforcing public decency laws. No more Twist contests, no more Wild Elephant dances. But Tulagi's had renewed its lock on being the #1 place to hang out, and the Flash Cadillac band members had launched a career for themselves. They performed for years at the Troubador and other nightclubs in L.A., and earned several guest spots on various TV shows and movies. All because they discovered how to generate so much fun that people would be willing to get naked on a public dance floor.

Lt. Hugh Thompson never wanted to be a hero. He certainly did not want national attention for his role in the My Lai massacre incident. In his mind he had just done his duty. As the trial approached, the grief and stress became intense. Thompson suffered severe lack of sleep, loss of weight, as well as the alienation by many of his fellow soldiers. They accused him of causing harm to the military, of possibly being a traitor, and a disgrace to the uniform. Post-traumatic-stress-disorder (PTSD) was not known or understood at the time, but it was a very real issue for him.

Yet the military trial centering on the question of war crimes at the hands of U.S. soldiers did garner the national attention that Thompson wanted very much to avoid. Harsh cross-examination by the Senatorial committee was often focused on him, and tried to position him as irrational, and someone who had ordered his team in the helicopter to point their guns directly at their fellow U.S. soldiers in order to protect themselves while Thompson offered First Aid to the wounded. At one point he actually thought the interrogation commission might file charges against him for interfering in a military operation.

The consistent answers from Lt. Thompson before the panel demonstrated a heart of reason and integrity. His solid position had to be balanced against so many others that claimed he was a threat to the military system of obeying a commanding officer. It made some in the press feel like the outcome could only be a "coin-flip", determined by whomever a person might chose to believe.

A timely interview by newsman Mike Wallace may have helped to sway the court's decision. Wallace aired a personal conversation that he had with Pvt. Meadlo, who confessed on national television to obeying specific orders to shoot unarmed civilians. With a quivering voice he acknowledged killing frail old men and numerous young women and little children at point-blank range. Even the stoic reporter Wallace could not hide his dismay.

In the trial, two Private First-Class soldiers acknowledged in graphic detail some of the other gruesome atrocities that had occurred that day. Shooting young girls. Chopping out tongues. Gang-raping a woman as she was dying. Spraying rapid gunfire through dozens of unarmed Vietnamese that were huddled together. As they replayed their memories of that day, one soldier had no sense of guilt, dismissing the entire episode as "soldiers who were simply following orders." The other soldier corroborated the story, but hung his head in shame. One week later he quietly took his own life in an act of suicide.

The conclusion of the trial left both the prosecution and the defense with a sense of grave disappointment for our country. Lt. William Calley was found "Guilty of War Crimes" for personally murdering 22 unarmed women and children. He received a sentence of "Life in prison". Even though more than 500 other civilians had been ruthlessly killed that morning by 104 U.S. soldiers, Lt. Calley was the only man that was actually convicted and punished.

It was a humiliating day for the Army, because that verdict went on the permanent record. In their minds "war crimes" might be a tool of our evil enemies, but American military personnel could not possibly stoop that low. A national poll conducted by Newsweek Magazine, however, later revealed that only 9% of the public approved of the verdict, and 79% disapproved. While in prison, Lt. Calley received an average of 10,000 letters of support each day. Indiana Governor Edgar Whitcomb ordered flags to be flown at half-mast in honor of Calley. Mississippi Governor John Williams said his state was considering seceding from the Union because of the unfair verdict.

In an ironic twist, President Nixon continued to attempt to impose his will on this case in an effort to reduce the embarrassment to our military. First he ordered Calley's release while this case was appealed. A few months after Calley was actually held in prison, Nixon ordered that his sentence to be reduced from "Life" to "10 Years." Two years later he was permanently paroled after serving a total of only 3½ years.

Was justice served for anyone in any way in this case? How could it ever be? Added to this tragedy, it would be 30 more years before the Army could truly shed its façade and have any complete closure on this pathetic episode. For those three decades Lt. Thompson's hope for exoneration for his honesty and integrity would have to wait. . . and wait . . . and wait.

Angela Davis

Charles Manson

Jimi Hendrix

Shootings at Kent State University

CHAPTER 8

"1971 – AMERICA IN DISARRAY"

"Some folks are born made to wave the flag,
Oooh, they're red, white, & blue . . .
It ain't me, it ain't me, I ain't no Senator's son, son,
It ain't me, it ain't me, I ain't no fortunate one . ."
Creedence Clearwater Revival

"Power to the people, power to the people . . .
Say we want a revolution
We better get on right away
Well, you get on your feet and into the street.
Singing power to the people, power to the people . . ."

John Lennon

By 1971, the word "revolution" was a frequent subject in the national dialog. No longer were the activists content merely to talk about ending the war, or merely talk about equal rights for Blacks, or merely talk about economic justice. It was time for a complete overhaul of the system. Revolution was the answer. And two books arrived on the scene this year to fuel that heart for revolution.

Author Saul Alinsky published his book that became a veritable "recipe" for such a revolutionary mindset, and he did so with an attitude of intellectualism. *"Rules for Radicals"* quickly became a best-seller, and established itself as the new "bible" for activists with any cause that sought change. Alinsky had been a community organizer in south Chicago, and was passionate about improving the conditions for the impoverished through the tool of collective community action. His general contention was that meaningful change could most easily be achieved by first creating social chaos. Once that vacuum existed, the opportunity would be ripe to replace an out-dated system with something completely different.

His book instructed the reader to try to polarize people primarily on political and economic issues, and secondarily on religious and racial passions. His vision stated that cultural instability would create a desperate demand for a new course of action out of necessity. If people felt unstable or insecure, they would more quickly move to a new position of thinking.

"Rules for Radicals" offered 12 general principles for accomplishing dramatic change. "Ridicule" was one potent weapon, for example, not just against corporations or governments in general, but targeting specific individuals. Utilizing that guiding tenet would create more energy and longevity with supporters. Another axiom was that if a "negative" was pushed long enough, it would become a "positive" in the eyes of the public. Those persons that had been undecided would always shift to side with the underdog.

Alinsky also taught the importance of finding a common enemy with one's audience, and then to be relentless in attacking that entity or person. Whether the target was a local politician or a local agency, cultural change would be accomplished because the masses were effectively unified with a clear sense of focused opposition.

Interestingly, Saul Alinsky had very little time to utilize the success of his book. He died the next year, at the age of 68. He had only begun in his mission to move America toward a social state by controlling education, religion, and class warfare. Although he himself was a radical leftist, in the ensuing years his theories became a Primer for both ultra-radical as well as ultra-conservative strategists in their pursuit of change.

The second such book published this same year was also targeted to the revolution-minded audience, and authored by William Powell. Unlike Alinsky, however, his underlying attitude was that of anger.

At the age of 19, Powell was incensed when he received his draft notice, and could not imagine himself wearing an Army uniform or trudging around Viet Nam. So in 1969 he began spending full days at the New York Public Library, pouring over electronics manuals, survivalist guidebooks, and even declassified military documents. His vision was to create a "How To" book utilizing violence as an acceptable means for bringing about political and cultural change.

After two years of research, the dream became a reality when his book *"The Anarchist Cookbook"* hit the bookstores in the spring. The contents included detailed instructions as well as illustrations for such things as making dynamite at home, converting standard shotguns into grenade launchers, or making one's own LSD. His "cookbook for revolution" sold more than 2 million copies in a very short span of time.

Some might have read it merely for tantalizing entertainment, but more than enough of Powell's readership put its teachings into practice. The Weather Underground found it very useful in making simple bombs that they could disperse around the country. Timothy McVeigh followed it explicitly in his Oklahoma City bombing of 1995, and it also was the guidebook for the Columbine High School shooting of 1999.

Prior to his death, William Powell acknowledged on numerous occasions that he regretted ever having written his book.

It was no longer an honor to go to the White House. By the time the two-year anniversary of President Nixon's inauguration arrived, the environment and morale throughout the White House staff was toxic. Those men closest to the President – including H.R. Haldeman, John Erlichman, and Charles Colson – did not trust each other, and functioned with competitive ego trips of their own. They took time carefully to measure the square footage of each man's office to know within a square inch who had the largest space. They also carefully measured the distance from their office door to the door of the Oval Office, as a factual basis for who had the most influence with the Commander-in-Chief. About the only thing they enjoyed doing together was treating all other Republicans with a smug animosity. State and national leaders within the party felt their arrogance, and a schism continued to widen.

For the other employees within the White House, everyone knew the pay was good, but they never bothered to tell other people where they worked, unless they were at a government function. Mentioning that fact at a restaurant or grocery store might reduce the level of service. There were occasional death threats that came by mail or phone messages. And they certainly were not ignorant of the statistics pertaining to the weekly protests around the country, which vilified anyone associated with the President.

Richard Nixon himself was showing early signs of severe paranoia. He had the FBI tap the phones of known war protesters such as John Lennon. Nixon demanded that they find sufficient drug charges that could force Lennon to be deported and moved back to England on a permanent basis. His fear stemmed from that fact that 18-year-olds could now vote, and Lennon held enormous sway over the opinions of those young adults. He had to be destroyed in any way possible.

Nixon's temper grew noticeably shorter, his language more and more profane, and any conversations with his staff seemed distant or disconnected. His vindictive anger toward anyone on his "enemy list" – and particularly the media – created a contagious environment of ridicule and revenge. He took the time personally to edit the invitation list of which media companies would or would not be allowed to cover his daughter's wedding in the White House. And in a secret step of universal distrust, he had a sophisticated tape recording system set up in the walls of the Oval Office, to capture any conversation that took place there. He felt it might someday provide important information on what disloyal persons might be saying behind his back. Little did he realize that his tape recording system would soon be a major component of his very own undoing.

March 1st was a wake-up call for the FBI. All of the protest marches and sit-ins sprinkled all over the country could be the responsibility of the local police and the National Guard. But when lives are threatened or intentional destruction of property is involved – and particularly bombs – the FBI must be called in. This particular morning a bomb went off in one of the restrooms in the Capitol Building in Washington, D.C. No one was injured, but extensive damage took place.

It was very clear that this was not a mechanical problem of some sort from the lack of proper maintenance. It could not be a gas line explosion, or a clog in a main water line. The blast was too powerful and too localized. Investigators had spent less than a day looking for clues when the police station received an anonymous phone call. The muffled male voice on the line did not identify himself, but said that they were part of the Weathermen organization, and that they not only took credit for the explosion the day before, but that they would continue to bomb random locations until the Viet Nam War was ended.

This took protesting to an entirely different level. American Law Enforcement had to be on edge at all times.

After four years of legal battles, the U.S. Supreme Court finally ruled that Muhammad Ali would be permitted to box once again. In March of this year Ali returned to the ring to challenge Heavyweight Champion Joe Frazier in what was billed as "the Fight of the Century." The irony was that Frazier personally had lent Ali large sums of money during that four-year gap so that Ali could afford to stay in reasonable boxing shape.

University concerts had shifted from "sock-hops" to rock & roll "bashes." Venues had shifted from auditoriums to stadiums. The University of Colorado hosted *"The Rolling Stones"* that spring, and the 53,000-seat stadium was packed to over-flowing. Concert promoters placed full-page ads in the Denver and Boulder newspapers, with a tag-line at the bottom of the page which read, "BRING YOUR BEST STUFF." Since the word "drugs" did not actually appear, the papers reluctantly published it. But everyone knew what it meant. And everyone complied.

Joints were being shared throughout the duration of the concert. More than 100 lids of marijuana were thrown from the stage into the outstretched hands of the crowd. If the *"Guinness Book of World Records"* had kept such statistics, this may have been the largest drug party to date. No one will ever know for sure. But everyone got "baked" in the Colorado sunshine that day.

In April, an auto magazine conceived of another segment of rebellion that had an unusual sense of adventure and entertainment. Due to the oil embargo and the rising price of gasoline, highway speed limits had been reduced to 55 mph. Even the emptiest stretches of Interstate Highways in the western states had to comply with the national restriction.

As a reaction against that government edict, the first annual cross-country race was established, called the "Cannonball Sea-to-Shining-Sea Memorial Trophy Dash." It was an effort to defy government restrictions, and create a rebellion behind the wheel of a car. The starting point and end-point for the race were the same for every driver, but there was no specified route, and no particular rules, to traverse the country. A Ferrari was the winner that first year, driving the 2800 miles in less than 36 hours. The driver admitted to exceeding 170 m.p.h. on several segments of the trip.

There was no cash prize. There was no trophy. Just bragging rights. The satisfaction of going against the laws of the land was enough of a reward. This annual race was held five years in a row as a light-hearted way to flaunt the need to oppose limitations on one's freedom. As its popularity began to grow, however, law enforcement felt it was necessary to shut it down as a hazard to highway safety. The success of this cross-country challenge became the central theme to a very profitable movie, entitled *"Cannonball Run."*

One of the more glamorous jobs during this era was that of working for the commercial airlines. Pilots and stewardesses – as they were called then – were envied as "jet-setters" because of their domestic and international travel opportunities. Travel by air was considered a luxury, since just over 80% of all passengers were businessmen. In an effort to perpetuate an elite or select image, the airlines maintained strict hiring guidelines for their stewardesses. Some airlines chose uniforms of hot pants, mini-skirts, and go-go boots as standard attire for their flight crew. Braniff Airlines had all stewardesses take off one layer of their uniform while standing in the aisle of the plane during mid-flight. Airline stewardesses could not be married, they were expected to dress "properly" even on those days when not on duty, and had to be weighed every 90 days to make sure that they were not the slightest bit over-weight for their height. On the job, the women were required to wear girdles, false eye-lashes, and to be "extra friendly."

The National Organization of Women tried to sue the airlines, claiming that these practices were demeaning to women. But the creation of this sexy image persisted. One stewardess did a centerfold photo-shoot for Playboy Magazine. Mattel released a "Stewardess Barbie Doll." Advertising campaigns for most airlines went overboard to solidify that perception of sexy stewardesses. Examples included:

- one airline had a series of ads that did not show any of their planes, but rather showed individual photos of some of their stewardesses, and the only ad copy read "FLY ME"
- Continental Airlines chose an ad campaign that featured photos of selected stewardesses, with an accompanying tag line which said "WE REALLY MOVE OUR TAIL FOR YOU"
- The most blatant may have been this print ad, which pictured stewardesses welcoming passengers into the airplane as they

boarded. It read, "Every passenger gets Warmth, Friendliness, and Extra Care. . . And someone may get a Wife."

Flight crews would typically travel three or four days at a time, and then have a corresponding number of days off. During those working trips, the airlines provided hotel rooms and per diem meal expenses for their employees. This created a most unique environment for both pilots and stewardesses. The combination of the sexual revolution in general, the free hotel rooms provided by the airlines, being anonymous in cities away from home, the opportunities to meet fascinating people on their flights (particularly celebrities or executives flying in 1st Class), as well as the perceived attractiveness of working in the airline industry all blended to create a sexual frenzy for many of these airline employees.

While it would never be reasonable to suggest that this mindset was universal among airline employees, there were more than enough crew members taking full advantage of this system to make it legendary. A pilot having sex with a stewardess while on a "dead-head" flight. Male and female crew members sharing their hotel rooms while on a layover trip. Or stewardesses giving their name, number, and hotel key to a handsome passenger. The standard joke of the day was that stewardesses would bring their food and beverage cart down the airplane aisle and offer "Coffee, Tea, or ME" to their customers.

Most stewardesses chose to live together with one or two other airline employees in apartment buildings that were easily accessible to their home airport. These buildings became known as "stew-zoo's." One such apartment complex in Chicago had to have its entire plumbing system replaced because it had become clogged with thousands of used condoms. "Free love" wasn't just for the hippies.

Matt was an occasional hunting buddy of Mark's, ruggedly handsome, and carefree about anything in life. In the spring of this year, Matt had to fly from Denver's Stapleton Airport to LaGuardia in New York City to attend a funeral for his uncle. In order to save a little money, he booked a ticket on a "red-eye" flight, leaving just before midnight, and arriving in New York early the next morning. It was a six-hour flight he would never forget.

The Boeing 707 could hold almost 300 passengers, but there were less than twenty people on board that night, all seated in the Coach section. After take-off and the standard safety announcements, Matt settled into perusing his latest copy of *"Playboy Magazine."* His reading was soon interrupted by one of the stewardesses.

"Excuse me," she said, "but our flight tonight has no meal service, and our plane is virtually empty. If you would like to move up to the 1st Class section, we can offer you a free drink."

"You don't have to ask me twice on that," Matt said with grin. He slid out of his seat and followed her toward the front of the plane. The spacious leather seats in 1st Class felt luxurious, and Matt picked a window seat to enjoy the night-time view of the city lights in the distance below. All of the cabin lights were off so that other passengers could sleep if they so chose.

"What sort of drink sounds good?" the stewardess asked.

"How 'bout a Scotch on the rocks?" he said.

Four minutes later she returned with two drinks – the Scotch for him, and a glass of sparkling water for herself. To Matt's surprise, she sat down in the seat next to him and started chatting. Matt put his magazine away, and enjoyed the conversation. After some time, she asked if he wanted a refill.

"Sure, why not?" he replied.

She returned momentarily with another drink and resumed the conversation. As she did so, she gently put her hand on his knee while she was talking. Matt wasn't sure what to do about that, but she solved that question for him. A few minutes later she reached into the overhead compartment and pulled out a small blanket. She unfolded it, gently threw it across his lap, and proceeded quietly to give him a hand job.

By the time Matt got home from the funeral four days later, he couldn't even remember the name of that stewardess. But out of loyalty, whenever he did need to travel, he always chose to fly that same airline for the rest of his life.

In the spring of this year, the movement for equality for African Americans witnessed two "advances" which bolstered the morale of every black person. During the past year, Chicago had been a test market for a television show called *"Soul Train."* Targeted exclusively to the African American audience, the program featured live dancing to the latest soul, R & B, and hip-hop music. All of the dancers, the emcee. as well as the guest musicians were black. Sponsors sold products which were exclusively marketed to the African American demographic.

The one-year experiment was a raving success, and in '71 *"Soul Train"* was syndicated into 13 other major city markets. Patterned after *"American Bandstand",* the TV show became a cultural phenomena, show-casing new artists, new fashion, and new dance moves. Numerous over-night careers were made by musicians that were invited to perform live on the program. Young adults – both black and white – watched the show for the next 35 years, making it the longest-running show of its kind.

In April, the Civil Rights movement received a second "step of progress" in the form of a major victory from the U.S. Supreme Court. With a single stroke of the pen, the highest court endorsed an issue that had not been resolved by years of marches, sit-ins, and passionate speeches. And the court's decision was UNANIMOUS. Typically the court could not unanimously agree on the most trivial items such as when it was time to break for lunch. The norm was that the court would always be divided somewhat on any given case, which is why the Constitution established that the Supreme Court should be comprised of nine Justices. But this case made the rare statement that there was no equivocation or debate.

The Justices all agreed that racial segregation was wrong, and that as a pragmatic step toward school integration, busing of students was now a necessary step to assure that students of any race received an equal opportunity for a worthwhile education.

Turmoil subsequently broke out in many communities. Parents took to the streets, waving signs and yelling their disapproval. Vacant school buses were burned or mechanically disabled. In the meantime the young students were innocently caught in the ebb and flow.

But the court's ruling was enforced, city by city. School districts had to reallocate resources such as books, science lab supplies, and sports equipment in an attempt to make schools "equal." In some districts they chose to swap teachers as well, so that a Caucasian instructor was assigned to teach at a predominantly black high school, and vice versa. One such teacher received so little respect from the new students that she gave up on any attempt to teach anything, and just let the students play poker for an entire semester. The objective was not easy, but it was a necessary beginning. Such an edict cannot change hearts overnight that have accrued an attitude of hatred, or developed a long-term rationale for separate communities for different races.

This singular issue launched the national political aspirations of Alabama Governor George Wallace. His formal opposition to the policy of busing pulled back the covers on the hatred that still lurked in the minds and hearts of so many parents. Both state and national elections would be impacted by this decision. Yes, the Court had spoken, but it only intensified the level of urgency from voices on both sides.

The Court might have been unanimous, but the country was still so divided.

April 24th set a new high-water mark for protesting the Viet Nam War. More than 500,000 young men and women from across the country jammed onto the Washington Mall, surrounding the Washington Monument and the reflecting pool. It was a new record attendance for any cause that was being held on the Mall, and that record would hold for more than 25 years. (Simultaneously a crowd of more than 125,000 gathered on the opposite coast, for the same purpose – to gain media attention and generate new enthusiasm for everyone to go into their local communities and speak out against the war.)

This was a peaceful gathering, assembled to hear rallying cries from leading activists, as well as to hear from two young veterans who had just returned from Viet Nam – one of them now confined to a wheel chair. It was a moving experience for everyone in attendance, and later became a memorable scene in the movie *"Forrest Gump."*

Just ten days later a gathering of a different kind took place in Washington, D.C. This was a militant assembly of more than 20,000 protesters, who were given instructions on trying to disrupt Government business of any kind. Clusters of people blocked the main entrances to numerous buildings. Others marched in large numbers in the streets, so that traffic was unable to move. There was to be no burning of buildings, just creating gridlock for any person trying to get from Point A to Point B.

For a couple of hours it actually worked. Police finally established a system of arresting hundreds at a time, and "herded" them to the Mall, which became a large "holding pen", patrolled by hundreds of officers, mostly on horseback. By mid-afternoon, the police held just over 12,000 protestors "under arrest" on the sprawling lawn of the Washington Mall. Traffic had returned to normal, but the police had no possible plan to actually arrest so many. By late in the day all but two were released because there was no realistic place to put them. Protestors were emboldened, convinced that this pattern of "the law of large numbers" might force the government to change. They were determined to win. Somehow. Some way.

On June 13th the government's façade over "information management" regarding the war took a giant hit. Daniel Ellsberg had secretly participated in a research project within the Defense Department, seeking to document everything regarding the U.S. involvement in Viet Nam from its very inception. Secretary Robert MacNamara had previously ordered this exhaustive study because he believed it would be helpful to the government at a later date. More than 7,000 pages of documents became a part of that file, which became known as the "Pentagon Papers." But the report proved to be anything but helpful for the Pentagon or the White House.

The early documents recorded how the U.S. provided secret support for Ngo Dinh Diem to become the President of Viet Nam, including laundered cash and smuggled military equipment to do so. Memos gave written instructions for covert operations or rigged elections. A few years later the U.S. withdrew its support of Diem, and covertly supported the military coup that assassinated him. Official written facts showed that the three previous Presidents had also lied to the American people regarding what was actually taking place in Viet Nam. Other classified documents revealed that in the early '60's the U.S. was looking for an excuse to enter Southeast Asia at any reasonable location as a means of containing China since it was believed that China was already plotting against the U.S. Further documents confirmed that our military had gone into Cambodia and Laos illegally to bomb possible supply depots. For the integrity of the White House as well as the entire Defense Department, the Pentagon Papers were damning.

As a conscientious objector to the war, Ellsberg began to speak at anti-war rallies, and refer to some of the facts and statistics that he had uncovered. He was consequently arrested and charged with espionage, conspiracy, and stealing U.S. government property. President Nixon was insistent that the "Pentagon Papers" report was a classified document that should never be made public. His henchmen were instructed to make private threats to any major newspaper that would consider putting those files into print, and also to conduct "dirty tricks" against Ellsberg to destroy his credibility.

The New York Times was the first newspaper to release information from the Pentagon Papers. The White House immediately demanded a legal injunction to be issued which would prevent any further revelations because all those documents were registered as "classified", and thus threatened the security of the United States. The Times complied with that legal blockade, and suspended any further publications of the Pentagon Papers.

The Washington Post was not so obedient. Since they were not specifically named in the court's restriction of the New York Times, management gambled the entire future of their company by publishing more and more documents from the Pentagon Papers files. Their integrity gave them the courage to operate under the freedom of the 1st Amendment, knowing that if a higher court decision was rendered against them, it could send them to prison for treason.

Citing a national emergency, the White House demanded that the Supreme Court suspend any studies on other cases, and convene with only one day's notice to deliberate this debate, and then issue a verdict within another 24 hours regarding the need to protect these classified documents. Their filing requested that all such related documents remain held in secret by the U.S. government.

The Supreme Court ultimately disagreed with the President and his attorneys, however, and concluded that Ellsberg had legally made copies for himself, and was protected by the 1st Amendment to express his own mind, and as such, this information was legally available to the public domain. In a monumental vote of 6 – 3, the Court issued a statement that in a land of freedom such as ours, "the press is empowered to preserve the *governed,* not to preserve the *governor.*"

As owner and publisher of one of the two most influential newspapers in the country, the Post's Catherine Graham was willing to lead the way, and more than a dozen metropolitan newspapers around the country were quick to follow by reprinting their Pentagon Paper articles. The daily release of shocking and damning details was a resounding victory for freedom of speech, and a crushing defeat for Nixon and anyone else that wanted to manipulate or hide information.

In an unexpected connection, the legal charges against Ellsberg were ultimately dropped after the Watergate investigation uncovered the fact that President Nixon had also instructed the "White House Plumbers" to discredit Ellsberg In any way possible. In the process Ellsberg became an heroic celebrity for the growing crowds that distrusted the government and opposed the war. The Washington Post ultimately received the Pulitzer Prize for its courage in making those documents available to the American public.

And in so doing, the noose around Nixon's throat tightened just a bit more. He had no idea he was now living on borrowed time.

As with most universities across the country, the University of Colorado had an agreement with the City of Boulder that no hard liquor could be sold within 500 feet of the campus borders. Thus 3.2 beer was the beverage of choice at any establishment near the University, to be consumed in enormous quantities. In late summer, Tom stumbled across a loophole in that policy. The law read " . . .500 feet, using standard pedestrian access." Even though Tulagi's was one short block from the University "as the crow flies", the actual sidewalks to get there measured slightly more than 500 feet. Tom smelled opportunity.

He invited a University administrator and a Boulder City Police officer to join him in measuring the exact distance for the official record. Yep. 514 feet. They all agreed that Tulagi's was exempt from that particular legal parameter.

Using his enormous creative capacity, Tom quickly went to work. He scraped and borrowed enough money to make a generous offer to buy 50% of the popular bar. The owner agreed. Tom immediately filed for a liquor license, and – to the shock of the city as well as the CU student body – it was approved. Within a short time Tom was pouring mixed drinks every night, and during the day working to book rock & roll bands to play there.

On such short notice, the first artist that was able to perform was a relative newcomer to the Country Music scene, named Bonnie Raitt. The club was packed out every night for her four shows – not so much because they were fans of her music – but for the novelty of being able to legally order hard liquor. While many musicians had an ego the size of Alaska, Bonnie showed that she was a class act both on and off the stage. When her show was done and the crowd had left, she came out from her dressing room and helped the staff sweep the floors and clean up the bar area. Rare talent combined with genuine humility assured her that she had a long and enormous career ahead of her.

Just two weeks later Tom booked another new band that someone had heard in a coffee house in Aspen. Tom needed to fill the dates, so he agreed to pay them $100 per night for five nights, and to perform two shows each night for that fixed price. There were only 40 people at the first show, but from then on every show was packed. Word of mouth spread quickly that this group was something special, and every night thereafter there was a waiting line to get in. The group called themselves *"The Eagles"*, and they would always fondly remember that their real "coming out party" for their stellar career took place that week in Boulder.

In the coming months, some of the best bands in the country performed at Tom's club, including The Dooby Brothers, The Grateful Dead, and The Allman Brothers Band. It was a money machine for Tom.

The liquor license approval had opened the floodgates. Now booze and drugs were taken to a new level. Tulagi's became a destination point for musicians and music lovers alike. It was a small precursor to the notorious "Studio 54" in New York City. Word quickly spread throughout the music world. When any given band arrived, the group manager had two questions: the second question was "Where is the sound board?", and the first was "Where is the Blow?"

On the afternoon before each band's engagement was to begin, the musicians and their crew went out for dinner at the Red Lion Inn, peacefully secluded five miles west of town in the mountains. Without the risk of police wandering by, they consumed large quantities of drugs and alcohol together. The restaurant staff even new the drill. If the band provided their own drugs, the waiters sometimes served the cocaine to the entire crew on an elegant mirror etched with a large wagon wheel.

Needless to say, bands loved coming to Boulder.

Life on this earth ended for another rock & roll musician on July 3rd. As the lead singer for "The Doors", Jim Morrison had become the symbol for living a life of complete rebellion from normality. He rocketed to the forefront of the entertainment world by using his genius to write brilliant lyrics and music while living a life of extreme excess to the point of self-destruction.

Often times performing while drunk or stoned, his audiences cheered him on, wanting to live a life with no limits vicariously. At his concerts he was arrested more than once for public indecency, including fully exposing his genitalia to the crowds. Reports of his excessive drug abuse on a daily basis became legendary.

At a press conference in Miami he expressed his world-view in blatant terms. "I've always been attracted to ideas that were about revolt against authority," he said. "I like ideas about the breaking away or overthrowing of established order. I am interested in anything about revolt, disorder, chaos – especially activity that seems to have no meaning." That was an accurate summation of his life.

He died in Paris, France, from a drug overdose at the age of 28. Although he had married in his early 20's, his primary female companion for the last two years of his life was not his wife. Following his death, a Will was discovered that declared that his girlfriend – and not his wife – was the sole heir to his entire estate of more than $2,000,000. Morrison's parents as well as his wife contested the will in probate court.

The court delays created dire circumstances for Morrison's girlfriend. Because she had become accustomed to fast living, and now suddenly had no means of income, she turned to prostitution. It was almost two years before the courts made a final determination that the Will was valid as written, and that she was in fact to be the only recipient of Morrison's assets. During those months and months of court maneuvering, however, she had also became a heroin addict, and subsequently died from an overdose just two months after the judge's favorable verdict. She was only 27.

By law, her parents then became the next legal heirs to the estate. Morrison's widow as well as his parents would still receive nothing. Morrison's parents once again filed court papers to refute that court decision, claiming that she was not officially married to their son. Rather than seeing more and more money chewed up by attorneys, the girlfriend's parents stunned the court by offering a 50-50 split of the estate, and Morrison's parents quickly agreed. None of them had any idea of the eventual wealth that they now shared.

Prior to his death, Jim Morrison and The Doors had sold more than 5,000,000 albums. Thanks to the re-release of some songs, and the publication of some of Jim Morrison's poetry, the estate of Morrison sold more than 25,000,000 more albums in the ensuing years after his death. As a result, Morrison's parents 50% share made far more money from his musical works than Jim had made for himself.

As a final celebration of his legacy for rebellion and living life contrary to cultural norms, to this day his most devoted fans continue to travel to Paris to visit his gravesite, to do drugs and have sex in front of his gravestone, as a statement of solidarity with the man who exemplified living with no limits. Jim Morrison would have been proud.

Tom did have at least one college friend that was not a part of the frequent campus protests. Dave was a rare exception that felt more constructive change actually might come about by creatively working WITH the Establishment rather than trying to destroy it.

Ecology had become a new issue for the country. Air and water pollution had reached alarming levels in numerous cities. "Doom and gloomers" forecast a rapidly approaching day when all of mankind would have to wear gas masks, and most of humanity would die from the lack of breathable air or sanitary water. A few examples of such unbridled pollution in the news included:

- toxic chemicals in 55-gallon drums were frequently discarded in vacant lots in NYC
- truckloads of used oil were discarded into public lakes or the ocean
- large plastic bags full of used hypodermic needles washed ashore in New Jersey
- portions of Lake Erie caught on fire due to floating patches of oil sludge and debris
- numerous areas of public land had become "volunteer garbage dumps" for old appliances
- and other items that would not burn
- smog had become a major health concern, particularly in New York, Chicago, Denver, and

L.A. When weather conditions were right, more than 80% of the suns rays were blocked by smog. A recurring joke was that breakfast restaurants had to serve a "Denver Omelet" with its own brown cloud.

In order to address such abuse of the environment, concerned citizens created "Earth Day" as an opportunity for adults of all ages to find creative ways to help the planet. Individual efforts as well as state and national legislation were welcomed. Following the passage of the Clean Air Act, there was a growing awareness for the need of helping the environment in any practical way possible, no matter how small the incremental step might be. In that light, Dave's two roommates developed a notion that they might literally run across the entire United States as a publicity campaign against water and air pollution. They asked Dave to travel with them as their "advance man."

Tony and Joel had trained for the previous two years by running at least ten miles per day. They also did extensive research on the most progressive and effective legislation available in the U.S. to counter water pollution and air pollution, including specifics on how Mayor Richard Daley and his staff had cleaned up the Chicago River. Those selected legislative documents were then rolled up into a small baton that the runners carried with them every day.

Their cross-country adventure took place during that summer of '71, using the name "The Save America Run." They charted a coast-to-coast course from Long Beach, California, to Long Beach, New York, to give it a bit of a "hook." Their schedule was to run 32 miles per day, six days per week, as they traversed the country. The actual running took 4 – 5 hours each morning. Once their daily run was out of the way, Dave's responsibility was to schedule as many constructive appointments as possible for the runners during the rest of their afternoon. There was often a small press conference with the local media at the end of each daily run segment. Sometimes there was a personal meeting with a Governor, a State Senator, and always the local Mayor. Every such meeting included the presentation of a copy of the water and air pollution legislation hidden in their baton.

As an honorary "thank you", Tony and Joel received dozens of "Keys to the City" at these receptions, which of course don't unlock a thing. Local service club organizations such as Kiwanis or Rotary Clubs provided a venue for a free meal and a welcoming audience on a daily basis. From city to city, these gatherings of community leaders had already grown so tired of the many rebellious protests by other college students and hippies, so this positive approach by the Save America Run team provided a novel and refreshing contrast. There had been incidents within the previous year where college students had dumped a 55-gallon barrel of oil sludge onto the office lobby of an oil company, or strewn buckets of dead fish into the headquarters of a Defense Department contractor. Business and community leaders only saw such disgusting actions as foolish and unproductive. Because of Tony and Joel's pragmatic and constructive approach, as well as their passionate conviction in sharing their perspective of finding positive solutions for improving our country by diminishing its pollution, they consistently were met with standing ovations.

National media did not pick up on the story until their 94th running day when they splashed into the Atlantic surf in Long Beach, New York, right on schedule in mid-September. The next day, Dave had arranged for them to be early guests on NBC's *"Today Show"* with Joe Garragiola, then a national news radio interview with Gene Rayburn, followed by interviews on all of the New York City news outlets. The following day they drove to Washington, D.C., to appear before the House of Representatives, the Public Works Committee, the Environmental Protection Agency, and a private meeting with Illinois Senator Charles Percy.

In the ensuing months, numerous cities in random corners of the U.S. passed their own anti-pollution legislation based on the written samples provided by these two young runners. The smallest city to do so was Aspen, Colorado, and the largest was Detroit, Michigan. The overall experience proved that many civic leaders were in fact open-minded to make progressive changes regardless of where those ideas may have originated, including from college students. As true community leaders they were not only visionary, but displayed a willingness to adapt when worthwhile opportunities became available to their communities, no matter what the source.

These running brothers may have been the first hint of a radically new approach – a small but growing shift in the pursuit of change. These were young Americans constructively helping to improve America with valid solutions, not just to protest or complain about what was wrong. There were other young people that were slowly beginning to rebel against negative or random acts of pure opposition, and instead sought to offer pragmatic suggestions as well. "Caring for planet earth" became a part of the social conversation. When possible, "recycling" became the newest practice for early adapters. Worthwhile as it might be, it would be a few more years before these isolated phenomena would slowly become a significant trend. America's conscience, however, had now been awakened by young and passionate adults, and the environment began to make a gradual correction into a positive slope.

Inflation in America was approaching an annualized rate of 10%. Every economic variable was on the decline except the unemployment index. The government had to keep printing money to meet the military obligations that were dragging on. If the economy did not improve, Richard Nixon knew that it would be a major detriment to his re-election efforts in the coming year. In an act of desperation, the President asked all of the television networks for an hour of prime time broadcasting to allow him to talk directly to the American people. It became a ploy that he would need to use numerous times during the next 30 months.

On the evening of August 15th, Nixon went on the air from his desk in the Oval Office, and announced his drastic measures for an economic turn-around. First, he was taking the US Dollar off of the Gold Standard, which would allow it to float in trading against other international currencies. Second, he announced a wage & price freeze for the next 90 days. The vision was that all food and commodities would not change in price. All companies could not give any pay raises to their employees for those three months. The expectation was that inflation would drop to almost 0% for that time period, and once those restrictions were lifted, inflation would re-settle at a more manageable rate.

That may have been the vision. Reality was something quite different. Reality looked like the image of pinching a garden hose so tightly that no water could escape for a short period of time. But the water pressure continues to build so that once the hose is un-pinched that backlog of water must rush out with a far greater force. The ill-advised decision of the President created the worst financial crisis for our country since the Great Depression.

In late November the 90-day clampdown was over, and prices immediately jumped at a double-digit rate. Pay raises also returned, even if companies had to lay off more people to get there. It was nothing but an economic maelstrom. By early December the U.S. dollar was devalued for only the 2nd time in history.

President Nixon was now perceived as an abject failure. With the economy moving backwards, the President was seen as incompetent in not being able to lead our nation back to a healthy state. As the war continued to consume millions of dollars and hundreds of lives each month, the President was also seen as a failure in not finding a solution for peace.

Someone once said, "it's lonely at the top." In Richard Nixon's case, it could not have been more true.

Every minority or special interest group now demanded equal rights. And standard rules of etiquette had fallen by the wayside. The amplification of those demands would just have to be increased until satisfaction was met.

September 9th witnessed a sad example of this mindset, coming from a source that nobody would have expected. Prisoners in the Attica Correctional Facility, located in western New York state, secretly organized in a revolt for fair and humane treatment. Regardless of ethnicity, these men claimed they were harassed, beaten, starved, or put into isolation without just cause. A daring protest seemed to be their only choice.

Following dinner that evening, in what appeared to be a routine process for everyone to return to their cells, prisoners suddenly tackled three of the security guards, disarmed them, and held them hostage in one of their cells. A fourth guard witnessed what had happened, and rang the emergency alarm. Within a few seconds the inner atrium was filled with additional armed guards, holding all other prisoners at gun-point. However, the hostage takers refused to give up their captives, and demanded a meeting with the Chief Warden, with news media to be present, to negotiate their demands for better prison conditions.

The guards claimed they could not negotiate with prisoners, and demanded the release of their fellow guards. It was a verbal stalemate that would become a nightmare.

The next day the demands became more intense. The prisoners holding the guards issued a new demand for them to meet with the Warden, or they would kill one of the guards within the next hour. When no response was offered, they fulfilled their threat. They stripped one of the hostages down to his underwear, shot him in the head, and threw his body into the center courtyard.

When the remaining two hostages realized that their own survival was unlikely, they tried to negotiate with a new twist of their own. They claimed that there were at least two prisoners in the facility that were placed there as secret informants. The guards would be willing to identify them if their own lives could be spared. But after being physically beaten and held at gunpoint, the guards gave up the names of the two moles without any assurance of protection.

Within a few minutes the armed prisoners walked across the inner atrium, identified the traitors, and shot them both at point blank range. When the outside guards heard the additional gunfire, they assumed that all the hostages had just been killed, so they rushed in and began firing their rifles at the cell where the hostages were being held, killing several prisoners that were standing outside that cell. What they did not know was that the armed prisoners had temporarily moved to the other side of the prison, and their new line of sight left the guards as sitting ducks. The prisoners returned gunfire, and two more guards were killed before the others could retreat once again to safety outside of the secured doors.

The revolt would last four more days, with the occasional exchange of teargas and gunfire. But never any meeting with the Warden. The impasse finally ended when the prisoners had run out of ammunition. As the smoke cleared, there were 10 dead prison guards, 32 dead prisoners, and numerous inmates that were wounded.

Who knows how many lives could have been spared that week if those involved would have chosen to dialog rather than debate. Discuss, rather than argue and threaten. Prison conditions remained deplorable at many such facilities across America. It would be another eight to ten years before needed changes would begin to take place. Amazingly, those improvements ultimately came about because someone from the White House staff ended up in prison. But that's another story for a later time.

Binge drinking was a frequent problem at any university, and CU certainly had its share. Three fraternities lost their charter in the fall of '71 because of frequent arrests for disturbing the peace, or under-age drinking. The University's Administration was not proud of the fact that Playboy Magazine consistently listed this school as one of the top three party schools in the country. Yet they agreed to student's demands that fall to provide co-ed dorms, which only entrenched that reputation. (An amusing note in this transition was that girls living in those men's dorms used their decorative touch to plant flowers in the urinals.)

There were some harmless forms of rebellion that even provided amusement or entertainment. Homecoming carried an annual tradition of a parade of floats, carefully constructed by each of the sorority houses. But this fall no sorority member was nominated to be Homecoming Queen. In a last-ditch effort to have someone wear the crown, the school mascot was nominated. That happened to be a 700-pound female buffalo named "Ralphie." Homecoming was a smashing success that year, although it was difficult for the queen to keep the crown on her head. It is likely the only time in American history that a Homecoming queen ate her entire bouquet of flowers.

"Streaking" was another amusing form of innocuous campus rebellion. The fad had become a national phenomenon. At first some individuals chose to run naked through a classroom just to disrupt the class. Those that wanted a bigger audience streaked through the Student Union, or across large portions of the campus. Another popular choice was running naked on a public street for several blocks, just to amuse the traffic.

One evening more than 200 CU students – including men and women – decided to enjoy a "group streak." Their run took them through the campus, screaming with delight as they jogged past classrooms, faculty offices, and the administration center. To add some adventure, they entered the Student Union and took turns getting some food or asking for a cup of ice water from the cafeteria staff. Most of the kitchen workers just chuckled as they served everyone glasses of water. One attractive coed behind the counter asked if she could take her "dinner break". She stepped from behind the counter, stripped naked, and joined the bouncing bodies as they headed off to other points of the campus. Someone snapped a picture before they left, which appeared on the front page of the local paper the next day.

If there were a competition for "audience size" the 2nd place trophy must go to the two young men who streaked across the football field at half-time in front of 55,000 cheering fans. Before security guards could corral them, they ran through another exit and disappeared into the maze of campus buildings adjacent to the stadium. But 1st place would be awarded to a young man who managed to wind his way past back-stage security at the 46th annual Academy Awards in Hollywood, and raced across the stage wearing nothing but a smile. Millions of viewers joined host David Niven in a moment of laughter as he adlibbed about the unexpected guest's "shortcomings."

Ah, the carefree days of youth.

The subject of drug abuse and police corruption gained national attention on October 18th. After two years of secret investigation, the Knapp Commission announced their findings, which shocked all of America. In the city of New York, more than 50% of all police officers on the city's drug task force were "dirty", taking cash under the table from the drug trade. Citizens were baffled, wondering how law enforcement could become such a large part of the problem when they had been hired to be part of the solution.

Frank Lucas was an African American who chose to circumvent the established drug trafficking which had been controlled exclusively by the Mafia. He set up his own elaborate system for packaging and delivering heroin that was twice as potent for half the price. He even flew to Thailand and Cambodia to establish direct relationships with his sources. Within months he had taken over the city heroin market, and was personally netting more than $1 million per month.

His "empire" included several night clubs, a large network of prostitutes, and several legitimate businesses – such as auto repair or dry cleaners – to serve as the "fronts" for his distribution. The majority of the city's police and detectives were also receiving monthly cash payments to look the other way.

When Lucas was finally arrested and convicted, he received a sentence that would far exceed his lifetime. He then negotiated a new deal with the judicial system, and agreed to become an informant for the police if he could receive a reduced sentence. He had already destroyed thousands of lives – not only those that became addicted to the drug itself, but those that became addicted to the extra cash they received in exchange for their jobs and their integrity.

Frank Lucas was able to survive because he never became a "user" himself. Hollywood later chronicled his life in the movie *"American Gangster."* It demonstrated once again that the only winners were those who never became enmeshed in those drugs in the first place.

Every city in America now had to investigate its own police and detective forces. Drugs had far more power than people ever imagined. And if it could happen that extensively in New York City, it could happen anywhere.

By late fall, President Nixon was beginning to lay the groundwork for his re-election campaign in the coming year. He knew that as the incumbent, he could use his present position to great advantage. On October 29th, he tried to do so in the role of Commander-in-Chief. At a White House briefing, he enthusiastically announced an immediate reduction of more than 20% in the number of U.S. troops in Viet Nam. That would lower the American head-count there to 196,000, which was the fewest in the past 5½ years.

The President hoped for a "standing ovation" as a national response. Instead, reactions were tepid. Was the glass half full, or half empty? Yes, it was a step in the right direction, but it meant that there were still 196,000 men risking their lives in a war that fewer and fewer Americans really believed in. The general public was unimpressed.

Nixon soon realized he would have to do much more – whether it be legal or illegal – to achieve another term in office. Nothing was going to stop him from getting there.

Tom was notorious for betting a lot of money from time to time when playing pool at the Golden Cue. He also was known for betting a lot of money from time to time playing poker when he could find a worthwhile game. But on Thursday, December 30th, Tom made the biggest bet of his life . . . by betting his entire future on a verbal promise from the White House.

Tom had only one semester left on his school deferment with the military draft. Because his birth date had the misfortune of being drawn with a very low number in the lottery system, it was a guarantee that he would immediately be drafted the day after his school deferment expired and his allotted eight semesters were done. But good fortune – or Divine intervention – smiled on Tom that chilly December day.

A very successful Wichita businessman by the name of Bill Graham had been in Boulder to meet with Tom's father. When their business was completed that morning, Bill needed a ride back to Stapleton International Airport in Denver. Since all the bus lines and shuttles were running a minimal schedule during that holiday break period, standard choices for rides to the airport were closed. At the last minute Tom's father asked Tom if he could provide a big favor by driving Mr. Graham to the airport on short notice. That 35-minute ride would forever change Tom's life.

Tom had recently traded in his Corvette Z-28, and now had a new Mustang Cobra. He looked forward to any excuse that could get his new car out on the highway. Once they had exchanged pleasantries in the car, Tom and Bill rode silently for several miles. Then Bill broke the silence with an unexpected question.

"So, Tom," he queried, "what is your status with the draft?"

"Well, I still have a 2-S school deferment," he answered, "but I'm in my senior year, so it runs out next June."

Bill studied Tom for a moment, and then continued. "That's most interesting," he said. "My son is in virtually the exact same situation back at Wichita State. And we have been following this very carefully." He paused to pull out his pack of cigarettes.

"Smoke?" he asked. Tom gladly obliged, and opened the ashtray for both of them to use.

Bill spoke with quiet authority, and Tom was quickly transfixed. "I don't know if you have paid attention to the news lately," Bill said as he stared ahead, "but here is what's happening. The Paris Peace Talks have struggled to make any tangible headway in finding a conclusion for the Viet Nam War. So in a step of negotiating in good faith, the U.S. has offered to suspend completely the military draft for the first 90 days of this next year. They are now waiting to see if the North Vietnamese will respond in kind."

Bill paused, as if that was profound. Tom shook his head and blurted out, "So, what's the big deal about that? I already have a deferment that goes for the next 5 or 6 months."

"No, no, here's the point," Bill said calmly. "The way this draft lottery system works, you can only be "at the front of the line" for 90 days as far as the Draft Board is concerned. If you are 1-A for 90 days and are not drafted, in essence your turn would be done, and you would then fall into a secondary category. A new wave of young men with numbers from 1 to 365 would move to the front. From that point on you could only be drafted if there were a national emergency where every possible person in the entire lottery system would need to be called up."

He dragged on his cigarette a moment before explaining further. "Here is what my son and I have decided," he said, pointing his finger at Tom. "We felt the smart move was for him to go to our local Draft Board office and voluntarily cancel his 2-S school deferment this week. That way, next week he will enter 1972 at the very top of the list – but only for the next 90 days – with a 1-A draft status. So if there truly is no draft for 90 days as the U.S. has proposed, he is free and clear. Granted, if our government reneges on that promise before those 90 days are up, my son is screwed and will get drafted right out of school. But we figured that it was a sure thing that my son is going to be drafted anyway on the day after he graduates this spring. So we decided it was worth the risk."

Now Tom was the one staring quietly at the road ahead. *Could it really be that easy?*, he thought, as his mind raced a thousand miles per hour. *A simple, legal way to put the imminent draft in his rear-view mirror! Permanently!*

"Well, it's up to you, of course," Bill added. "But I hope you give it some thought. Today happens to be the last day you could do that, since the Draft Board offices are closed tomorrow for the holiday weekend, and next Monday will be too late since we will be into January already."

Tom tried to stay focused on driving, but his mind was totally elsewhere. A few minutes later he dropped Bill off at Stapleton Airport, shook hands, thanked him, and returned home. His driving speed increased the closer he got to Boulder. He didn't have time to talk this over with his parents. He didn't take the time to stop for his usual drink at Tulagi's. Instead, he drove straight to the Draft Board office, nervously explained his intent, and signed the cancellation form for his 2-S deferment. He beat the deadline by one hour. He was now classified as 1-A as of December 30th, which meant from this moment on he was at the very top of the draft list entering 1972. He had just bet his life on a verbal promise from the President of the United States, who was reputed to be a frequent liar. This was either the smartest or the dumbest thing he had ever done. He just had to hold his breath for the next 90 days.

It was an exceptionally cold December morning, almost too cold for snow to fall. "Deputy Dawg" had spent a miserable night trying to contend with the elements. He had broken into another cabin in Boulder Canyon, but it served as little more than a windbreak since there was no available source of heat. He even attempted to use a mattress as an extra blanket, but it was too clumsy to be helpful.

As daylight broke through the frost-covered aspen trees, he decided he would hitchhike up to Nederland, and purposely get arrested again so that he could get a warm bed and a little food at the Nederland jail. Once he got to the shoulder of Boulder Canyon road, it took less than two minutes to catch a ride, because that morning every driver felt badly for any person that had to be standing outside in the extreme frigid air.

His ride was kind enough to drop him off in front of the Nederland grocery store. Deputy Dawg may have been the first customer of the day, and the grocery store manager was still opening up the cash registers. "Good morning," Deputy Dawg said as he approached the grocer. The clerk cringed a bit as he studied the hippie's unkempt shoulder-length hair and tattered clothes. But his forced smile quickly turned to a frown as Deputy Dawg continued. "In a minute," he stated very matter-of-factly, "I'm going to try to shoplift a whole bunch of crap, so you might want to call the police right away, and get it over with."

At first the grocer wasn't sure if this filthy-looking hippie was actually serious or not. But when Deputy Dawg grabbed four or five random things from the first shelf and calmly headed for the exit, the clerk ran for the phone. It took Marshall Forbes almost ten minutes to get there, yet the officer was surprised to find Deputy Dawg still pacing back and forth in front of the grocery store waiting for him.

This was a hippie that the Marshall had arrested several times in the past, and he was recognized right away. "DAMMIT, Dawg," the Marshall said with a scolding voice as he got out of his police car, "what are you up to now?"

Deputy Dawg did not try to hide his discomfort. "Hey man," he replied through chattering teeth, "I stole this stuff so I guess you need to arrest me again, right?"

The Marshall shook his head in disbelief. Too often he had arrested hippies and taken them down to the Boulder jail in hopes of getting rid of them, only to see them back in Nederland later the same night. He knew Dawg just needed a warm bed and a good meal. With a sense of frustration he opened the back door of his car, and let Dawg get in. *This is not what I went to law enforcement training for*, he thought. As they drove back to the police station, the Marshall let himself get angrier and angrier. *This is not what tax payers should be providing — a free Bed & Breakfast to these hippie drug-head bums that don't make an effort.'*

Deputy Dawg willingly entered the Nederland jail cell for the fourth or fifth time, and scarfed down the modest food that was later offered to him. Marshall Forbes went about his other tasks for the rest of the day, but seethed with increasing measure every time he looked at the disgusting guest sleeping in his jail cell.

The winter sun had set before 5 p.m., so it was quite dark outside when the Marshall got up from his desk and put on his coat to head home for dinner. But he paused as he got to the station door, and instead turned back to his desk, took a small pistol out of the lower drawer, and then went back to the jail cell. "Hey Dawg," he said, with an artificial smile, "gimme' your hands. We're goin' for a little ride."

Deputy Dawg seemed confused, but reached his hands through bars so that he could be handcuffed again. Once they got into the officer's car, he broke the silence. "So what's up? Where are we going?" Dawg asked.

The Marshall took a moment to answer. Finally he looked into his rear-view mirror so that their eyes could meet. "You know, Dawg . . . I'm sick and tired of your kind . . . coming around here over and over, and just making trouble for us." He squinted with a greater sense of conviction as he continued. "I don't want you around here . . . so I'm taking you to a place where you won't come back."

Deputy Dawg wasn't sure what that was all about, but it clearly made no sense when they stopped at a small road construction site about three miles south of town. A Boulder County road crew had just finished putting in a new box culvert to accommodate a small stream that ran under the highway. Now all that remained on this project was for their back-hoes to refill and pack the dirt around the culvert.

"So, what are you doing?" Dawg anxiously asked, as the Marshall pulled him from the back seat.

"Just shut up!" the Marshall replied, as they walked to the edge of the road, and then slowly side-stepped their way down the steep embankment next to the culvert. Once there, the Marshall forced Deputy Dawg to his knees, and placed the pistol at the back of his head. *'I'm doing this for the good of my country, I'm doing this for the good of my country,'* the Marshall kept telling himself. *'And I'm doing this for the good of our community, too.'*

The echo of the fired bullet had long dissipated before it reached the ears of any other human being. Rushed with adrenaline, the Marshall almost forgot to remove the handcuffs from the lifeless body. He retrieved a small shovel from the trunk of his car, and covered Deputy Dawg with a couple of feet of loose gravel and road material. He then quickly checked for any other remaining evidence before getting back into his car and driving home.

The next day the construction crew unknowingly finished the job. As they filled in the final touches of road material around the culvert, they created a 22-foot grave that would never be disturbed. Only one angry law enforcement officer would ever know the full story of what was buried there.

Daniel Ellsburg

Civil Rights march

Marshall Renner Forbes

Jim Morrison / the Doors

CHAPTER 9

"1972 – TREATING A TERMINAL PATIENT"

"If you listen you can hear it
. . . all the signs are right this time.
You don't have to try so very hard,
If you live in this world
You're feelin' the change of the Guard."

- Steely Dan

Women managed to take center-stage throughout 1972 in every possible facet of American life. In spite of the vast diversity of their roles, the one common thread was that women were now taking ground-breaking steps which had previously been considered exclusively ruled by men.

In January Shirley Chisholm became the first Black Congresswoman to announce her candidacy for President. Like Margaret Chase Smith before her, the news media tried to "puff" the novelty of the story for a while, but her party gave her little room for any traction. Yet the brief sound bite was a psychological lift for black women and white women alike.

The Boston Marathon was traditionally the most prestigious long-distance race on American soil. In 1972 the planning commission announced for the first time that women could register to run in that race. It had taken five years of petitioning by Kathrine Switzer and her friends to get a favorable response from the Boston Athletic Association. It was a monumental step for equality of all women in the world of sport.

Anna Mae Hays had recently been named the military's first female to be promoted to the rank of General. She had previously served as a nurse in WWII and set up military hospitals during the Korean War. At the conclusion of her promotion ceremony, General Westmoreland not only gave her the shiny silver star insignia for her uniform lapel, he also gave her an awkward kiss on her lips. Although he claimed it was the new protocol for congratulating female generals, it was clear that the military was not comfortable with this breakthrough for women.

The women's movement, under the leadership of Gloria Steinem, gained the legal rights to re-issue the Wonder Woman Comic Books. They used the symbolic image of Wonder Woman as a standard for strength, power, and equality for women, and even adapted her character to become an activist for additional women's rights.

In the spring, Angela Davis was released from prison. Her freedom demonstrated a two-fold advancement for women – African American women celebrated her leadership as an activist, and White women celebrated the demonstration of a woman receiving equal treatment from the judicial system.

Linda Lovelace gained notoriety for women in yet another arena. She played the lead role in a breakthrough movie called *"Deep Throat."* Prior to this movie, pornography was associated with sleeze, only to be shown on low-rent back-street screens. In an unplanned merger with the sexual revolution now going mainstream, *"Deep Throat"* established a new genre of "porn chic" movies. Unlike earlier stag films, this included a serious plot line and the highest quality of background music mix. For some, Lovelace was seen as a celebrity instead of a cheap sex object, expressing the cultural phenomena of the legitimacy of any sexual experience.

The movie went viral. Both male and female ticket holders waited in lines going around the block – even for the mid-day showings. Voices of opposition in some states tried to declare the illegality of the movie based on state obscenity laws. But that confrontation only seemed to accelerate the demand and success for the movie. In a few months, Linda Lovelace starred again in *"The Devil In Miss Jones"*, which surpassed *"Deep Throat"* in both attendance and financial success.

Not all women celebrated her success as true progress. Understandably so. But women were definitely making a name for themselves nonetheless in all areas of American culture.

The week of February 21 was truly historic in all the annals of American politics. Richard Nixon was desperate for a political win of any kind. The Viet Nam war was a quagmire, and continued to produce greater and greater protests against the country's military presence in southeast Asia. The economy was sliding from bad to worse, and his program for a "wage and price freeze" did nothing to curtail the rate of inflation.

Thanks to the secret arrangements by Secretary of State Henry Kissinger, Nixon got his much needed "win" this week. He and his wife, Pat, flew on AirForce One to China to meet with Chairman Mao and other key leaders in Beijing, seeking to normalize U.S. relations with China. There had been no formal communication between China and the U.S. for more than 25 years, and no diplomatic ties whatsoever.

Even though Chairman Mao was severely ill, he personally spent two hours in a private conversation with Nixon. Mao knew that the visual statement to his subordinates was far more important than any specifics they might talk about. It indicated that he too wanted to pursue this international relationship because of what it might mean for his own country.

Other elements of the trip were simply secondary. As honored guests, Richard and Pat Nixon visited a few Chinese schools, hospitals, and factories, driving through the busy streets of Beijing, slowly weaving their way through thousands of smiling pedestrians and bicycle riders. (One item of particular interest was not discovered until they had returned to the White House a week later. Upon studying the satellite footage of their motorized tour in China's capital city, it was apparent that several hundred bicyclists would smile as they rode past the President's limo, then go behind a wooden barricade, quickly ride ahead about 100 yards, then re-enter the main street and ride past the limo once again. It was a pattern that was repeated throughout the day in an attempt by the Chinese government to show a throng of happy faces as the norm for their local culture, proof that the Chinese urgently wanted to make a great first impression.)

Without question this was Richard Nixon's shining moment during his six years in office, and far exceeded his goals for the trip. The President wanted to have an image with the American voter as an effective international leader. It could solidify his re-election efforts before the real campaign even began. He also hoped to create a wedge between China and the USSR, as well as a commitment that China and Taiwan could peacefully coexist. He got all that and more.

The breakthrough from this initial dialog awakened a sleeping giant. China slowly began to enter the 20th Century, and unleashed its vast population to become a manufacturing juggernaut for the benefit of the free world. Capitalism slowly became a part of the Chinese economy, and the cross-section of the entire continent shifted. Modernization of their cities produced such an economic boom that it ultimately shifted the balance of the world banking system.

Richard Nixon basked in that singular success for the rest of his life. Every President should have his moment in the sun.

By now, drug use was commonplace for anyone under the age of 30. *Time Magazine* identified Boulder as one of the busiest hubs for drug usage anywhere in the country. Every restaurant and bar in town had a "quiet corner" for those patrons that wanted to do drugs. Extensive experimentation helped people find what suited them, based on the desired effect, the cost, and the relative availability.

"Blow", or cocaine, was the most expensive, going for $80-$100 per gram, or $2800 per ounce. When inhaled into the sinuses, it provided an enormous physical rush for several hours, but because of its high cost was limited to individuals with ample cash on hand. It became the drug of choice for rock musicians and other wealthy celebrities. These artists claimed that activities such as creating new music or having sex were greatly enhanced when on a coke high. Cocaine was often "stepped on" or "cut", meaning it was diluted as it moved down the supply chain to the final end user.

LSD (lysergic acid diethylamide), or simply "acid", was the standard hallucinogenic drug of the time that sent users on a "trip", leaving a person's mind stimulated for a few hours while in a state of heightened awareness. It was usually taken in pill form, on small pieces of blotter paper, embedded in tiny "window panes" of gelatin, or it could be a liquid drop served on a cube of sugar. "Orange Sunshine" was the most common acid available, and was purchased in five to ten units at a time. Mescaline – known to some as "Peruvian Marching Powder" – was a milder version of acid, and was also easy to find.

Similar hallucinogenic substances have been used by humans for hundreds of years. Native Americans, for example, had used the peyote plant in religious ceremonies for its mind-expanding properties. "Magic mushrooms" (psilocybin) could be inexpensive, but could also be risky. The best ones offered a mild hallucinogenic ride for three to six hours, but eating the wrong mushroom could make a person sick. PCP (phencyclidine), or "angel dust", was also a popular hallucinogen, and was versatile in that it could be taken as a pill, snorted, or "fired up." Long-term use, however, proved to be both addictive and permanently mind-damaging.

Heroin was the hard-core choice, for people that wanted a complete escape. Injected by a needle directly into a vein in its liquid form, snorted, or smoked, it simultaneously offered extreme exhilaration and extreme risk. Addiction was certain with continued use, and because consistent potency was impossible to manage, heroin was responsible for the majority of overdose deaths.

Speed (methamphetamine) became very popular on college campuses, particularly during finals week. This "pick-me-up" pill accelerated the heart rate, and could keep a person awake for 60 hours without the need for sleep. "Soapers", "Quaaludes", and some eastern drugs such as Secanol had an opposite effect, leaving a person feeling like dead weight, or "as limp as a dishrag" for a couple of hours. Originally these extreme muscle relaxants or depressants were legally taken by football players following a strenuous game. Eventually they became the precursor to common date rape drugs.

Far and away the most popular drug was marijuana. It carried many other names, such as "Mary Jane", "weed", Ganja", "grass", "pot", "Jay", "roach", and at least 1000 others. Smoked in the form of small cigarettes, it was relatively inexpensive, it created a mellowing sensation, and it greatly reduced any sense of pain, yet seemed to have very little addictive properties. Users described it as a "mental buzz or fog", or a profound sense of relaxation. Avid users found other creative means of enjoying this drug, such as baking the marijuana leaves into a brownie recipe. Others claimed that inhaling the smoke through a water-pipe, or "bong", provided a faster and longer-lasting buzz.

In future years there would be greedy scientists that would secretly become involved in carefully manipulating some of these drugs in order to enhance the performance of professional athletes. Enormous businesses developed for ways respectively to detect or mask illegal drugs in an athlete's body. Major league baseball, cycling, and track & field would be particularly marred by this pharmaceutical phenomena. The integrity in professional football, wrestling, and weightlifting would also be forever diminished by illegal steroids. Individual athletes as well as entire countries would be banned from the Olympics because of repeated drug usage to give themselves a competitive edge.

Debates would rage for decades regarding the advisability of legalizing any of these drugs. But for the early '70's the government, the FDA, and the general public did not understand the need or benefit of any of these drugs, and thus continued to insist that they all remain illegal. The resulting "war on drugs" would prove to be impossible for law enforcement to contain fully.

In February the Paris Peace talks took a bad turn. In spite of the U.S. offer to eliminate the military draft, North Viet Nam walked out of the talks on the 24th. After repeated attempts to renew any peaceful discussions, the U.S. delegation felt they had no recourse but to renew the military draft at an aggressive rate. But they waited to do so until April 1st, in order to honor their initial offer of a 90-day reprieve. America's image and credibility might matter in the coming weeks as negotiations continued.

As that time-window of a 90-day moratorium of the draft expired, Tom was ecstatic with his good fortune. His gamble of cancelling his school deferment just three months ago had actually paid off, and he was now virtually exempt from the risk of any military duty. Only a complete national emergency would be able to get him.

To celebrate, Tom and his girlfriend asked two other couples to go with them on a three-day ski weekend in early April to Vail. One of the other women had the use of her parents' condo almost any time she wanted, so that made the deal even better. The ideal spring snow conditions caused everyone's anticipation to increase like the altitude as they drove up Interstate 70.

Everything in Vail was glorious that weekend. After their second day of skiing, the three couples had a nice dinner and settled in around the condo fireplace, enjoying two more six-packs and sharing two joints that Tom had provided. In a short time everyone was feeling quite mellow. To this day nobody remembers exactly – or is willing to admit – who first suggested that they swap partners for the night, so that everyone would sleep with someone else.

At first, Tom's friend Jake objected. He honestly thought he was in love, and wanted to be faithful to his girlfriend. They had been living together for more than a year, and he was secretly considering a marriage proposal. But he was quickly outvoted, 5 to 1. When he realized that his girlfriend was OK with the idea, he shrugged his shoulders and quietly said, "OK, what the hell. Let's go for it."

The random selection process then had to be settled. The guys agreed that they would each put their cigarette lighters into a ski cap. The girls drew toothpicks of different lengths to determine in which order they would pull a lighter out of the hat. Tom's lighter was drawn third, but was selected by the most attractive of the three women, who happened to have larger than average breasts.

Tom felt that fate had generously smiled on him for the second time in one week. Everyone retired to bed with their new partner, and enjoyed the evening as assigned couples. The sexual revolution meant freedom of experimentation, and this particular night certainly fit that description.

In April, President Nixon and his National Security Advisor, Henry Kissinger, met in secret to determine the best strategy for the continuation of the Viet Nam War. They knew that the Presidential campaign would consume the summer and fall months, with the election to be held in November. There could be no hint of weakness before the American people that might cost them the office of the White House for four more years.

They finally agreed in private that the U.S. should allow the South Vietnamese government to fall to the communists, but only after the fall election. Consequently they had to develop a plan that could extend the war for a minimum of seven or eight more months. The first step of their two-fold strategy was to significantly increase the bombing of North Viet Nam, including supply routes as well as the capital city of Hanoi. Large B-52 bombers were sent on daily runs to wreak devastation on the countryside.

North Viet Nam responded with its own counter-strategy, which was a major military offensive into South Viet Nam on the ground. This ultimately became known as the "Summer of Flowers", to commemorate the enormous death toll that this took on their military forces. The Viet Cong were determined to win – no matter what the cost, or how long it might take.

The second step of Nixon and Kissinger's strategy was to place mines throughout Haiphong Harbor, which was the bay surrounding the North Vietnamese port of Hanoi, to prevent any Russian or Chinese ships from entering the harbor to re-supply the Viet Cong. The combination of these factors created a brief sense of the U.S. actually winning the war. Short-term momentum was suddenly on the U.S. side.

Nixon's favorable rating soared in the polls. He just had to hang on until November. He didn't fully realize that his biggest political opponent that summer was not the Democratic candidate that would be running against him, but rather the terminal "cancer" of his own character. The absence of integrity will eventually catch up with anyone. For the most powerful man in the world, this time-bomb was already ticking.

The daily protests on the University of Colorado campus carried a heightened pitch in May because of the B-52 bombings in North Viet Nam. Agitators with bull horns were yelling at students as they walked between classes, and insisting on handing out literature to everyone that came near their information tables. Occasionally they created enough congestion that some students were unable to get to their classes on time. The activists would become very angry with the more conservative students that just wanted to go to class, get their degree, and get on with life.

At first it only seemed that the anti-war activists just had a little more passion with their opinions, but would not act on those emotions. That assessment was wrong. Late in the afternoon on the 21st of May the vocal leadership left the lawn area in front of the Student Union, and galvanized a small group of about 50 people to go across the street and march through the small business district of "The Hill." Chanting "STOP THE WAR NOW!! STOP THE WAR NOW!!", they slowly made their way down the center of the street, so that no traffic could get through.

Tom happened to be inside the Golden Cue playing pool as the marchers moved past their windows and headed toward Tulagi's. "Holy crap!" someone yelled in the pool hall, "Let's go out there and join the march!" It looked like fun, so Tom dropped his cue stick ran outside with the others.

The novelty quickly picked up momentum, and students from nearby fraternities and sororities ran from their rooms to join the excitement. Store owners became very nervous, and called the Police. Even though law enforcement responded within minutes, by the time any officers arrived on the scene there were more than 1000 students milling in the streets, chanting slogans and jumping up and down.

Boulder Police had never been confronted with this size of challenge. Every available officer was dispatched to the area, and their radio calls were rather frantic at first. They certainly didn't want to start shooting people, but there were far too many students involved to think they could arrest everyone. Thankfully, the officers chose a strategy of "containment without interference." Police lined up elbow-to-elbow in full riot gear and created a human perimeter on the streets. Then they let the protesters continue their yelling. But if any additional students from the outside tried to join in the mayhem, police would not let them in.

The revelry continued for more than an hour without any major incident. To some students it just seemed like a large "pep-rally." No buildings were burned, no windows were broken. Finally police opened two fire hydrants and used fire hoses to disperse the crowd. For a brief moment students over-powered the police and turned one of the hoses on the policemen themselves. After a brief wrestling match, the officers regained control. The only arrest was one coed that took off all of her clothes, and had to be taken away for "indecent exposure." Several officers volunteered for that "service duty." As the crowd got bored with the random yelling and the wet clothes, they slowly began to disperse, and things soon returned to normal.

But a seed had been planted. Local anti-war protesters realized they had started something new, and needed to capitalize on the energy that had just been created. Throughout the night and into the next morning, word began to spread throughout the entire campus that a much greater protest march would begin the next day at 1pm. Nobody would want to miss this.

By noon the following day more than 3000 students were already waiting on the campus lawn, wondering what might happen. Sandra felt conflicted as she sat at her classroom desk, listening to activists outside who were going from classroom building to classroom building, yelling "GET YOUR ASS OUT OF CLASS. GET YOUR ASS OUT OF CLASS." While she certainly didn't feel that she supported the war, she did feel that she had an obligation to take her studies seriously and strive to get the best grades she could in her courses. In her mind – and many students like her – these protesters were just lazy. Her greater priority was getting her degree, so she chose to stay in class that day.

By 1 p.m. there were over 5000 students that had showed up. A few leaders began making announcements into their bull horns, inviting everyone to begin slowly making their way east through the campus. Occasional chants would begin, including "NO MORE WAR", or "STOP NIXON NOW."

There was no specific plan to such a spontaneous march, other than to move through the campus and hopefully continue to gain more and more participants. But by the time they reached the other edge of the campus 45 minutes later, more than 10,000 were involved. Tom and his friends felt empowered, like this might make a meaningful statement to anyone who could watch this on the news. They were suddenly a part of something much bigger than themselves.

Then events took a very unexpected twist. When the marchers reached the far edge of the campus, most assumed they would turn around and walk back from where they had come. But the leaders kept walking east another block, directly on to Highway 36, which was the major traffic artery between Boulder and Denver. Cars careened to a stop or pulled onto the shoulder of the road. The giant mass of bodies continued to pour on to the high-speed highway as if they had found a new residence. Announcements over the bull horns asked participants to find a place on the highway and have a seat. All four lanes were immediately closed off, covered with a wave of humanity at least 400 yards long. It was now impossible to get in or out of Boulder by this route. A gas station on the corner abruptly closed and padlocked all of its doors at 4pm so that no students could steal or damage any of their items on the shelf.

Law enforcement was over-whelmed, and frantically called Denver Police for assistance. Boulder's police vehicles were useless, so policemen were on foot, trying to arrest a few of the ringleaders. If they used a smoke bomb or tear-gas, the protesters just threw it back at the police. Ryan had just recently returned from his tour of duty in Viet Nam, and happened to be riding into town on his motorcycle that afternoon. When he saw the massive crowd, he got off of his bike and tried to find a vantage point where he could watch. Instead, because of his military jacket, he was mistaken as a key agitator by one of the police officers, and arrested. He spent the night in a Denver jail before anyone would listen to his story, and he was then released.

After a few hours, students began to rotate out of the mob to briefly go back to their dorm room to get some food for everyone, or make a run to a fast-food restaurant. Others gathered a little firewood, and built a few small fires in the middle of the highway. Those fires likely may have saved lives during the night, because some cars would otherwise be traveling too fast to stop in the middle of a darkened highway. Eventually the Highway Patrol placed a few flares a mile down the road, and closed the highway to any vehicular access near Boulder.

For many students – including Tom – this was their most significant protest of the entire war. But what a memorable scene it was. The CU student body kept the highway closed for almost 48 hours. National news carried photos of students huddled under blankets when the temperature dropped during the night. Hundreds of local citizens stopped by to witness firsthand what was happening. Sometimes there was singing, sometimes chanting anti-war slogans. Sometimes a person would try to give an extemporaneous speech on the coming new world order.

Ultimately tear-gas was used to disperse the crowd, and students peacefully returned to their dorms. It felt good to get back to a comfortable bed anyway. But Boulder had made another national statement. This was no ordinary war. This was not politics as usual. And America was growing more and more restless with the need for an acceptable resolution. Something had to give.

May 15th witnessed another would-be political assassination. Alabama Governor George Wallace was campaigning once again for the office of President. His singular message of racial separation and the elimination of mandatory school busing was gaining more and more traction as white people in northern states grew tired of the marches, sit-ins, boycotts, and riots. He had won five states outright in the previous election, and this time the early polls actually showed him running neck-and-neck with any of the other leading Democratic candidates in the primaries.

During a routine campaign stop in Maryland, several rifle shots were suddenly fired. Wallace crumpled to the stage floor, along with two of his campaign staff. Although none of the men were killed, Wallace's bullet wounds left him in critical condition, and paralyzed from the waist down. The next day, as he clung to life in his hospital bed, he won the Democratic primaries in Maryland and Michigan. Clearly he was now the party front-runner. Racial hatred was winning.

But his recovery was excruciatingly slow. It was three months before he was released from the hospital, confined to a wheelchair for the rest of his life. His campaign efforts came to a standstill. He returned to Montgomery and slowly faded from public life. No other candidate picked up the mantle of his message, and the segregationist movement faded with him.

Wallace was a microcosm of the southern mindset, with a deep racial prejudice that had festered for 200 years. Over a lengthy amount of time during his forced retirement, he finally began to see the fallacy of his thinking. Twenty years after his final Maryland campaign speech, he invited civil rights leaders to his office in Alabama. Sincerely seeking reconciliation, he asked for their forgiveness. He apologized for the many roadblocks to equality that he had helped to assemble. And – in the spirit of Martin

Luther King – he was forgiven.

Yes, change was coming to America. Sometimes just one heart at a time.

Frank Wills was content to hold a very boring job. He was an introvert that really preferred not to work in close proximity with other people. As the night-watchman at the Watergate Building in Washington, D.C. he could often times work his entire shift without seeing more than two or three people. And even if he did, he was thankful that he was not necessarily obligated to have a conversation with them. His daily goal was to punch in and punch out on the company time-clock, and then quietly return to his modest home. In his wildest dreams he could never have imagined that his name could become a house-hold word nationwide, or that he would be at the entry point for the greatest political scandal in the history of the United States.

Making his routine security rounds late one night in mid-June, he discovered two doors with tape carefully covering the door latches so that they would not lock when the door was closed. His first inclination was to search the building quickly on his own to see if anyone was there that should not be there. But his intuition told him this was too precise to be some juvenile prank, so he called the police instead, concerned that a serious burglary might be in progress.

Without turning on any sirens, three police cars responded, and proceeded to make a thorough search throughout the Watergate Building. The officers did not know that the Democratic National Committee had chosen to set up their campaign headquarters there. When the police reached the floor rented by the DNC, they discovered five men going through files and tampering with phones. Although cleanly dressed, none of the five burglars was able to produce a personal ID. The only pieces of paper in two of the men's pockets had the name of "Howard Hunt" on it, as well as a private phone number within the White House. Very strange.

All five were taken into custody. All five refused to talk. All five were photographed, finger-printed and held while those prints could be cross-checked for any previous criminal records. But there were no matches. Very strange indeed.

It took several days of investigation before the police realized this case held enormous significance. This had actually been the second break-in into this building by these men. Initially they had come three weeks earlier over the Memorial Day weekend, intending to set up multiple phone "bugs", and search the Democratic Headquarters' files for cash or any specific hints of campaign strategy. They had also photocopied numerous documents that might prove helpful for Nixon's campaign strategists. Because the initial phone bugs were not working properly, they had to come back on this night to correct the problem.

One of the five arrested was James McCord, who was employed that year as the Security Chief for the re-election commission of the Republican Party. He had previously been a CIA officer, and was an electronics expert. But the police still had no idea of the ultimate ramifications of this arrest. What was their motive or intention? It took months to understand fully.

Also arrested were: Frank Sturgis, who had served in the U.S. military, and then later served the CIA as an undercover operative; Bernard Barker, a citizen of Cuba and a CIA operative who had tried to overthrow Castro. Eye witnesses also linked him to the assassination of John Kennedy, because he was seen standing on the "grassy knoll" in Dallas at the exact time JFK was shot; Virgilio Gonzalez, another Cuban citizen who was an activist against Castro, and whose specialty was a locksmith; and Eugenio Martinez, a CIA operative that had also broken into the offices of Daniel Ellsberg's psychiatrist a year earlier, while looking for information that could destroy Ellsberg's character and credibility.

Behind the scenes, the two master-minds for this caper were E. Howard Hunt and G. Gordon Liddy. They both were currently employed as top campaign aides to Richard Nixon. Hunt was an officer in the CIA, and specialized in break-ins, clandestine operations, and dirty tricks. As a hobby, he wrote numerous spy novels, incorporating some of the secretive experiences he had seen or heard through his associations at the CIA.

Liddy was a lawyer, and former FBI agent. Acquaintances described him as a cold-hearted man with no soul. His methods of self-discipline were chilling. As a boy he hated the fact that he was afraid of lightening storms. So on one particularly stormy night he slipped outside, climbed a tree, and spent the entire night staring down the frequent blasts of thunder. By morning he no longer feared lightening. He also grew up with a hatred of rats. So one afternoon he trapped a rat, killed it with his bare hands, cooked it over an open fire, and ate it. That permanently eliminated his fear of rats. As an example of his "obsession with no limits", he even plotted to kill Jack Anderson, a syndicated newspaper columnist who frequently opposed the President. For Liddy, a worthwhile "end" could justify any "means."

President Nixon had recruited all of these men because he held a deep and intense hatred for the American media, which he felt was conspiring to oppose the war and trying to find ways to make him look bad. And he held a deeper disdain for those unknown persons within his own staff that were frequently leaking confidential information to the press. In an effort to stop those leaks, he personally empowered a few men that he referred to as his "Plumbers", for the expressed purpose of stopping those leaks.

The President authorized them to do whatever was necessary to get the upper hand with the press as well as with the Democratic Party, as long as it was not traceable back to the White House. At their discretion, they could do such things as tapping phones, stealing confidential documents, bribery, or other dirty tricks. More than $3,000,000 in cash was secretly held as a slush fund that was at their disposal. These kinds of choices had earned the President the nick-name of "Tricky Dick."

Other devious plans were already in place to undermine the upcoming Democratic National Convention in Miami. A yacht was chartered, staffed with a half-dozen prostitutes, stocked with ample amounts of food and liquor, all of which would remain on board as the boat was anchored off-shore. Key Convention Delegates would be invited to a private "reception" on the yacht, secretly photographed while having sex, and then later bribed for any helpful information they could provide at a later date. A classic example of "dirty tricks."

The day after the arrests at the Watergate Building, all the news outlets reported briefly on a "burglary" or a "break-in" at the DNC. Since no one was injured, and no property seemed damaged, the item seemed like minor news. There was no immediate connection to the White House. There was no awareness as yet of the national drama that was just beginning. But it was about to shake our political system to the core.

In late June Tom was invited by his friend, Larry, to go out to the Boulder Airport to go skydiving for the first time. The idea of such an adrenalin rush sounded great to Tom, so he agreed.

The local airport was quite small, and only handled single-engine or twin-engine prop planes. Drug runners used the airstrip every week because it was "off the radar" from the FAA, but convenient to the Boulder customer base. Typically there were less than ten take-offs or landings on any given day.

But when Tom and Larry arrived, the airport was abuzz with planes, cars, and FBI agents everywhere. "You don't have any weed with you today, do 'ya?" Tom quickly asked before they got out of the car. "No, I'm clean," Larry replied. "Well, then we've got nothin' to hide," Tom said. "Let's find out what the hell is going on."

As soon as they stepped out of their vehicle, two of the FBI agents immediately approached them and began asking several questions. The agents were friendly, but very focused. The FBI was scouring every small airport In the United States, particularly any airstrip that offered skydiving opportunities. Their objective was to ask every private pilot and every skydiver if they had any information on D.B. Cooper.

Less than a year ago Cooper had hijacked a commercial plane in a most daring manner. He held the passengers hostage until Federal agents brought more than $200,000. in cash on board. He then instructed the pilots to fly the Boeing 727 in a circular pattern over the Pacific Northwest for several hours, while the rear staircase of the plane remained open. At some unknown moment D.B. Cooper then parachuted out of the back of the plane, carrying the cash with him in a backpack.

The FBI had reason to believe that Cooper might be friends with other skydiving advocates, and also might have gravitated to Boulder because of the large hippie population that was living "off the grid." Tom and Larry had no such information to offer, and were soon allowed to proceed with their adventure of Tom's first jump. The unexpected interrogation combined with the successful skydiving trip made the day doubly memorable for Tom.

(As a follow-up, the D.B. Cooper incident remains the only unsolved air piracy crime in American history)

The summer months brought nothing but bad news from Viet Nam. In June a U.S. military plane accidentally dropped napalm on a small group of South Vietnamese troops and civilians. When a nine-year-old girl * realized her clothes and skin were on fire, she ripped the flaming cloth from her body and began running down a dirt road while totally naked and shrieking in pain. A news reporter happened to be walking with some American troops that were approaching that village, and captured that scene with his camera. The photo became known as "Napalm Girl", and was one of the most lasting images of the entire war. That single photo was attributed with raising anti-war sentiment across America.

(* The little girl's name was Kim Phuc Phan Thi. She would survive the war, although her back, arms and neck were covered so extensively with burn scars from that fateful day that her body could never sweat. Consequently she suffered lifelong pain and discomfort in the Viet Nam heat and humidity. Raised in the religion of Cao Dai, she believed all religions were equal, seeking any and all divine beings. It would be 13 more years before she would discover a source of forgiveness, and extend that forgiveness to those soldiers that destroyed her country, her village, and her personal health.)

Just one month later the news from Southeast Asia was even more pathetic. It was not the first time that a U.S. celebrity had traveled to North Viet Nam, but it may have been the most notable. In July actress Jane Fonda requested a visit, and the North Vietnamese government was quick to agree. They knew that publicized moments like this would help them to win the psychological edge in the war, and also could help to shift the negotiation process at the Paris Peace Talks.

News footage was taken of Fonda walking through the streets of the capitol city of Hanoi with their political leaders, smiling and visiting with some of the local merchants. She told her hosts that the U.S. POW's were guilty of war crimes for the bombing and killing of innocent civilians. She urged the North Vietnamese to hold out against U.S. imperialism. She was then taken to a military installation where she climbed on top of a large anti-aircraft gun and straddled the 16" barrel for a photo. That single image was able to polarize further Americans in their convictions regarding the war.

In a surprise move, her hosts also took her to a prisoner-of-war camp to meet some U.S. pilots in captivity, and to prove that they were being treated well. It was all a carefully scripted charade. When Jane Fonda was introduced to prisoner John McCain, he walked forward and shook hands with her. In that moment he secretly passed a small piece of paper to her, which contained a written description of the inhumane treatment that was actually taking place. It was a calculated risk on his part that seemed like an opportune step to improving their prison conditions, and possibly forcing a move toward their release, if she could just get that information to U.S. authorities when she returned home.

Instead, to the prisoners' utter shock and dismay, Fonda glanced at the note and then handed it to her hosts who were the Viet Cong guards. Within an hour after her departure from Viet Nam, the guards began to mercilessly torture those prisoners within an inch of their lives. When John McCain returned to the U.S. at the conclusion of the war the following year, he described in great detail his personal ordeal because of Fonda's betrayal. It was gut-wrenching for anyone to hear.

Many military Veterans were never able to forgive Ms. Fonda for her actions that day. They labeled her as a Communist and a traitor, and gave her the nickname of "Hanoi Jane." A few months later she married Tom Hayden, one of America's most vocal personalities in ending the war and opposing traditional values in the U.S. Together they continued to speak of their opposition to Washington and the war effort. But to her credit, when the war was finally over, she apologized deeply for her actions in North Viet Nam, and has tried since then to converse with U.S. veterans when given a chance. She admitted on numerous occasions that this particular day in Hanoi might have been the worst mistake of her life.

But this war was so ugly, and forced so many people to do or say things they would later regret.

Chess Club on any high school or college campus had typically been the exclusive turf for the student body nerds. But that standard profile changed in dramatic fashion this summer.

As a young boy, Bobby Fischer had become an American phenomenon in the chess world, winning national tournaments from the time he was just 13 years of age. He was the youngest person ever to win the U.S. championship, and youngest ever to become a candidate for Grand Master. He dropped out of high school at the age of 16, convinced there was nothing more of importance for him to learn, and focused almost all of his time on chess. He began to demand a chance to play for the World Championship, and finally got his wish in the summer of '72. The Russians had dominated this arena for decades, and Boris Spassky was now the current world title-holder.

After lengthy negotiations as to where to hold the contest, Reykjavik, Iceland, was chosen as the host city. The entire match was scheduled from July through September, consisting of 21 games, and a winner-take-all cash prize of $250,000. Each game was worth 1 point. If a particular game ended in a draw – which is quite common in tournament chess play – each contestant would receive ½ point.

Because of the heightened Cold War between the USSR and the USA, this match received unprecedented news coverage, and billed it as the "Match of the Century." It might as well have been called "Good Verses Evil." Daily updates were given front-page priority on all the national newspapers. Television's nightly news carried a lead story on any updates. As the match got underway, Spassky won the first game outright, and won the second by forfeiture because Fischer demanded they play in a different room of the hotel. But from that point on it was a downhill "crash and burn" for the Russian champion. He only won one more game out of the remaining 19, and was mentally crushed by this arrogant American who had not yet reached the age of 30. The final score was 12 ½ to 8 ½. Media's use of "Total Domination" would be an understatement.

Bobby Fischer was placed on the cover of *Sports Illustrated*, and was offered more than $5 million in product endorsements, all of which he declined. For a short time he was considered the most famous person in the world. Americans relished the satisfaction of any "defeat" of the Soviets because America desperately needed some kind of win to bolster the national psyche.

Fischer, however, became more and more outspoken in his rebellion toward American culture, and lived his life as a personal form of protest. He chose to reside outside of the U.S. because of its "military obsession and the evils of capitalism." He went "underground" for several years, refusing to pay any taxes to the IRS, and ultimately forfeited his world title years later for refusing to schedule a challenge match with another opponent.

Chess, on the other hand, exploded in worldwide popularity. During the next few years, participation in high school and college campus chess clubs throughout the U.S. more than tripled. Chess was suddenly cool, thanks to the free-spirited attitude of a genius nerd named Bobbie Fischer.

Tom decided it was time to make some noise. On a dare, he and a friend had hacked into the University of Colorado's main computer. They found they were able to create a bogus payroll for the entire campus staff, and had access to blank checks for the CU accounting department. They could have produced paychecks in any amount if they so chose. It was mischief – without a doubt – but could carry a prison sentence if Tom was ever discovered.

Once again, cooler heads prevailed. His older brother, Brian, was still focused on changing America. He convinced Tom to ignore that purposeless crime, and instead join him in Miami for the Democratic National Convention in mid-summer. It was of utmost importance that this political convention would produce a mandate to end the war immediately, and to stop the oppression from the hands of capitalism.

In early July Tom and two friends climbed into a VW van and headed to Miami, host city for the 1972 Democratic National Convention, which was held in the downtown section of the city. The gathering for this political mountaintop started with such optimism and excitement. In the Convention Hall, enormous portraits of John and Bobby Kennedy served as a backdrop to the stage, as a reminder of the great leaders that had recently been at the helm of their party.

The delegates from every corner of the country truly felt that this time the election was theirs for the taking. Americans seemed tired of the war in Viet Nam, and now the Democrats had the person and the platform to call for an abrupt end to that war in futility. Many Americans already hated the President, and even more felt he could not be trusted. The election should be in the bag. Yet is was New York's Mayor John Lindsay, on the other hand, who said, "Somehow this political party has a keen instinct for committing suicide." He may have been the singular prescient politician of the entire event.

This was the first political convention ever to debate abortion rights and gay rights for consideration on the official party platform. South Dakota Senator George McGovern was tabbed to be their presidential candidate. He had briefly run four years earlier following the assassination of Bobby Kennedy. And for the four years since then he had continued passionately to talk about the liberal positions that he felt were over-due for the American public – an immediate end to the war, complete amnesty for all draft-dodgers, decriminalization of pot, and absolute abortion rights for women. Many delegates at the Convention, however, felt that some of those party platform planks might be too aggressive or extreme for middle-America's voters to accept.

The convention floor was anything but unified on those issues. Governor Jimmy Carter led a "Stop McGovern" movement at the last minute. When it came time for McGovern to select his running mate for the ticket, more than 30 well-known Democrats said "No Thanks", including party leaders such as Hubert Humphrey, Ted Kennedy, Walter Mondale, and Edmund Muskie. McGovern finally got his "prom date" with Thomas Eagleton, Senator from Missouri.

Due to limitations of Convention space, and to accommodate new Convention rules that could make room for more McGovern delegates, the mayors from Chicago, L.A., Boston, Detroit, San Francisco and Philadelphia had to be removed from the convention floor. That did not help to generate any enthusiasm in those metropolitan areas. By the time the official delegate voting was complete, it was 3 a.m. At that late hour Eagleton and McGovern gave their acceptance speeches to a paltry audience that was a small fraction of those that had been listening six hours earlier. It was another historic example of not yet understanding the power of television, and thus the Democrats missed any chance for a "convention bounce" in the polls. Consequently McGovern's Convention message of "COME HOME, AMERICA" got off to a slow start.

As the ensuing campaign began to progress, Democrats continued to shoot themselves in the foot. All of the initial polls showed that McGovern would beat Nixon by a comfortable margin. But doubts began to surface that he was too tied to the ultra-radical voices that only ranted about ending the war – with or without honor. Republicans were able quickly to position McGovern as an evil extremist, as someone striving for "amnesty, abortion, and acid." It was much too far to the Left for the general American voter. The language of the conservative farmers throughout the Midwest was even more blunt. Bumper stickers surfaced which said "OUR COUNTRY WAS BUILT ON BLOOD, SWEAT, & TEARS. NOW McGOVERN WANTS TO GIVE IT TO HIPPIES, DRAFT-DODGERS & QUEERS." As a proud contrast, Republicans kept drumming their goal of "Peace with Honor."

Presidential candidate McGovern could not buy a break. Few celebrities strongly endorsed his candidacy. Barbra Streisand finally agreed to give a fund-raising concert at the Forum in L.A. because of her loyalty to the party. She packed the place out, with ticket prices ranging from $6 – $100. The gross was over $300,000., but by the time expenses were paid, only $18,000. was donated to the candidate's coffers.

Just three weeks into the campaign, the Democrats suffered another self-inflicted wound. It was revealed that several years earlier V.P. candidate Thomas Eagleton had taken electro-shock therapy and mental health treatment for clinical depression. With the associated risk of having a mentally unstable running mate, McGovern had no choice but to drop him from the ticket. His new VP of choice was Sargent Shriver. But the sudden appearance of instability on the Democratic campaign created a horrible public relations image that needed to be overcome.

An additional major self-inflicted wound was the discovery that George McGovern had secretly tried to negotiate with the North Vietnamese, asking them to withhold any definitive peace agreement until after he was in office so that he might bask in the glory of that success. That attempt at such a hidden process was seen as detrimental to current peace efforts, and possibly treasonous for interfering with those persons that were currently in office. A weak apology ensued.

The AFL-CIO was the biggest labor union in America, and traditionally represented the single largest block of Democratic voters. For the first time in the union's history, the leadership officially endorsed the Republican ticket, and encouraged their rank-and-file to vote likewise. It spelled the final death knell for the Democrat's campaign. On election night McGovern could not even carry his home state, and the final count in the landslide defeat showed that 49 states sided with Nixon. The lone state that kept the outcome from being a unanimous whitewash was Massachusetts.

As George McGovern would later say, "I tried to open the doors of the Democratic Party, and when I did, 20,000,000 people walked OUT."

August was a month of great momentum building for the Republicans. On the 12th of the month, the last ground troops were ordered to leave Viet Nam. American media gave over-time coverage on this historical marker. Even though U.S. fighter pilots were still on daily call to give air support to the South Vietnamese troops, this was a significant step toward having all military back on American soil. Psychologically it looked wonderful.

Less than two weeks later, the Republican Party held its National Convention in Miami Beach, just a few miles from where the Democrats had convened. This truly was a "Grand Old Party" as delegates reveled in the convention hall, waving signs that said "FOUR MORE YEARS" and "AMERICA – LOVE IT OR LEAVE IT." Richard Nixon was re-nominated in a near unanimous vote. This time the acceptance speech was aired at a time when far more viewers across the country were still awake to watch television.

Outside the Convention hall, more than 3,000 protestors gathered each day, striving to make a statement against the war. Police were not about to have a replay of what had happened in Chicago four years earlier, so they had a much stronger show of force from the moment the convention began. State Troopers and Federal agents were also on hand for back-up support. Tear gas was used as soon as protestors began to march around the building. A few windows were broken, more than 200 were arrested, at least two needed medical attention for broken arms, but nothing more serious occurred.

Coincidentally Bobby Seale was back in town as one of the demonstration leaders. He had just been released from prison for conspiracy and inciting a riot as his sentence in the Chicago 8 trial 3 ½ years earlier. As the self-appointed head of the Black Panther Party, he now needed the renewed visibility. He was able to lead the crowd in a chant: "One, two, three, four! We don't want your f----ing war!!" Accompanying him were several Viet Nam vets that were also voicing their opposition to the war.

Insulated from those external disruptions, the delegates inside were nothing but jubilant. This may have been the first such convention that was carefully scripted for television. Celebrities such as John Wayne made brief appearances on stage, and assured the crowd of their support for the Republican ticket. Women were also given a place on the platform – another "1st" for this convention. Anne Armstrong of Texas delivered the keynote address, and Pat Nixon became the first "First Lady" ever to give a speech at a Republican Convention. There would be no voter bloc that was over-looked this time.

Political strategists and "Committee to Re-Elect the President" (CREP) members tried to ignore the discouraging economic trends that confronted the average American family. They shook off the word "Watergate" as meaningless old news. They positioned all protesters as "anti-American." Their singular task was to make the general public look through their lens, and see the world from their vantage point. That image had to last for three months to get them through the election. Three months. Just three more months.

Internally, however, Republican leadership was troubled. They were being given minimal information at best as to what was really behind the Watergate story. While at the Convention, Senator Bob Dole began meeting privately with every state leader in the party, with just one universal question. "What do you know about this Watergate thing?" He – and a few others – had begun to smell a rat. Yes, politics can be an ugly game at times, and anyone can make a mistake in judgment from time to time. But Dole also knew that forthrightness was always the best option in order to avoid even greater collateral damage. He prayed that this would not somehow damage the Party that he loved so.

Normally the Olympics are seen as an international celebration, and a time to watch in amazement as athletes gather from around the world to compete at the highest levels in their respective sports. But this August the quadrennial festivities wrote a tragic chapter in the grand history of that event.

Just a few hours after the opening ceremonies, Palestinian terrorists took 11 Israeli athletes as hostages. The entire city of Munich, Germany, went on lock-down as the police tried to negotiate with the captors. The demands of these terrorists included the release of 234 Palestinian prisoners being held in Israel, as well as the provision of a commercial jet to fly themselves and their hostages to a neutral country.

Two of the Israeli athletes were killed in the hotel before the remaining entourage made their way to the Munich Airport. Once they arrived, local police tried to ambush the Palestinians on the tarmac, but the attempt was a disaster. When the Palestinians realized they were under gunfire, they quickly murdered the other nine Israeli athletes, and killed one German police officer. Five of the eight terrorists were also killed in the heavy gunfire, and the other three were taken under arrest.

The Olympic Games contestants forced themselves to continue in a state of shock. But the news got even worse just one month later. Other Palestinian terrorists hijacked a Lufthansa plane and demanded the release of those three surviving comrades from the Munich prison for their murders of the Israeli athletes. This time the German authorities complied, and no other civilians were killed. But terrorism had "won" for the moment, and in so doing raised the level of fear around the world.

In America, FBI agents now realized that activists could no longer be treated in a rational manner. All the rules of their FBI safety training needed to change. Any confrontation with groups such as the Weather Underground would now have to be done with the understanding that passionate radicals would be willing to sacrifice their own life as well as the lives of others for the sake of their cause. But police and FBI agents had never dealt with such opposition. While there were many opinions, no one really knew what to do. Chaos was still commonplace.

Richard was feeling the pressure. Having dropped out of high school at the end of his junior year, he certainly had no desire to try to enroll in a Community College just to avoid the draft. He knew he couldn't fake it. But he also had no desire whatsoever to get shipped off to Viet Nam. The draft board knew where he lived, and had recently plucked his best friend off the street and into the Army. Escaping to Canada seemed to be the logical choice.

He stuffed a few changes of clothes into a back-pack, withdrew every cent from his meager bank account, and left East L.A. on a prayer.

Hitchhiking was easy in California since hippies were constantly shuffling up and down the coast. But once he got into northern Washington, it was a little trickier. He had to convince a commercial truck driver to let him hide in the back of his cab as he crossed into British Columbia to deliver a semi load of fruit.

Vancouver was nicer than Richard had expected, and he was pleasantly surprised to see so many Americans who had already made the same choice that he did. The counter-culture presence was very evident, and within a few hours he had found a place to crash with other draft-dodgers.

Work was hard to come by, given that he had no passport. "Tommy C" was a local Canadian who befriended Richard and the other "California strays." "Tommy C" knew where they could get occasional work on the docks unloading cargo ships, and get paid in cash at the end of each day. Most days they were panhandling, hoping for enough spare change to get a meal or two. Other than a disdain for America's involvement in Viet Nam, the main thing that this circle of friends shared was a great love for smoking marijuana.

As the months passed, "Tommy C" and Richard developed a special friendship because they loved making everyone else laugh. No topic was off limits. They would play the role of a dog trying to describe another dog's pile of crap, or awkward mistakes while having sex. But their best material revolved around exaggerated experiences with marijuana. During amateur night at a couple of local clubs they stole the show. Their irreverence was exactly what the audiences wanted. So when a night-club manager offered them a paid gig, they realized they needed a stage name for their comedy duo.

Richard experimented with several ideas, but didn't want to sound like they had "sold out" to the typical main-stream entertainment styles. They finally decided to play it simple, and just go with their single names. Tommy's last name was Chong, and Richard would use his own nickname of "Cheech." Thus "Cheech and Chong" was born.

Their "pot-themed material" was an instant hit. Flaunting the law by celebrating marijuana as a routine part of daily life gave them a distinct reputation. Regular bookings flowed in from numerous places in western Canada. They recorded some of their best routines, and the album sold briskly in the U.S. as well. The hippie and counter-culture loved them as one of their own. In less than a year, by mid- 1972, they had the #4 selling comedy album.

Although they made a few movies in the coming years, including the cult-classic *"Up In Smoke"*, their image was forever cemented in the role as a couple of stand-up stoners who were high on life, high on free love, and always wanting to get high. Chong later spent almost a year in prison on a drug bust, paid a $20,000 fine and forfeited over $120,000 in assets. But the rebellion of the counter-culture community paid them well, and Cheech and Chong made a career out of celebrating doing things that were against the law.

The Washington Post had sky-rocketed into national recognition following their successful verdict from the Supreme Court regarding the printing of the Pentagon Papers. Now publisher Don Bradley wanted to take this newspaper into the stratosphere. He seemed to be the only news executive that smelled a big story circling the Watergate break-in. He and his wife had been the closest of friends with John and Jackie Kennedy. To a few of his co-workers he would admit that he had a liberal bias, and a deep-seeded hatred for Richard Nixon. But more importantly, he had an obligation to cover the news – and UNCOVER the news – when a story was ripe.

Bradley assigned two of his beat-reporters to begin researching the details of the Watergate break-in. Bob Woodward and Carl Bernstein were given free latitude to call or visit anyone that they felt might offer worthwhile information. One of their earliest phone conversations was most interesting. Because the written name and White House phone number of Howard Hunt was in the pockets of two of the Watergate burglars, they decided to give Mr. Hunt a call. To their amazement, he directly answered the number they called.

"Hunt . . ." the voice said at the other end of the line.

Bernstein swallowed and answered. "Yes, Mr. Hunt, this is Carl Bernstein at the Washington Post." He paused, but there was no reply.

"I was wondering, Mr. Hunt," he continued, "do you have a comment as to why two of the Watergate burglars had your name and number in their pockets?"

Again there was a pause before he answered. "Holy shit!!" the voice said, and hurriedly hung up the phone.

That unusual phone call made it clear that persons in the White House were somehow connected to the burglary, and that this could become a monster story. With regularity, publisher Bradley kept giving his reporters space in the paper to present their incremental steps of progress. It was a brush fire that was gaining momentum.

By early September, the term "Watergate" was becoming a national point of conversation, and suddenly took on new urgency. Howard Hunt, Gordon Liddy, and the five Watergate burglars were indicted by a federal grand jury. Public curiosity was growing rapidly, thanks to the "scoop" reporting from Woodward and Bernstein. They were blessed with some important clues coming from a man only known to them as "Deepthroat." This source proved to be very knowledgeable about the political layers in Washington, D.C., but for the time being refused to provide his true identity.

If the three of them met at all, it was late at night in a darkened corner of a multi-level parking lot, so that the reporters could only stare into the glare of a car's headlights, but were unable to see the person with whom they were talking. It seemed too suspicious at first, but every clue from "Deepthroat" proved to be accurate. The anonymous voice kept hinting that this burglary was no small-time job, but had connections into the White House, and possibly to the President himself. He repeatedly told them to "keep following the money."

In the Oval Office, desperation was beginning to set in. John Erlichman briefly considered crashing AirForce One with President Nixon and H.R. Haldeman on board, which might solve everyone's problems. Haldeman advised the President that he needed to have the FBI shut down any further investigation into the Watergate break-in. Nixon agreed, and instructed the CIA Director Richard Helms to tell the FBI Acting Director Patrick Gray to "stay the hell out of this." Their assumption was that because Patrick Gray was in a temporary position, he would consult with the Deputy Director of the FBI, Mark Felt. It was known that Felt was aggressive in seeking further promotions, and would undoubtedly comply with anything that the White House might ask of them.

What the President and his personal advisors did not know was that Mark Felt had a little more integrity than they did. They had no idea that Felt was feeling very conflicted with those instructions from the very top, and had secretly volunteered himself to be the "Deepthroat" source to the newspaper reporters. Like a victim stuck in quick-sand, every time the President or his staff in the Oval Office tried to wiggle, it only made matters worse. And now with every secretive conversation that might take place in the Oval Office, Nixon's sophisticated tape recording system was running.

In mid-September a call came in to Marshall Forbes' office in Boulder

County. Another family was telling him that hippies had broken into their cabin in Boulder Canyon, and were refusing to leave. It was a story that was recurring far too often. The Marshall's level of exasperation grew with every minute as he drove to the given address about three miles away.

As he pulled on to the property, three hippies were already strapping on their back-packs and leaving. The fourth stayed behind. The Marshall stepped out of his car, and unholstered his pistol.

"Do you think you folks belong here?" he asked gruffly, as he approached the front deck.

The first three – two men and a woman – continued their departure, and didn't bother to answer. They walked down the short driveway to the canyon highway, and thumbed a ride into Boulder. The other man walked back into the cabin, so the Marshall cautiously followed.

"Just quit harassing me, man," the young man said with a belligerent tone. "If I want to ---"

"OK, let's get something straight," the Marshall interrupted. "First, this is NOT your property, right?"

There was a long pause. "Hey. It's a free country, man," was the reply. Marshall Forbes shook his head. "I think you need to go for a little ride with me. I know you've done this sort of thing before, and it cannot continue."

The long-haired young man offered no resistance, willingly accepted being put into hand-cuffs, and slid into the back seat of the officer's car. The Marshall locked and closed the cabin door, picked up the backpack, and threw it into the trunk of the car before driving back to town.

It's pointless to try to talk sense to some of these hippie-freaks, he thought, as he drove up the canyon. *It's just hopeless.*

As the Marshall filled out the paperwork at the jail, the young man only gave his name as "Sunshine." No last name, no address, no employer, no emergency contact, and absolutely no respect. He refused to answer any of the other questions that were asked of him. The Marshall decided to let the young man sit in his cell while he went out for dinner. Throughout his meal, he let his anger continue to rise.

By the time the Marshall returned from the local diner, it was dusk. When he entered the jail, his guest was sleeping on the floor of his cell. "Hey," he said, trying to startle the young man, "I think you should get up. We're going somewhere else."

Sunshine wearily got to his feet as the Marshall unlocked the cell door. They drove up a dirt road to an old abandoned mine without saying a word.

Sunshine realized something was horribly wrong when he finally got out of the car, and noticed that the Marshall was holding a small-game rifle.

"What the ---" he stammered.

The Marshall stared at him for a second, as he took the gun off safety. "You and your kind are such WORTHLESS human beings," he muttered through gritted teeth.

Sunshine started to run without any idea of where he was or where he was going. The first shot went through his back and knocked him down. The second shot – at much closer range – went straight through his skull.

The Marshall calmly put the gun away, and quietly went to work. He dragged the lifeless body to the entrance of the old mine, removed the wooden barricade over the entrance, and shoved the body down the mineshaft. *I don't like doing this*, he kept telling himself, *but there is no other solution. It's for the good of this community.*

He made three more trips back and forth from his car, carrying 40-lb. bags of lye. He dumped the contents down the shaft as a means of covering the potential odors of a decomposing cadaver. *No one will be looking for this scumbag anyway,* he convinced himself.

Marshall Forbes had a difficult time sleeping that night. *I am just one man, confronted with a huge population of hippies. They have no purpose or direction. But this incident was not a realistic long-term solution.* And he tossed and turned some more.

The next morning he called one of his hunting buddies. "Ed," he said with a tone of urgency, "I need a favor." He slowly pulled a small-game rifle and an old pistol from the back seat of his car, and took a deep breath before he continued. "Ed, I need you to take these guns and hide them somewhere so that no human being will EVER find them." He gave Ed a stern glare. "I don't want you to ask any questions, and I don't want you to tell me where these guns end up. No one should ever know, OK? NEVER!"

Ed nodded and left. He complied with the Marshall's directive and never did ask any questions, although he did have some suspicions. Those suspicions were finally confirmed more than 40 years later when the retired Marshall was lying in a Denver hospital bed, losing his battle with a terminal illness. He gave a detailed confession to two of his closest friends. He had to clear his conscience before he met his Maker. Those terrible choices had haunted him all of his life, but he ultimately died with that burden lifted.

As the year 1972 came to a close, President Nixon's anger consumed him. Even though he had just won 49 states in the national election, his public support was now plummeting once again. Demands for an official investigation into the Watergate scandal were gaining momentum. Inflation seemed out of control. The war in Viet Nam dragged on. And the blame for all of these was placed on his back.

Forget any goal of 'peace with honor', he thought. *Forget any agreement with Kissinger to just let the South Vietnamese government fall. Forget all those SOB's. I can still win this war, and in so doing, I can still win back some respect.*

On the 20th of December, Nixon called in his Generals from the Pentagon for a strategic meeting. As the Commander-in-Chief, he had grown tired of their negative reports and pessimistic projections. He announced his decision to increase the bombing of North Viet Nam dramatically to a level that had never been seen before. The target would be the capital city of Hanoi, as well as surrounding areas that held any concentration of North Vietnamese people. It offered the best opportunity to destroy supply lines for the Viet Cong. He ordered the largest bombing attack to commence over the Christmas holiday weekend. Although the military brass objected on the grounds that it would kill so many civilians, Nixon shrugged it off as the necessary consequences of war. Just do it.

The pilots followed their orders, and the devastating bombings took place for an entire week. The damage – and the death toll – was enormous. But the net result was the exact opposite of what the President had envisioned.

The North Vietnamese wrote songs of their resolute commitment to rebuild and to be one country, no matter what the cost. They would push on, to the last man if necessary. On the home-front, Americans were becoming more deeply angered and embarrassed at the new state of the war. The "doves" had always opposed this war. Now the "hawks" were reticent. There was no dignity or possible sense of victory when civilians were being slaughtered in this manner. It had to end. It had to end.

Mark Felt / Deepthroat

Secretary of State Henry Kissinger

Governor George Wallace

Washington Post Reporters Bob Woodward and Carl Bernstein

Senator George McGovern

Watergate Building

Jane Fonda in North Viet Nam

Napalm Girl

CHAPTER 10

"1973 – VICTORIES AND DEFEATS OF BIBLICAL PROPORTIONS"

"Where have all the soldiers gone,
Long time passin'?
Where have all the soldiers gone,
Long time ago?
Where have all the soldiers gone?
Gone to graveyards, everyone.
When will they ever learn?
When will they ever learn?"

- Peter, Paul, & Mary

Peace was at hand! After five years of little more than political bureaucracy, the Paris Peace Talks announced a sudden breakthrough. Secretary of State Henry Kissinger had been secretly meeting with Le Doc Tho, a high-level member of the North Vietnamese government. Tho was motivated by the fact that the U.S. was unexpectedly building a new relationship with China and the Soviet Union, which Tho felt could ultimately threaten their continued support for the Viet Cong.

On January 6th Tho and Kissinger agreed in principle to a handwritten peace document which held several critical stipulations:

- the U.S. would have to withdraw all remaining troops from South Viet Nam within 60 days after the official agreement was signed;
- both sides would release ALL prisoners-of-war immediately upon the signing of this pact;
- within 180 days a free election for all citizens would take place in the re-unified country of Viet Nam.

Suddenly there was the legitimate hope for peace. Could it really be possible after so many years of pointless bloodshed? Kissinger was confident that he was working with a leader that he could trust. The entire agreement, however, almost collapsed when South Vietnamese President Thieu discovered that these meetings had been taking place without his knowledge. He insisted that he be allowed to edit the existing draft of the peace agreement. When North Viet Nam balked at this suggestion, President Nixon immediately ordered the renewed bombing of Hanoi. That brought everyone back to the negotiating table, and the final "Paris Peace Accord" was officially signed on January 27th, 1973.

PEACE!! Peace at last. In the coming months, Henry Kissinger and Le Doc Tho jointly received the Nobel Peace Prize for their ability to bring this to fruition. The world collectively crossed its fingers that the war was finally over. Or was it? U.S. ground troops prepared to leave, but American military officials and the U.S. Embassy remained in Saigon for two more years. And South Vietnamese troops continued fighting the Viet Cong – and dying – for two more years.

The hangovers from the 1972 New Years Eve festivities had not fully worn off before Washington, D.C. had to begin cramming for the upcoming Presidential Inauguration on the 20th of January, 1973. Richard Nixon was being sworn in for his second term in the White House amid a flurry of national protests and scandals that created daily distractions. Any modicum of support for remaining Americans in Viet Nam was continuing to wane, even though the President was boasting that a peaceful exit was now in process. Civil Rights leaders were demanding more support from the President, feeling that he was too distracted with too many other issues to elevate the legislative gains they were seeking. And looming ever larger in the rear-view mirror was the growing rats nest surrounding the term

"Watergate." Political opponents now were smelling blood on this one.

Nixon tried to insulate himself even more from any voices of opposition, fiercely demanding absolute loyalty from his staff, and carrying a façade of optimism. He did his best to ignore the growing cries of protest that made the daily news. But that January one of the most unusual and unexpected protests managed to break through the invisible wall that surrounded the President.

As part of the inaugural celebrations, *"The Ray Conniff Singers"* were invited to perform for the President and First Lady, the White House staff, and their chosen guests. The musical chorale was comprised of 25 male and female instrumentalists and vocalists – all white – singing tight harmonies as they performed covers of some of the most popular pop tunes. It seemed like an all-American choice, perfectly catering to all of the middle-age and older adults that had helped put Nixon into office for another four years.

The performance began on cue, as they sang a couple of their well-known hits. But then something happened that was not "on the printed program." As the audience sat in stunned silence, one of the female singers stepped aside for a moment and rolled out a large poster that said "STOP THE KILLING." Their unanticipated message joined the

chorus of protesters across the country that wanted the heightened bombing of North Viet Nam to end. She then walked over to the microphone at center stage, took a deep breath, and addressed the President and the First Lady seated in the front row.

"Mr. President," she said, "stop the bombing! Stop the killing!"

She then returned to her place in the group, and the concert continued as scheduled. For the rest of the evening, however, applause was tepid at best. Nixon's smile was gone, and the room felt suddenly hollow. He could no longer hide from his detractors, even in the secured fortress of his "castle." His world was now quietly crumbling, more than he knew, slowly being consumed by multiple political cancers that he could not fully see.

In spite of its highly controversial and unpopular nature, the bombings did seem to stimulate the North Vietnamese back to the Paris Peace Table. Within a week an initial peace accord was signed between the two nations. It called for a gradual and scheduled scaling back of armed forces on both sides. This seemed to be as close to "peace with honor" that the U.S. could hope for, so the American delegates took it. The North Vietnamese knew that once the Americans were officially removed, the entire country would quickly be theirs anyway.

Within two weeks of the signed accord, 40 U.S. POW's were released.

Lt. Commander John McCain and his fellow Navy pilots stepped from their transport plane onto American soil for the first time in five years, got down on their hands and knees, and gently kissed the ground. It had seemed like an eternity surviving in the "Hanoi Hilton", but now they were safely home. Some wanted to disappear from the public eye, to just melt into a quiet neighborhood with their families. McCain chose to continue to serve his country honorably as a Congressman and Senator from Arizona for 36 years, and in 2008 was selected to be the Republican candidate for the office of President of the United States. Throughout his career he frequently spoke out against any notion of hasty military intervention because he had experienced its wrath first-hand.

January also witnessed one of the most historic and controversial decisions in the history of the U.S. Supreme Court.

Just a few years earlier, Norma McCorvey, of Dallas, Texas, was only 21 and pregnant with her third child. She decided to claim she was raped, and hoped thereby to seek a legal abortion. At that time Texas law allowed for abortion only under the circumstances of rape or incest. But since there had been no police report of a rape, the local court denied her request.

Norma then tried to arrange for an illegal abortion, but discovered that the local facility which once provided that procedure had recently been closed by the Dallas Police. Distraught and feeling helpless, Norma prepared to deliver another baby. Her fortune turned when a sympathetic lawyer offered to help her on a pro bono basis, choosing an entirely different legal strategy – one that would ultimately rock the nation.

Her lawyer filed a case against the Texas District Court seeking rights of personal privacy as provided under the 9th Amendment, and within that privacy provision made a claim to terminate her pregnancy. Instead of the anonymous name of "John Doe", Norma was legally represented as "Jane Roe." The Dallas County Attorney that represented the defense in this initial case was Henry Wade. Thus the recorded court docket before the judge listed this hearing as "Roe vs. Wade."

That case name would become historic. While some joked that "Roe vs. Wade" were George Washington's only options for crossing the Delaware, this was no joking matter. The District Court ruled unanimously in her favor, that the existing laws were in fact a violation of her rights to privacy as guaranteed under the U.S. Constitution. Although "Jane Roe" had won her case, the legal process was slow enough that she had already given birth to her 3rd child before the final verdict was issued.

Texas did not want the embarrassment of being held up as a state in conflict with the Constitution, so the State appealed the case to the Supreme Court the following year. After "Roe vs. Wade" was presented to the higher Court, deliberations were delayed twice while the bench took the necessary time to replace two Supreme Court Justices.

In late January of '73 the U.S. Supreme Court finally issued its verdict, almost 3 years after Norma McCorvey had first appeared in a Texas courtroom. By a vote of 7 to 2, the highest court in the land stated that the availability of an abortion was a fundamental right under the provisions of the Constitution. At first the written language of this decision emphasized the freedom of a doctor to perform an abortion. The writings in support of the decision tried to balance the protection of the health of the mother with the potential of human life, and tied that to the 3rd trimester of the pregnancy. It would be many years before the verbiage would be expanded to include this freedom under women's rights in general, and change the limitation to "fetal viability", or the potential for the fetus to survive outside of the mother's womb.

Newspaper headlines across America carried the news, not fully aware of the controversial firestorm that had just been ignited. Not only were there questions of adjudication by federal or state agencies, but this also brought a moral and religious debate to the forefront. A moral shift had just taken place on a national scale. When Tom saw the front-page story, he walked through the University of Colorado Library as well as a few classroom halls while yelling "YOU LADIES ARE FREE!! YOU LADIES ARE FREE!!"

"The pill" could legally prevent a pregnancy. An abortion could now legally terminate an unwanted pregnancy. Those two factors gave license for women to be as sexually liberated as they chose. The sexual revolution had first removed the "guilt" of free sex. Now these two social advances had removed the "risk" of unprotected sex.

In the immediate aftermath there were a few strange political scenarios that had to play out. California Governor Ronald Reagan was a champion for conservative causes, and a steady pillar for protecting and supporting the Constitution. In his defense of the Constitution and the nation's judicial system, Reagan became a leading voice for liberalizing the abortion laws in California. Conversely, Ted Kennedy – always a proponent of the more liberal left – was endorsing a "right to life" stance in Massachusetts because of the high concentration of Catholic voters in his district.

Women rarely spoke out on "Roe vs. Wade" over the next few years because this was not positioned as an issue of sexual equality. For more than 40 years this case has remained the most contentious decision in the history of the Supreme Court. Annual marches by both supporters as well as those in opposition have been held respectively since that noted verdict. For the first 20 years the opposition was exclusively a Catholic issue, and "evangelicals" would not join in large numbers until later.

Since abortion was legalized on that cold January day, an average of more than 1.3 million women have exercised that option every year. The trend line, however, has declined by more than 30% over the past 20 years, possibly because broader choices of contraception have become available. Norma McCorvey merely sought to change her life – but she ended up changing the world.

Less than a month after his re-inauguration, President Richard Nixon had another difficult announcement to make. The economy continued to flounder, and inflation remained at unacceptable levels. In another television appearance from the Oval Office, Nixon tried to explain to the American people that every U.S. citizen needed to take some "difficult medicine."

As of February 13th, the US Dollar needed to be devalued again by an additional 10%. Naturally there was plenty of "political spin" to support the change. American exports would increase as a result of this decision, which would improve the unemployment rate as well as reduce some of the national debt. Or so he promised.

Most economists were not so easily convinced. This was unprecedented territory, so previous examples did not exist to support his case easily. The general citizenry could only sit back and watch. The majority were already skeptical simply because Nixon's approval rating was plummeting. Everything the President did seemed to be working against him. This decision would prove to be no exception.

Within four months the lowered value of the Dollar forced the OPEC nations to reduce drastically their production of oil. World oil prices were pegged to the devalued Dollar, so other countries were suddenly paying much less in their own currency for their same shipments from OPEC. America had not seen "rationing" of any products since World War II. Now there were gas lines more than two blocks long, with cars sometimes waiting for four hours to get their turn at the pump. Vehicles frequently ran out of gas while waiting in line to buy gas. Drivers were limited to $10 in any one purchase. And many stations ran out of their gas allotment before the end of the day. If so, they just had to put out a home-made sign that said "NO GAS TODAY."

Within the coming year regular gasoline went from 36 cents per gallon to $1.50. The increase in all shipping or delivery charges forced every manufacturer's products to be raised correspondingly in price. Every American now felt the adverse impact of that decision. The choice to weaken the Dollar had inadvertently weakened all of the U.S. economy as well.

Also in late February, Native Americans made another concerted statement about their own issues. On the 27th, about 50 men from several tribes pulled off an armed takeover of Wounded Knee, South Dakota. They chose this particular site because it held the historical memorial of a massacre in 1890 of hundreds of American Indians. Now an armed occupation ensued for the next 71 days, officially led by the "American Indian Movement", or AIM.

AIM was the same organization that had taken control of Alcatraz Island in San Francisco's Bay in 1969, and a forced occupation of the Bureau of Indian Affairs in Washington, D.C. in 1972. In each takeover, their goals were two-fold. Not only did they seek equal rights for all Natives, but also asked for actual financial reparations from the U.S. government for having broken more than 1000 treaties with their various tribes.

The leaders of AIM had decided that utilizing civil disobedience should not be the sole domain of African Americans in their quest for equal rights. In this South Dakota incident, there were a few civil conversations with random news media representatives, but very little in the way of substantive negotiations with government officials.

After more than two months of measured "tolerance", U.S. Army jeeps arrived to support the local police and State Highway Patrol. Using bull horns, the officers announced that everyone was under arrest, and that no one would be harmed if they laid down their guns and walked out peacefully. At first, no one complied, and a short volley of gunfire took place from both sides of the barricade. Two tribal members were killed by army snipers, and one federal agent was wounded and permanently paralyzed. The Natives laid down their guns as soon as they realized they were vastly out-armed, and that the law enforcement agents had now been instructed to "shoot to kill."

Extensive national news media coverage gave the AIM movement the public empathy that they wanted. That new level of visibility helped slowly to awaken the conscience of Americans regarding the systematized mistreatment of Native Americans. Here once again were Americans that were willing to die for a cause that needed a place in the national conversation. Pity, however, is one thing, substantive action is another. Increased funding was approved for every Reservation. Approvals were given for each tribe to open casinos on their land as a tangible step to improve their local economy. What didn't change was the deplorable school system for the Native children, the extremely high levels of alcoholism, and the universal mentality of complete hopelessness.

To this day most of the reservations throughout the U.S. remain as nothing more than "third world countries" existing like islands of bleak despair hidden in the middle of America's abundance.

The Beatles had set a "high water mark" that no other musical band in history could hope to match. They had produced more #1 songs than any other group, and often had four songs at a time in the "Top 10." At their very pinnacle, however, they gave up touring and live performances because they were tired of the screaming fans that were having a great time but too noisy to appreciate fully the musicianship that they were witnessing. The "Fab Four" continued to sell millions of albums exclusively from their studio work.

Other bands had an opposite mentality. One noted example was an Australian group that came to America in 1973, calling themselves "AC/DC." They wanted to find the mania and then expand it. Their entire strategy was to focus on extremely loud instrumentals and howling lyrics centered on booze and sex. The intent was to get their listeners hot and sweaty, screaming along with the band, drinking to excess if necessary, to enjoy themselves. They had no concern for the critics that might pan the group as having limited musical ability. They only wanted to connect with the musical and cultural rebellion that was taking place, and catch a ride with those in a wave of ear-busting frenzy.

That strategy proved to be quite successful. Within just a few years their band had sold more than 200,000,000 albums.

The ultimate opportunity for decadence and luxury for rock & roll musicians reached an insane level in the spring of this year. Bobby Sherman, former teeny-bopper heart-throb, bought a used Boeing 720 for

$750,000, and spent another $200,000 refurbishing it to be the ultimate pleasure-ride in the skies for any band that wanted to charter it. His flying creation included a drawing room with a fake fire-place, a bedroom with a king-size water bed and private shower, a 30-foot sofa facing a 30-foot brass-trimmed bar and electric organ, a video system stocked with porno movies, and two to four "stewardesses" to cater to any and all whims of the passengers. The gaudy lights and finishes made the interior look like a slice of the Las Vegas Strip.

"The Starship", as it was named, was available for the modest sum of $2,500 per flight hour, plus fuel. The music world also referred to it as "Rock & Roll's Air Force One." *"Led Zeppelin"* was the first band to take a chance on chartering the plane. They felt they needed a PR bump because they had received some very bad reviews in Rolling Stone Magazine, which said they should change their name to "Limp Blimp." Zeppelin invited some of the press on to the plane to take a few photos of them, hoping for a new wave of publicity that might position them as incredibly successful.

The photos worked. Within a short time, Alice Cooper, the Rolling Stones, the Allman Brothers, Deep Purple, the Bee Gees, Elton John, and Peter Frampton were waiting in line to reserve the plane for their respective tours. Flight experiences on the Starship became legendary. When the Allman Brothers first boarded the party plane, lines of cocaine were already on the bar counter, spelling out "Welcome, Allman Brothers." Another band-member said his favorite memory of the plane was getting oral sex while flying through extreme turbulence. The Alice Cooper band used the plane's PA system to announce "Ball Scores", which was the number of women each band member had sex with the previous night.

The plane's longevity was short-lived, however, because its four engines were terrible gas-guzzlers. America was in a severe fuel shortage as it was, so band managers would often have to bribe airport fuel trucks in order to get refueled. In less than four years, the Starship was moth-balled, and then scrapped for parts. Gregg Allman later complained that the use of this plane was too excessive, and actually was the beginning of the end for their band.

Allen Ginsberg had lived many places before he finally chose Boulder to be his home. Ginsberg had already become a famous hero to everyone in the counter-culture movement. He was not only opposed to the Viet Nam war, but was opposed to ANY war. He was an outspoken advocate for legalized drugs and recreational sex with either gender, and stood in opposition to capitalism, materialism, Christianity, and any aspect of traditional American culture. He was one of the first to acknowledge openly his homosexuality, and defend it against any critic. In early 1973 he chose Boulder – not because of the scenery or climate – but because of the ample supply of drugs and free love that he found there.

As a poet, writer, and public speaker, he had first gained notoriety from his poem entitled *"HOWL!"* This literary work caused him and his publisher to be taken into court under the charges of obscenity and "printed pornography" due to its vivid description of sodomy and other sex acts. The judge ultimately found him "Not Guilty" based on the Freedom of Speech guaranteed under the 1st Amendment, thanks in no small part to the previous legal work of his late friend, comedian Lenny Bruce.

The historic Boulderado Hotel became his residence for the next few years. Ginsberg had begun to pursue Krishnaism and other Eastern religions. He built a strong relationship with Naropa Institute, the Buddhist campus in town and, under their educational umbrella, started a new branch for the school that he called *"The Jack Kerouac School of Disembodied Poetics."*

His written tirades made him a secret enemy of the State, as he sought to speak out against the capitalistic system as well as the U.S. military. He had co-signed an anti-war Manifesto entitled *"A Call to Resist Illegitimate Authority"*, and in conjunction with other writers vowed not to pay any taxes to the IRS as a protest to the ongoing war in Viet Nam.

Because of his admiration for communism and some of its heroes, he was soon invited to make extended visits to several communist countries. Both China and Cuba thought that he opposed everything in America, and that his presence in their respective countries would provide public relations opportunities for their own propaganda. But Ginsberg's support for homosexuality and drug usage made his stay very brief. Cuba abruptly deported him to Czechoslovakia, where he was soon arrested for public drunkenness and use of illegal drugs.

Even though he opposed the use of tobacco in any form, he was a strong advocate for the legalization of marijuana. He also championed the use of LSD, and actively worked with Timothy Leary to promote its use on a regular basis. In his writings on drug use, he repeatedly claimed that the CIA was involved in the production and sales of heroin coming out of Thailand and Laos. Those accusations, however, were never verified.

Upon his arrival in Boulder Ginsberg was treated somewhat as a celebrity, and his presence provided a rejuvenated stimulus to the voices of protest. He began meeting with the primary activists against the Viet Nam war, and together planned a rally and a march across the city. Just before CU's graduation ceremonies that spring, he notified the news media that the march was on.

Tom couldn't resist. Along with 1,500 students and hippies, he joined the others as they gathered at the Memorial Center on campus, and then proceeded to march down the middle of Broadway, which was the busiest street in the city. Numerous signs were waived in the air, stating "REMOVE NIXON NOW", "DUMP DICK", and "NO MORE DOUBT, GET NIXON OUT." Traffic had no choice but to find alternate routes, or just wait 20 minutes for the yelling procession to pass.

Unfortunately this was not as peaceful as other local protest marches had been. Maybe it was the fresh spring air, or the fact that graduation was less than a week away for many students. But adrenalin was running high. Some marchers began to break windows of houses or retail stores as they passed. Two students discovered a U.S. Postal Service vehicle that had just made a delivery, and noticed that the keys had inadvertently been left in the ignition. They stole the vehicle and drove it about a block before ramming it into a telephone pole.

The procession concluded their two-mile march in the center of Boulder, on the lawn of the old County Courthouse. Ginsberg and others gave impassioned speeches about the need to end the war, to impeach Richard Nixon, and to legalize drugs. Petitions were handed out, asking people to collect signatures demanding the resignation or impeachment of the President. But when one student in the crowd decided to throw a rock through a courthouse window, the Police had had enough. Tear gas was lobbed into the crowd from three sides, and the students hurriedly scattered without further incident.

Ginsberg had successfully established himself as a hero to Boulder's anti-war or anti-Nixon activists. When he died years later, his Will stipulated that 1/3 of his ashes would be buried near his boyhood home in New Jersey, 1/3 of his ashes would be buried next to a Buddhist shrine in India, and the final 1/3 of his ashes would be buried at the Shambala Mountain Center, a scenic overlook on the outskirts of Boulder. He never wanted to leave.

The Soap Box Derby was an annual tradition of pure "Americana", like baseball or apple pie. Young boys aged 6 to 13 from across the country

– with the help of their dads – created homemade "coaster" go-karts to compete for the national prize, which included a large trophy and a $7,500 scholarship to the college of their choice. These non-motorized carts rolled down a long ramp, moved by gravitational pull alone, and steered by the helmeted lads. Preliminary regional tournaments in almost every state pitted entrants to compete against each other two at a time. The top 120 to 150 competitors then travelled to Ohio every fall for the National Championship. And the nation's media faithfully covered this event each year, making it a familiar household story of "happy" news.

In this the 36th annual Derby Championship, scandal rocked the event to its very core, and ultimately brought it to ruin. Instead of the crude wooden crates that had competed in the early years, designs by 1973 were quite sophisticated. The winner for this year was Jimmy Gronem, from Boulder, Colorado, driving a coaster made of molded fiberglass. Jimmy was living with his adoptive guardian, Robert Lange, who was a very successful business owner in Boulder. Lange had even paid to have their Derby vehicle entry flown to California ahead of time to be tested in a wind tunnel. The sleek, futuristic design of his vehicle was credited with helping Jimmy win each heat with ease. At the national finale, he accepted his 1st place trophy and scholarship with total elation, and almost everyone assumed the story was closed.

But the next day, "the wheels began to come off." A few of the race judges had noticed that this particular vehicle seemed to have a much faster start than any of the other competing designs, and asked to thoroughly examine it. To their astonishment, they found a powerful magnet hidden in the nose of the cart, along with sophisticated and elaborate wiring. The electromagnetic circuit was only complete when the driver leaned back and touched his helmet to the pressure pad behind him. The starting gates for these derby races had every pair of entrants leaning their vehicles against a two-foot metal plate, which would simultaneously drop down at the starter's whistle, and the vehicles would coast down the ramp to the finish line. As a result of this starting process, the magnet in the nose of Gronem's fiberglass cart actually pulled the vehicle forward momentarily at a faster rate than mere gravity. From that point, no competitor could catch up to him.

The trophy and scholarship were forfeited immediately. Young Jimmy Gronem was sent home to Boulder empty-handed. Traditional America felt violated, that such a standard of wholesome competition had been sullied. But then things got even more ugly.

The Derby judges remembered that Robert Lange's own biological son, Bobby, had won the same national event just the year before. They insisted on examining that winning vehicle as well. Lange first claimed that the vehicle was missing, but then later stated that it had been disassembled. Search warrants were issued for his Boulder home and garage as well as his company warehouse, but no remnants of that vehicle were ever found. Lange ultimately agreed to pay a $2000 fine, and his entire family was banished for life from any further Soap Box Derby competition.

The Derby scandal once again put Boulder into the national news. But this time the local Chamber of Commerce was not happy with that visibility. Blatant selfishness and rebellion against American traditions was rapidly moving beyond the campus setting. Personal and business ethics were being blurred or ignored at an increasing rate. The cultural shift from "community" to "self" was becoming more and more pervasive. Individualism was supreme.

On May 17th, the Senate Watergate Committee began its nationally televised hearings, chaired by Sam Irvin. Normally any government proceedings would sound like the most boring television possible, aired only on C-SPAN. But this time America was transfixed. Every TV network as well as every national news publication was in a shoving match to find space for themselves to cover the proceedings live. Fireworks were expected, because the blood-bath had already started.

Earlier in the year, the five defendants in the Watergate burglary had all pled "Guilty" to all charges. Burglar McCord had also written a letter to the judge, acknowledging that some of his original testimony had been perjured because of pressure from "higher authorities", and that the burglary was not just a CIA operation as originally stated, but involved other governmental persons. Without directly saying so, his implication clearly pointed to key persons in the White House. Corruption and obstruction of justice were becoming more and more apparent at the highest levels of our government.

Less than three weeks prior to the start of these hearings, three of the closest advisors to President Nixon – Bob Ehrlichman, H.R. Haldeman, and Richard Kleindienst – all resigned at the President's request. Each of them was secretly promised that funds would be provided for their bail, and that their families would be well-cared for if they were willing to "take the fall" without implicating the President. White House legal counsel

John Dean had begun negotiating his own plea deal with the Watergate prosecutors, and as a result Dean was fired by the President.

During the Confirmation Hearings for acting FBI Director Patrick Gray, he had testified that John Dean had "unofficially" required daily updates from him regarding the Watergate investigation, and then that Dean had lied to FBI investigators. Gray was approved as the new Director of the FBI, but held that new position for less than two months. When it was discovered that he had destroyed secret files from the safe of Howard Hunt, he was forced to resign.

When burglar James McCord took the witness stand before the Watergate Investigation Committee, he dropped a new bombshell by stating that U.S. Attorney General John Mitchell had been the boss of the entire operation. The judicial net was widening once again, and the severity of the crime as well as the cover-up – although still unclear – was intensifying.

The findings of the new Senate Watergate Committee through May and June continued to make front-page news every day. With the prospect of prison on the line, John Dean became the first witness to contradict the President openly. He testified that he had been present in the Oval Office for at least 35 conversations regarding the Watergate cover-up. He also implied that a recording system had been installed in the White House two years ago, so that all such conversations were on tape, and those could be used to verify his assertion. He claimed he told Nixon that there was a cancer growing around the Watergate issue, but Nixon just told him to bury it. He also carefully described the moment he told the President that Howard Hunt and the "Plumbers" would need more than $1,000,000 in cash as "hush money" or they would rat out the White House, and that the President had assured him that money would not be a problem. The committee panel quickly appointed Archibald Cox to be an independent special prosecutor, specifically to oversee the investigation into any possible wrong-doing on the part of the President.

The dominos were beginning to drop, but even bigger surprises were waiting for this committee.

The Spring of 1973 saw another historic sports moment, which again had an unexpected connection to Boulder. A few years earlier, Colorado resident Penny Chenery had inherited a small Kentucky horse farm from her parents. And in 1970, with a stroke of luck or Divine intervention, she had been able to claim a reddish-brown thoroughbred colt when she and another horse breeder flipped a coin to determine ownership. For a year she and her staff just called the stallion "Big Red", but when it came time to try him out on the racetrack as a 2-year-old, her trainer decided they needed a more distinctive name. Their office secretary came up with the name "Secretariat."

After showing exceptional promise throughout that next year, the big red stallion qualified to be entered in the Kentucky Derby in May of 1973, the first segment of the "Triple Crown" of horse racing. As the most noted and prestigious of all horse races, the Kentucky Derby is commonly perceived by many as the "most exciting two minutes in all of sport." Rallying from the very back of the pack, Secretariat narrowly won that race with an amazing sprint to the finish, setting a new Derby record in the process.

A few weeks later, the Preakness race became the focus of national attention. The setting for this second leg of the Triple Crown was a rainy day and a very muddy track. That created a new dimension of danger, and necessitated entirely different strategies for racing. But Secretariat used the same approach that had worked for him before, and rocketed from last place to first place in the final home stretch.

Horseracing had not seen a Triple Crown winner in 25 years, so the mere prospect for that possibility inflated the hype and anticipation of the Belmont Stakes to stratospheric levels. The Belmont is the longest of the three races, and requires a higher level of strategy, pacing and stamina. Even non-horse-racing-fans took time from their Saturday schedules to watch that third and final leg of the Triple Crown. But any real suspense quickly faded shortly after the starting bell had been rung.

In any such race with world-class horses, the quality of competition is fairly equal. The science of selective horse breeding, the physics and regimen of ideal training, and weight restrictions on jockeys and tack all combine to make for a very level playing field. Almost always the margin of victory can be just a fraction of a second. Horses frequently win by a photo-finish, or just a "nose", or maybe half of a body length. A win of one or two lengths is deemed as a solid win. And anything more than that is considered "dominating."

On that spring afternoon of 1973, Secretariat did something unprecedented. Right out of the starting gate he bolted into the lead and never looked back. Rather than pacing himself for a race of such a greater distance, he seemed to sprint as though he were already on the home stretch. The initial cheering of the crowded grandstands transitioned into a quiet sense of awe and disbelief as his lead steadily increased. More than 10 lengths separated him from the pack as he went into the backstretch. By the far turn, that lead was more than 20 lengths. On the homestretch it was more than 30 lengths.

Such a margin of defeat seemed impossible. True racing fans would know that the finish time of 2minutes, 24 seconds is unreachable. In the 148 years of the Belmont Stakes, no horse before or since has ever come within two full seconds of that winning time. The degree of dominance is hard to compare. Could a baseball team win the World Series by 40 runs? Could a football team win the Super Bowl by 90 points? It carries that order of magnitude. Golfer Jack Nicklaus – among many other observers – called that performance the most amazing athletic performance he had ever seen in any sport in his lifetime.

Legends are extremely rare. But for a moment in time, a horse was able to make America forget about Viet Nam. A horse was able to make America forget about Watergate. Throughout the past forty-plus years since Secretariat walked onto a racetrack, he is still regarded as the greatest racehorse of all time.

Penny Chenery, owner of Secretariat, eventually retired and sold her horse farm. While she loved those Kentucky hills and the priceless memories they held for her, there was one and only one other place that she considered "heaven on earth." She retired there, and continued to live there until her death in 2017. . . in Boulder, Colorado.

In September, professional tennis recorded the most significant match in the history of its existence. But this was not an ordinary tennis match, merely to record which contestant had outplayed or outscored the opponent. Instead, this match rattled the social and political timber of America. It was Women's Liberation vs. Men's Chauvinism. It was professional women's tennis demanding equal prize money to that of the men's professional circuit. It was retirees demanding fair and equal treatment as elders in society. All of these issues came to a head on that fall evening.

Bobby Riggs, age 55, had enjoyed noteworthy success during his tennis career. At one time he stood on top of the world's stage for tennis when he swept Wimbledon in 1939 at the young age of 21, winning the men's single title, men's doubles, and mixed doubles championships. Throughout his career as a young amateur, later as a pro, and following his retirement from professional tennis, he frequently "hustled" other tennis players for money, including such antics as playing an entire tennis match while holding a bucket of water in his left hand, or wearing rain galoshes instead of tennis shoes throughout the match. So it was that the growing women's liberation movement now gave him the platform for his greatest hustle ever.

Whenever an opportunity had presented itself, Riggs repeatedly declared that women's professional tennis was vastly inferior to that of the men's tournaments, and even inferior to the Senior Men's players such as himself. His rant would always include a challenge that in his current retirement years he could still defeat any professional woman in a head-to-head match.

Billie Jean King, ranked #1 in the world in women's tennis, simply scoffed at the suggestion. She thought of Riggs as an old man with bad teeth that spray-painted his hair and waddled when he walked. But when CBS television offered $10,000 in a winner-take-all match, Margaret Court jumped at the opportunity. Court was Australian, happily married, a devout Christian, and had little or no interest in the political environment of the U.S. Court had won 13 major tournaments before she turned 25, and was the former #1 player on the women's circuit. Now ranked as the #2 woman in the world, and having just won the Grand Slam – all four major tournaments – a couple of years earlier, she assumed this match would be nothing more than a light workout at best. Her confidence in this decision was bolstered by the fact that this "gimmick match" offered a higher cash prize than any of the professional women's tournaments that she had ever won. She gave no thought to the significance of the cultural ramifications that were at stake.

Wrong decision.

Riggs trained rigorously for the event for three months, spending hours every day running and playing tennis. He hired a nutrition coach, who convinced him to consume high amounts of proteins and vitamins, and no booze. To taunt his opponent, as well as to irritate the national media and the entire women's movement, he frequently wore his WORMS t-shirt for his workouts, which stood for "World Organization for the Retention of Male Supremacy." At press conferences his mantra was "Women who can, do. Women who can't, become feminists." Such baiting only caused the hype to grow.

On Mother's Day afternoon, May 15, Tom and several of his friends gathered in his Boulder apartment to watch the event on TV. There was some casual sparring between the sexes, but everyone there tried to enjoy the novelty of such a unique sporting contest as entertaining fun. However, once the match had started, it was clearly the men against the women.

Everyone in Tom's apartment laughed as they watched Bobby Riggs present Margaret Court with a dozen roses before the match started. But the chivalry ended there. As soon as the contest got underway, Riggs used every trick shot, back spin, lob and finesse in his repertoire. Tom had lettered in tennis on his high school championship team, and recognized some of the subtleties of what was happening. Every time Riggs would use sharp back spin or a drop shot, Tom would shout, "Watch this, she's going to hit it into the net!"

American feminism as a whole, as well as the organization for equality in women's professional tennis, were both on the line that day, and both sadly came up empty. Male chauvinists across the country were buying beers for everyone when Riggs won the match in straight sets, 6-2, 6-1. Riggs quickly labeled it "the Mother's Day Massacre." From that moment on, his hubris reached a level that could make both Mohammed Ali and Joe Namath proud. Billie Jean King, on the other hand, was livid. She knew she now had to accept Riggs' next challenge. The credibility of women's professional tennis as well as the entire women's movement depended on it.

Promoters scrambled to get in on the spectacle. The Houston Astrodome was chosen to be the venue since it was the largest indoor domed arena in the country, and was aptly called "the 8th Wonder of the World." This time the purse was $100,000. as a winner-take-all best-of-five-set contest. Billed as the "Battle of the Sexes", more than 35,000 people attended the match, which is still the highest paid attendance for any tennis match in U.S. history. More than 90 million watched on live television, which far exceeded the TV audiences for any of the Super Bowls prior to that time.

The arena floor took on a circus-like atmosphere, and symbolic showmanship was at its finest that September evening. During the warm-ups, Bobby Riggs was paid an extra $50,000. to wear a bright yellow "Sugar Daddy" jacket, which was the logo and name of a candy company. He entered the cavernous arena riding in a rickshaw that was being pulled by a dozen female models in bikinis. Billie Jean, however, stole the focus of the pre-game activities. She entered the Astrodome in a Cleopatra-style carriage, held aloft in her royal throne by four bare-chested male body-builders dressed in the style of Egyptian servants. Just prior to the beginning of the match, gifts were also exchanged at the center of the tennis court. Riggs presented Billie Jean with a large lollipop, and she in turn gave him a live baby pig, as a direct reference to him being a "male chauvinist pig." The entertainment value of such pre-game antics exceeded all the pre-match expectations.

Early in the match, Riggs had the temporary lead. But Billie Jean had studied the film of Margaret Court's mistakes, and did not fall for his drop shots and lobs. It soon became apparent that the 26-year discrepancy in age was surfacing in their respective stamina and velocity of serves. The initial drama rapidly waned as Billie Jean took control, and won a dominating victory in three straight sets. (In true "hustler fashion", it was later learned that Bobby Riggs had placed some major bets against himself in Las Vegas so that he was sure to win big money either way.)

There had been numerous protests and marches in cities across the U.S. in support of women's equality during the previous eight years. Large gatherings of women had publicly burned their bras. Women's press conferences on a national platform had demanded equal pay for equal work. Legislation on behalf of women was submitted state-by-state, called the "Equal Rights Amendment." Yet all of those variables combined could not shift the mindset of Americans as much as Billie Jean King did in less than two hours on that humid September night in Houston.

Although the six-figure paycheck to Billie Jean King was more than twelve times greater than any women's tournament that she had ever won, the money in and of itself was insignificant to her. The world literally changed on that night. Credibility for professional women's tennis shifted dramatically. Support for the equality of all women's sports to mirror that of men's sports gained traction. Equality for women in the corporate workplace suddenly became a valid concept.

A few weeks later Billie Jean was honored as the #1 most admired woman in the world, edging out Israel's Prime Minister Golda Meir. She forever remains the equivalent heroic breakthrough idol to all of women's sports just as Jackie Robinson was to breaking the color barrier in major league baseball. She could always take pride in the fact that in one entertaining evening she had changed all of America . . . for the better.

More than 40 years later her tennis racquet from that match with Bobby Riggs was auctioned off for $125,000. It is without question the most expensive piece of women's sports memorabilia ever sold, and serves as a tangible reminder of her historic position in the world of women's sports and women's rights.

Vice President Spiro Agnew was never mentioned in the many White

House conversations revolving around the Watergate cover-up. First impressions were that he was an innocent by-stander, that he was squeaky clean, and just might come out of all of these investigations unscathed.

But first impressions can be more than misleading. Evidence from a different investigation surfaced that he had been anything but squeaky clean while in his previous position as the Governor of Maryland. In October of this year, witnesses came forward claiming that Agnew had accepted large sums of money as bribery payments in exchange for preferential treatment to select particular highway construction companies. Other acts of corruption and obstruction of justice surrounded those cash payments.

In typical political fashion, his first response was to deny, deny, deny, and suggest that these were false charges concocted by unhappy construction companies that had not received the winning state contract. He also tried to claim that as the standing Vice President of the United States, he must be immune to any such investigations into events from more than seven years earlier. But prosecuting lawyers persisted, showing that eight different Maryland construction companies had budgeted 5% of all contracts to be in the form of kickbacks, and half of each of those specifically went to Agnew. Records also revealed that he was continuing to receive payments from those construction companies while he was Vice President, and because of that fact the statutes of limitations had not expired. Some of those individual payments had been larger than his Vice President's salary of $62,500.

When the evidence became too compelling, Agnew negotiated a quick plea deal. He agreed to plead "no contest" to charges of income tax evasion as long as the greater charges of political corruption were dropped. He was fined $10,000, required to pay more than $150,000 in late fees to the IRS, and sentenced to three years probation. He was also disbarred from practicing law in his home state of Maryland. His abrupt fall was very disappointing to the most conservative arm of the Republican Party because he had been the first to rally great support around the idea that the national media was controlled by the Liberal Left. Agnew had no idea at the time that if he could have just survived another ten months in office, he would have become the most powerful man in the world.

Disgraced on a national stage, and bitterly angry that the President had not said or done anything in his defense, Agnew abruptly resigned from office, moved back to Maryland, and disappeared from the political scene. To get back on his feet, he borrowed $200,000 from his friend, Frank Sinatra, to start a consulting company. He used his six years in the

White House to his advantage, and capitalized on relationships that he had accumulated around the world. For the next 20 years he participated in a random assortment of international deals. As one example, his company brokered a contract to produce all of the Iraqi military uniforms for Saddam Hussein.

He never spoke to Richard Nixon again, and when Nixon died in 1994, Agnew initially declined to attend the funeral. But at the last minute he finally agreed to go. Yes, both men had been publically humiliated, but after so much time, wounds need to heal and life needs to move on.

In the fall of '73 the sexual revolution was becoming more and more apparent in Boulder by moving beyond the CU campus or the hippie communities. A pastor of a very conservative, Bible-teaching church was asked to resign when it was learned that he was having sex with two of the married women in his congregation. Other sins might be acknowledged and forgiven, but that was a failure that the church would not tolerate.

For the first time at least three of the high school athletic coaches in town were openly dating high school senior girls. Only ten years ago that act would have cost them their job. Some of those girls had been presumed to be sexually active before these relationships began, but as those friendships became "steady" it removed all doubt. The driving force of "unconditional tolerance" was moving people to accept such things that had at one time been an unthinkable taboo.

And that fall one of the most bizarre examples of sexual abandon took place at the notorious Pioneer Inn. In addition to its frequent fist-fights or daily drug deals, this rustic bar had built a reputation for unusual parties. Halloween was often the most notable for the year.

This particular year the October 31st festivities became legendary in the community. About seventy-five very creative or crude-costumed men and women arrived that night to compete for the $75. cash prize for 1st place with the best costume. Vern and Cindy had both grown up together in Boulder County, and remained good friends even though they were now married to other spouses. Vern's wife had to work on that night, and Cindy's husband didn't want to bother getting into a costume. So the two friends decided to coordinate their efforts, and went together to the party as "Little Miss Muffett and the Spider."

By midnight the booze and drugs had kicked in pretty good for everyone, and the bar was rather boisterous. Each contestant was asked to take a turn standing on the bar, and the patrons would vote for favorite costumes based on their whistling and clapping. When it was Vern and Cindy's turn, they stepped onto the bar and received their share of the applause. They were confident they might be in the final top five.

But then something unexpected happened. Four or five of the guys grabbed Cindy and proceeded to carry her on their shoulders as they marched around the bar area, chanting "MUFFETT, MUFFETT, MUFFETT . . .", and then returned her to the bar. Every parent knows that in the traditional children's nursery rhyme, the storyline said Little Miss Muffett was seated on a tuffet, and when the Spider sat down beside her, it frightened Miss Muffett away. But this night was not going according to any traditional nursery rhyme script. This night, when Little Miss Muffett was returned to the bar, the Spider proceeded to hike up her long floral dress and have sex together on the countertop in front of 75 cheering customers.

The vote was unanimous, and Vern and Cindy split the 1st Place prize money. And in so doing, they demonstrated once again that for some, sex no longer had any boundaries or limitations whatsoever.

In the fall of '73 "the most dangerous man in America" finally went to prison . . . for the 34th time. He never carried a gun, never robbed a bank, and never murdered anyone. Yet the President of the United States called him the most dangerous man in America. Why?

Timothy Leary had become the #1 voice in America for legalizing all drugs, and using those drugs in a regular, managed, and beneficial manner. His mantra of "turn on, tune in, drop out" introduced more young adults to drugs than any dealer in history. And his unlikely journey to get there became a bizarre, adventure-filled scenario worthy of a Hollywood movie.

Leary's career began as a genius psychology professor at Harvard University, working in a most unusual research endeavor with graduate students. Because LSD and other hallucinogenic drugs were legal at the time, he was forcing his students to take measured quantities of various drugs to obtain a measureable spectrum of reactions. He claimed his findings could cure alcoholism, homosexuality, and criminal behavior with the regular use of LSD. He was disillusioned, however, with the snobbery and elitism of the Ivy League, and was somewhat relieved when he was fired from Harvard.

Poet Allan Ginsberg had learned of his research, and asked to be his partner. He offered to introduce Leary's psychedelic services to celebrities, artists, and intellectuals. Two of those new "customers" were young members of the wealthy Mellon family, who purchased a 64-room mansion for Leary, and called it Millbrook. For the next five years, Leary regularly hosted "research parties" there, focusing on the extensive use of drugs. Coincidentally, G. Gordon Liddy was the local Asst. District Attorney, and had Leary and his guests arrested on numerous occasions on trivial charges. Those repeated FBI raids on Millbrook eventually forced its closure.

In 1966 LSD had been officially banned in the U.S. in spite of Leary's testimony before a government hearing. He had argued that such drugs were "like a car . . . dangerous if used incorrectly, yet highly beneficial if used wisely." His passionate defense claimed that regular usage of these drugs could enhance spiritual growth, a deeper pursuit of knowledge, and greater personal development. Leary considered himself a hero for the ages, likening his role to Jesus or Socrates, having a comparative impact on humanity.

In '67 he had published a brochure entitled *"Start Your Own Religion."* His self-created religion circumvented the law by using LSD for "spiritual learning." The following year he announced his candidacy for Governor of California, running against Ronald Reagan. His campaign slogan was "Come Together, Join the Party." Reagan called Leary "a kingpin, hell-bent on unraveling the normal order". A year later John Lennon wrote a song for Timothy Leary, entitled *"Come Together."*

But his blatant use of various drugs during the middle of the campaign got him arrested again. Because of his history of repeated distribution and personal use, he was sentenced to 20 years for drug possession. His near-perfect score on a psychology test, however, allowed him to be assigned to a low-security prison, working with a landscaping crew.

Leary got a secret message delivered to the Weather Underground through a mutual friend, asking for their assistance in an escape plan. The Weather Underground was happy to help, since their objective was to create chaos and disruption within any element having to do with the establishment. On an appointed morning, Leary quietly walked away from his landscaping crew and was whisked away in a VW van owned by the Weather Underground. He was not missed by the prison guards until roll-call later that evening. By then he was already in Arizona, and his escape precipitated one of the craziest manhunts on a global scale in FBI history.

Using a false passport, his first stop was Algeria, under the protection of the Black Panthers. The Algerian government recognized the Panthers as legitimate representatives of the U.S., even though the only members there were also hiding from U.S. authorities for other crimes. They supported Leary's opposition to traditional American culture, but were not pleased with his obsession with LSD. Panther leaders were willing to break the law if it benefited their followers, but the risk of jail-time for somebody else's drugs was not acceptable.

Leary struggled to get along with his hosts, and developed a particular friction with Eldridge Cleaver, because their "missions" were so very different. The members of the Weather Underground forced him to send a written cable to the U.S. media in which he thanked them for helping make his escape from prison. The Weather Underground was continually looking for recognition for every disruption possible. Leary reluctantly did so because he needed a place to call home. He even plotted with Bill Ayers and other Weathermen to coordinate a major domestic terrorist attack in a major U.S. city. But he realized it was time to leave his temporary "guardians" when he discovered that the Algerian government was secretly negotiating his extradition to the U.S. in exchange for increased oil and gas allotments.

His next stop was Beirut for a brief stay, then on to Vienna, Austria in '72. This provided a much easier setting in which to hide since he was now surrounded by other Caucasians. But it also provided a much higher cost of living. He sent telegrams to several of his "Millbrook associates", including Hugh Hefner, urgently asking for money. It generated a meager response. A few thousand dollars arrived from the Mellon heirs, but nothing close to what he needed. His final act of desperation was to sell his personal rights to tell his life story, which was the only remaining asset he owned.

Leary moved on to Kabul, Afghanistan, thanks to an unexpected friendship. The nephew of the king shared his love for LSD, and offered him a modest but comfortable home. Leary thought he might spend the rest of his life there, limiting his "trips" to daily LSD hits with his host. But the CIA learned of his whereabouts thanks to some illegal phone-taps, and federal agents captured him without incident. The man-hunt was over. "America's most dangerous man" was in custody. President Nixon felt a momentary sense of victory in the midst of his own battles with the law.

Back in the U.S., Leary was held on $5,000,000. bail, which was the largest bail set for any U.S. citizen in history. In the fall of '73 he was sentenced to 15 years for drug possession, and assigned to solitary confinement in Folsom prison because of his previous prison escape. Coincidentally he was placed in a high-security cell next to Charles Manson. Although the two men never met face to face, they developed a friendship from talking to each other through the walls.

Four years later Leary was released from prison. He married for the fifth time, and continued to speak out on the social benefits of legalized drugs. In a profound twist of irony, he met his old nemesis, G. Gordon Liddy, who had also recently been released from prison for his participation in the Watergate break-ins. Because of their shared experience of incarceration, they became friends. Over a couple of drinks they came up with the idea of working together on the public speaking circuit. Their presentation was a public debate on numerous issues such as drug legalization, abortion, gun-control, and population control. Leary defended the liberal perspectives and Liddy the conservative views. Their strong entertainment value created a high demand, and Leary made more money from those debates than at any point in his life.

Until his dying breath, he never deterred from his convictions that well-managed use of hallucinogenic drugs would benefit every adult.

Egypt and Syria launched a surprise attack on Israel in early October. Their combined man-power vastly outnumbered the Israeli army. In desperation, Prime Minister Golda Meir threatened to use nuclear weapons as a last-ditch resort to defend her country. Her only other salvation was if the United States would be willing to airlift weapons and supplies on an emergency basis. But when she called and pleaded for help from President Nixon, he balked.

Nixon felt his reputation was already on thin ice with the American people, and he wasn't sure he should risk a hasty decision that might have further negative ramifications for him politically. Helping to fund another war could be extremely unpopular, given the public perception of Viet Nam. He picked up the Oval Office phone and made his own call for help, not to the Pentagon, not to his Chief of Staff, but to Rev. Billy Graham.

"Billy," he said, once they were on the line, "you offered to pray for me if I ever needed it, and I think now is the time."

"Of course," the evangelist replied, "I'm glad that you would call."

The President took a few moments to explain the Middle East predicament, and Graham took a few moments to pray for him, for the U.S., for Israel, and for peace. After a short conversation, the call seemed to be over, but Graham suddenly added one more thing.

"Mr. President," he said, "it is certainly not my place to be advising the White House, or any other political position for that matter. But I feel compelled to share something with you." There was a lengthy pause before he continued. "The Bible does say that there are dire circumstances for those nations or people that curse the nation of Israel, and there are blessings for those nations or people that bless the nation of Israel. I just wanted to mention that."

The next pause was even longer. The President finally responded. "Thank you for your time, Billy", was all he said, and hung up the phone.

The following day the United States sent extensive weaponry and supplies in an emergency shipment to the southern border of Israel. When Egypt and Syria realized their advantage was gone, they withdrew their troops and the war ended as abruptly as it had begun.

The world never knew how close it had come to experiencing another nuclear explosion, but for the passing comment of an American citizen that had no political or military position.

By late October and early November the quagmire of the Watergate investigation had reached a crescendo pitch. Numerous testimonies before Sam Irvin and the investigating panel had become contentious, and kept alluding to the tape recording system in the Oval Office. The clear implication was that the President might know far more than he was letting on. The definitive questions were "What did he know?" and "When did he know it?"

Three months into the investigation, special prosecutor Archibald Cox had officially asked President Nixon for copies of all the tapes from the previous two years. The President replied that he had recently had the taping system disconnected, but would not give any tapes to the prosecutor or the Watergate committee because of the confidential nature of items pertaining to national security.

Cox was not satisfied with that answer, and hinted that he might submit a legal subpoena for the tapes, which would force the President to cooperate. Nixon was furious, but knew the threat was serious. Feeling more and more that he was getting cornered, on Saturday, October 20th, the President called in his Attorney General, Elliot Richardson, and demanded that he fire the special prosecutor Cox. Nixon did not have the legal authority to do so himself, but since the Attorney General had appointed Cox to this position, Richardson did have the legal right to recall the appointee. But the Attorney General refused, and instead, immediately submitted his resignation from office.

Not deterred in the least, Nixon called in the Director of the FBI,

William Ruckleshaus, with the same assignment of firing Cox. But again, Ruckleshaus refused to be a part of some action that had no merit, and he also resigned immediately.

Now Nixon was moving from desperate to frantic. He called in Robert Bork, who had recently become the Solicitor General for the Justice Department. When given the same assignment, Bork considered resigning, but chose to follow through with the orders. He called Archibald Cox and notified him that he was being fired. In his stead he appointed Leon Jaworski as the new special prosecutor. Their only hope was that the newly appointed prosecutor would back off on the President.

Those stunning job changes in such rapid succession became known as the "Saturday Night Massacre." President Nixon was feeling like he was surrounded with crooks. His "plumbers" had been arrested, and pled guilty. They were deemed crooks. His Vice President had just been forced to resign in disgrace less than two weeks ago. A major crook. Several of his staff had admitted that they perjured themselves while giving testimony before the Watergate panel. A clear implication of being crooks.

As the news broke regarding the Saturday night firings, Nixon's support ratings plummeted to a new low. Protests were organized – not for Civil rights, not for the Viet Nam war – but for justice and impeachment. Marchers carried new signs which read, "HONK FOR IMPEACHMENT" and chanted "JAIL TO THE CHIEF."

On November 17, President Nixon again asked the television networks to give him 30 minutes of prime time broadcasting so that he might address the American people. Glaring into the TV cameras with his jaw muscles clenched, Nixon firmly stated, "I AM NOT A CROOK." That would become an historic moment in his legacy, because more and more people were beginning to think otherwise.

Placed next to him at his desk was a stack of three-ring binder notebooks. Nixon assured the American people that these notebooks contained the transcripts to ALL of the tapes from the Oval Office, as well as the tapes themselves. This was everything that Special Prosecutor Jaworski was requiring. It sounded compliant, thorough, and humble.

But in true "tricky Dick" fashion, it proved to miss the mark once again. One of the tapes had an 18 ½ minute blank space, where the audio had been completely erased. Excuses were offered that were almost childish in nature, including that his personal secretary accidentally put her elbow on the "record" button while she was on a phone call. In this latest public relations exercise, Richard Nixon had intended to improve his standing with the special prosecutor as well as the American public. Instead, he only made things worse.

⊗

1973 had been another successful year for breakthroughs and advances for women. For the first time, women were allowed to serve as jurors in all 50 states. South Carolina and Mississippi were the final two states to make that shift. Now when the courts provided a "jury of your peers", it truly came without gender limitations.

Late in this year, Nancy Friday also took women's ideas and women's concerns to a new plateau. She published her book, *"My Secret Garden"*, which created a national stir. The manuscript shattered the cultural taboos of the day by going into great detail regarding the erotic daydreams of hundreds of everyday women. The sizzling copy provided an immediate invitation for her to appear on every radio and TV talk-show across the country. Often times the titillating candor had to be carefully censored on live programs, particularly those that aired in the daytime.

In a bit of irony, the book was quickly panned by the national leaders of the women's feminist movement, because they wanted the conversation of women's rights to concentrate on political or economic equality. As a result they tried to portray Ms. Friday as nothing more than an unscientific gossip columnist. Rather than backing down, however, the author countered by saying that any of those feminists that disagreed with her were actually lonely women because they were "anti-sex" and "anti-men." The intriguing debate certainly helped to sell more copies of her books.

Whether her liberating perspectives were accurate or not, Nancy Friday successfully elevated the female mind into the conversation of sexual freedom. The world of fantasy was now a factor that men and women shared.

⊗

By the end of the year, drug usage was becoming commonplace – not just with Boulder's high school or college students – but even with middle school students aged 12 to 14. Parents as well as school teachers were becoming distraught at the discovery of LSD in kids' lunch pails. Usually it was in the form of liquid drops soaked into a sugar cube.

The typical source turned out to be an older brother or sister. Maybe the middle-schooler had stolen it from them. Or maybe it was a gift. But in any event it gave a new sense of urgency to "parent-teacher conferences"

314

that took place every fall and spring semester. Where would this attitude of experimentation and rebellion end? Or was society on a downward slope with no upturn in sight?

One thing was clear . . . no one had an answer.

President Nixon and Vice President Spiro Agnew

John Dean at Watergate Hearing

Sam Irvin, Watergate Committee Chairman

Billie Jean King and Bobby Riggs

Timothy Leary

Native American Activist Russell Means

CHAPTER 11

"1974 – BEGINNING
OF THE END"

"Come, you masters of war
You that build the big guns
You that build the death planes
You that build all the bombs . . .
I hope that you die, and your death will come soon.
I will follow your casket by the pale afternoon
And I'll watch while you're lowered down to your deathbed
And I'll stand over your grave 'til I'm sure that you're dead."

Bob Dylan

Every New Year's celebration is supposed to have fireworks and sparklers. 1974 began with great fanfare and celebration, and the Watergate committee certainly added to the "fireworks" that were taking place to begin the new year.

Early in January the new prosecuting attorney, Leon Jaworski, submitted a formal request to the White House for 500 tapes pertaining to recorded conversations surrounding the Watergate break-in and the ensuing cover-up. Once again, President Nixon refused. Neither side was going to give an inch of ground voluntarily. Jaworski realized he was going to need a legal subpoena, and thus force the President to comply against his will.

During the first week of this new year, Gordon Liddy and Howard

Hunt were found Guilty of their Watergate burglary charges. Another shoe just dropped, and the investigating committee was convinced they were steadily moving toward the ultimate target. They had time on their side, and the President did not.

Nowhere were the boundaries of normalcy being so tested as they were on college campuses. Throughout the spring semester, the University of Colorado had to contend with some unusual challenges among its own faculty. The counter-culture mindset of the students was contagious enough to "distract" some of the instructors.

A sociology professor submitted a request for "ethnography research", which is the practice of in-depth study of a specific culture by experiencing and living within the community of that particular culture. Such a request was always approved and funded by CU, in the hope that new discoveries would be published and thereby enhance the reputation of the professor as well as the University. But this particular request for research funds was suspect at best. The professor proposed doing a sociological study of a local hippie commune. He was given a full year's salary to not shave or get a haircut, to have frequent group sex and unlimited sex with multiple partners individually, and experiment with a variety of drugs on a daily basis. The University could not rescind the approved proposal, because ethnographical study was apparently taking place.

Two other single professors were disciplined by the University Regents for having female students living with them. Because the young women were no longer minors, such a consensual relationship was not illegal. But the University was concerned about the image and reputation of the school, and the questionable appearance this would have for the integrity of all faculty. One concern was that co-eds might pursue such a relationship strictly to get a good grade. Although the University asked them to terminate those relationships voluntarily, for a time, both professors refused to change their living situation.

But that ended a few weeks later when one of the professors hosted a party at his home. Several of the students – male and female – were playing "naked tag" outside in the snow. When neighbors finally called the police with charges of "disturbing the peace", the school had had enough. Three days later the professor was dismissed by the University because such a "scene" was unacceptable for a faculty member.

One other embarrassment occurred in this same semester when a different faculty member hosted a party for other professors, and offered marijuana to everyone. Someone complained to the Office of the President, which meant some form of disciplinary action had to take place since that invitation had to do something illegal. The hosting professor was put on probation, but the actual cause was not recorded in his file because that would document that the University was tolerating something outside the law. Instead, the President sent a strong letter of reminder to all employees of the University, reiterating the expectation that all the recipients should be law-abiding citizens, and conduct themselves in a manner reflective of the high standards of such a reputable organization.

These kinds of incidents demonstrated how traditional boundaries for morality or adherence to the law in America were becoming more and more fluid.

In early February, the civil rights efforts for African Americans received a major boost from a most unexpected source.

MAD Magazine had at one time carried the lead torch for comedic satire for many years, willing to mock anything and everything that was held dear by American society. It targeted a wide range of subjects from patriotism to the organized church, from the U.S. military to standards of morality, and from Hollywood celebrities to financial success in general. Nothing seemed off limits. But it tended to steer clear of mocking racial inequalities, possibly because hatred and prejudice continued to generate such frequent domestic hostility.

But satire found a new voice this year when the ultimate parody on racism landed on "the big screen". Hollywood had already shown its support for racial equality in numerous acting roles of a serious nature. This twist was to use comedy and satire as a form of scoffing at those who continued to hold on to such ignorant tendencies as racism and ethnic prejudices.

Utilizing a collaborative written effort from a black comedian and a white comedian, the shared goal was to appeal to all races through raunchy humor. Richard Pryor and Mel Brooks produced a script that light-heartedly mocked all profiling on the lone basis of ethnicity, including Blacks, whites, Chinese, Native Americans, and the Irish. Not only was the general mindset of racial bias something to be laughed at, but any person holding such an attitude became the butt of the joke as well. Although blatantly "politically incorrect" throughout the zany story, the movie's underlying message of equality for all mankind resonated with the audience to such a great degree that it became an all-time classic. Yes, civil rights leaders unexpectedly owed a huge "THANK YOU" to the movie *"Blazing Saddles."*

There was one bizarre and near-fatal event surrounding this movie project. As co-writer, Richard Pryor had slated himself to take on the Lead Actor role as a black sheriff living in a small town of white citizens in the Old West. But just a few days before camera crews were to begin shooting the film, Pryor had a horrible drug mishap while free-basing crack cocaine. The coke burst into flames right in front of his face, and he was immediately rushed to the ER with extreme burns. Several skin grafts were necessary, and doctors considered it a minor miracle that he even came out of the ordeal alive.

While everyone associated with *"Blazing Saddles"* was openly thankful for Pryor's survival, they privately agreed that the public relations fallout would be too great if he remained in the film's lead role. Consequently the producers scrambled to find a "plan B", and actor Cleavon Little was given the greatest break of his career. America was the ultimate beneficiary, however, because this brilliant and hilarious slap at racial prejudice was loved by millions.

February 4th dawned as a quiet Monday morning on the campus of Cal-Berkeley University. Most students were trying to find the energy to begin the new week of classes. Others were sleeping in after a full weekend of partying. Every new week began with the same routine of lazy recovery.

Nineteen-year-old Patty was a sophomore, and lived off campus with her fiancé in an upscale student apartment just two blocks from the university. Traditional America called that "living in sin." But Patty had been a rebellious child all of her life, and insisted on continuing to disappoint her parents for the sake of her own choices. She had been kicked out of two parochial high schools for excessive rule infractions, so this was just another step in her quest to satisfy herself rather than her family.

Patty managed to make it to two of her three classes that day, spent a little time at the library and the Student Union before she and her future husband then returned home to enjoy a light dinner together. A normal weekday evening seemed to be ahead for them, watching a little television and enjoying sex before calling it a day.

But that evening proved to be anything but routine. A dented, rustic-looking sedan quietly coasted into the parking lot around 9 p.m. Two men and a woman stepped out of the car, took their semi-automatic guns off safety, and quickly busted through the front door of Patty's apartment unit.

Her boyfriend was watching the living room television, wearing only a pair of sweatpants. Before he could reach the touch-tone phone on the living room wall to call for the police, the men tackled him, beat him up, and held him on the sofa. "Don't make no trouble," one man hissed into his ear, "and nobody gets killed!"

The woman barged into the first bedroom, looking for his roommate. Patty had been sitting in front of the vanity mirror, brushing her hair, and turned to face her assailants with a look of panic. *'What is this,'* she thought, *'a robbery? -- or a gang rape?'*

"That's her," the woman yelled. "I know that's her. We're good!" She paused for a moment as she studied the young co-ed.

"Put on your shoes," she continued, as she addressed the young victim at gunpoint. "You're coming with us."

As the woman grabbed Patty's purse, one of the men put a blindfold on Patty, tied her hands behind her back, hoisted her onto his shoulder, and carried her out to the car. In less than six minutes of total turn-around time, the three kidnappers were back in their vehicle with their captured treasure muzzled and hidden in the trunk of their car.

Patty Hearst was the grand-daughter of the great industrialist William Randolph Hearst, who for many years had been regarded as the wealthiest man in America. The Hearst family's greatest assets were the ownership of numerous national magazines and a majority of the primary daily newspapers across the U.S. Patty had grown up taking her lifestyle of wealth and luxury for granted. The Hearst Castle – also known as San Simeon – had often been her childhood playground for games of "hide-and-seek" with friends, oblivious to the many tourists standing in awe as they studied the pieces of art and the collection of "castle ceilings" that the Hearst family had accumulated. Few persons in the entire country could command the potential ransom value that Patty might carry on her head.

Her captors were part of a secret gang that was a strange but dangerous mix. Blacks and whites, men and women, sophisticated as well as uneducated. And a smattering of hardened criminals. They called themselves the "Symbionese Liberation Army", or SLA, and their stated goal was to destroy the capitalistic state of America through guerilla warfare. For this group, campus sit-ins or marches were considered worthless child's play. Such civil disobedience had become useless and inadequate. Instead, the charges of arson, grand theft, and murder – including that of an Oakland police officer – were already on their hands.

Within a few hours the FBI had mounted a massive manhunt to a greater scale than anything since the Lindberg kidnapping of 1932. The Hearst family secretly paid a substantial sum of money to the FBI to add numerous full-time agents to the effort. FBI personnel set up an office inside the Hearst estate, and staffed it around the clock. Because of the celebrity status of the family name, Mr. and Mrs. Hearst held daily press conferences in front of a large contingent of media reporters while standing in their front driveway, pleading for the captors to safely return their daughter to them. Although the FBI worked feverishly, the SLA managed to avoid immediate capture because of living "off the grid", and fiercely intimidating anyone who recognized them. Committed anarchists such as this proved hard to follow.

The kidnappers kept Patty blindfolded and hidden in the closet of their small San Francisco home. A portion of every day was devoted to reading ultra-radical literature to her, trying to explain their perspective on the need to overthrow American culture and economics. They were not physically abusive, and kindly shared equal portions of their meager supply of food with her. But it was several days before Patty began to feel comfortable with her captors, gradually becoming more and more convinced that they did not intend to harm her seriously.

Within a few weeks the kidnapper's first ransom demands were published in the Hearst newspapers. Rather than asking for any cash for themselves, they required at least four million dollars worth of groceries to be distributed to needy families in the inner-city of several metropolitan areas. It was meant to demonstrate the need for a complete redistribution of wealth in America.

Against the recommendation of Governor Ronald Reagan, the Hearst family complied, and the historic food give-away plan – although chaotic and problematic – was implemented. Two weeks later, the SLA sent another brief audiotape to the Hearst newspapers with a voice recording of Patty herself assuring her family that she was OK, and also saying that she had officially joined the SLA, had taken on the name of "Tanya", and now supported the SLA's means of extortion or crime to bring down America. Her abrupt mind-shift may have been the result of brainwashing, it may have been a classic example of the "Stockholm Syndrome", or it may have been a clever ruse to make her captors put down their guard. If so, Patty played the part to perfection.

The FBI continued to pursue thousands of leads, but repeatedly came up empty. The first real break surfaced two months after the kidnapping. Two successful bank robberies in the San Francisco area in April produced surveillance-camera footage that clearly showed Patty as one of the bank robbers, wearing a wig and carrying a semi-automatic rifle. Now the Hearst family had a valid reason to be optimistic that the FBI would capture the entire gang, and the family would be able to prove that their precious daughter was an innocent victim of armed threats and mind control. The parents had no idea that their little girl quickly found herself in a consensual sexual relationship with two of the gang members, and was avidly working with her new friends to plan creatively how they could all take down the capitalistic system championed by her family name.

In May the next major clue landed in the lap of the FBI. The getaway van from the San Francisco bank heist was discovered in Los Angeles. Undercover police followed it to an unassuming safehouse of the SLA. Dozens of agents were called in to surround the building, and a massive shootout ensued. America watched on live television as the SLA and police exchanged gunfire for several hours. Smoke bombs and tear gas eventually caused the dilapidated building to catch on fire, and it quickly burned to the ground. Yet none of the kidnappers chose to leave the flames to run outside. The charred bodies of six SLA members were later found in the rubble, including the known leader, but no hint of Patty Hearst anywhere. Most of the group's guns and money were also destroyed in the inferno.

The FBI had no clear knowledge of how large the SLA might be, but knew that Patty was still at large. It so happened that the rest of the gang – just three in number including the young heiress – were out getting groceries and running various errands when the shootout had occurred. Once they reconvened, the remnant SLA members readily agreed that the Feds were too close for now, and they needed to "be invisible" for some time. For one night they stayed near Disneyland, hoping to blend in with the thousands of tourists. The next day they drove from Anaheim back to Oakland, easily mixing in with the hippie community that was there.

After catching their collective breath, they sat down with a few friends from Cal-Berkeley to develop a new plan. More than anything, they needed just to lay low for an extended while.

One of the other radical Cal students suggested they hide out in Boulder. Another mentioned that they had friends from New York that owned a small farm in eastern Pennsylvania. It was a long drive, but definitely would get away from any of the FBI agents that were nosing around. Because those radical students felt that the dead SLA members were martyrs for the cause, they were very willing to sacrificially give some money to Patty and the other two remaining members of the group. As soon as they had collected enough money to live on for a few months, the trio headed east.

In spite of unrelenting efforts by the FBI, no meaningful leads came up during the rest of that year. Patty and her new friends stopped in Boulder for two days, then continued on toward the Amish country of Pennsylvania. They had not given up on their commitment for a radical upheaval in America, and would resurrect the SLA once again. But things didn't quite go according to the plan.

In March, the tangible steps of the Watergate investigation became solidified. Dwight Chapin, Deputy Assistant to the President, was convicted of lying to a grand jury, and stepped into prison for a 9-month sentence. Seven other members of the White House staff were formally indicted, including Mitchell, Haldeman, Ehrlichman, Colson, Strachen, Mardian, and Parkinson. The noose around the President was now tightening.

In April, special prosecutor Jaworski issued an official subpoena to President Nixon, demanding the release of 64 specific tapes. The Supreme Court voted 8 – 0 that the President MUST release the tapes. Never in its esteemed history had the White House been confronted in such a way. But instead of turning in the actual tapes, two weeks later the President submitted written and edited transcripts of the conversations that were contained on the tapes. Jaworski was not satisfied.

Nixon was named as unindicted co-conspirator. Now the sharks were circling in a smaller and smaller orbit. The following month actual impeachment hearings began before the House Judiciary Committee. Two months later the court case was concluded in "The United States v. Nixon". The Supreme Court unanimously determined that the President could not withhold subpoenaed material, and must surrender the actual tapes to the investigators. With that decision, Congress began the preliminary steps to impeach the President.

Two of the tapes had particular significance to the Watergate committee. First was a tape with 18½ minutes of blank space. Was it incriminating evidence that had been intentionally erased? Logic would certainly move a person to that conclusion. Or was a person to believe President Nixon's personal secretary, who claimed she had inadvertently held the "erase" button while she was transcribing the tapes? In and of itself, it was compelling but not definitive.

The second tape proved to be the "smoking gun." This contained a conversation between President Nixon and Haldeman on June 23rd of 1972 – just a few days after the original Watergate break-in – in which the two men talked openly about formulating a plan to block any investigations that might surface. The evidence on that second tape was considered "black and white", and the committee now had what they needed. It was just a matter of filing the necessary papers, and then taking a vote in Congress. The President was toast. His remaining time in office would be a matter of days, not months or years.

"If you can do it, then so can I."

Too often those words are nothing more than a childish excuse, and usually end up getting someone in trouble. For three years the Weather Underground had used bombs as an attempted method for forcing political and social change in America. Using bombs for the purpose of destroying government or military buildings was their signature "calling card." More than 1000 of those bombs – an average of three per day – were detonated somewhere in the U.S. in an effort by Underground members to bring about a revolution.

By the middle of 1974 other activist groups were considering copying the Weather Underground to gain attention, notoriety, and favorable change for the benefit of their members. Black Students of America (BSA), The American Indian Movement (AIM), and the SDS were already on the FBI's "watch list" in Colorado. Boulder police had received occasional informant tips that various groups of protesters within the city were plotting to use a bomb. So far – thankfully – every one of those leads had proven to be false.

That all changed on the first Monday in May. Neva Romero was a 21-year-old senior at CU. She was the campus leader for an organization called "Los Seis", (later changed to "United Mexican American Students"), which was protesting for equal rights for Chicanos. They were frustrated with the creeping pace of social justice, and had taken over a small faculty office building, demanding that the University fire a particular administrator. Late in the afternoon she drove to Chautauqua Park on the edge of town, and sat in a car with a young attorney and his wife. As they talked, Neva cradled a bomb in her lap that was to be placed somewhere on CU's campus later that evening. For reasons unknown, the bomb exploded pre-maturely, and all three passengers were killed instantly.

Boulder Police were baffled, because Los Seis members had not seemed to be an apparent threat for such violence. But just two days later, it happened again. On Wednesday, May 5th, Francisco Granado and three other Mexicans parked their car in the Burger King parking lot. Final plans were being made regarding exactly where to place the bomb that was in a small suitcase in the middle of the back seat. Again, the bomb exploded prematurely. Francisco, as well as the two men in the back seat, were all blown into pieces. He left behind a 25-year-old widow and a young son. The person "riding shot-gun" had his leg blown off, but managed to survive.

Six people dead in less than 48 hours. The Los Seis group immediately claimed that the police had secretly killed them all in an effort to prevent the growth of another radical group. Others believed it was white supremacists acting out of fear or revenge. After weeks of investigation, the official police reports for both cases declared these to be "operator error", and that all died as the result of an accident.

Both incidents served as a deterrent for radical groups anywhere in the country, and demonstrated the need to reconsider their methods. Today the "United Mexican American Students" still revere these young people as martyrs for their cause. They claim that Neva and Francisco were heroic examples of what a revolution necessarily entails.

Music continued to branch into new directions. Disco became the rage, although it was strongly opposed by true lovers of rock & roll. "Studio 54" in New York City emerged as the most elite nightclub in the country, offering pulsing disco music and live dancers as a backdrop in an opulent setting for the most expensive clubbing, sex, and drug appetites.

John Lennon continually made news in the music world, even when he was not performing on stage. A trend of the early '70's was for rock & roll bands to try to create "hidden messages" in their album covers. Some were psychedelic patterns with disguised words, such as the Beatles *"Sgt. Pepper's"* album. Others required that the buyer must hold the album up to a black light for the message to appear.

In 1974 Lennon chose to collaborate with Harry Nilsson on one such creative album called *"Pussy Cats."* The cover was a photo of a cluttered living room filled with an eclectic collection of random furniture and knick-knacks. But the clever message was provided in two large children's blocks placed on the floor on opposite sides of the area rug that was in the center of the room. The sides of the blocks that faced toward the front had a capital letter "D" on the one on the left, and a capital "S" on the one on the right. The hidden sequential message read "D" plus "rug" plus "S", or "D-rug-S."

While it was cute in its simplicity, it spoke to a very dark side in John Lennon's behavior. In spite of the fact that he was one of the three most prolific song-writers of the 20th Century, and reaped the rewards of that success to a greater extent than any song-writer in history, drug abuse was now taking a toll on his life. That summer, while he was stoned and drunk at a party in New York City, he had sex with another guest while his wife was watching, and the other guests were listening in.

The ensuing scandal only got weirder. His wife, Yoko Ono, decided John needed a break from their relationship. Her bizarre solution was for him to have an extended affair with her house-keeper. John willingly obliged, and spent the next year in L.A. with her maid.

While he was living in California with his new partner, John began to use harder drugs, and became addicted to heroin. It caused him to act highly irrational at times. One evening he and his "temporary" girl friend went to a night club in L.A. to listen to the Smothers Brothers. John began heckling the duo, and the disruptions became so loud that security was asked to escort him out of the lounge. On the way to the door he assaulted another woman in the audience. As a result he spent that night in a California jail. It was a pathetic example of "drugs gone bad."

John Lennon proved to be a strange dichotomy on a world-sized scale. He "preached" peace through his music, but in his later years was known to have fits of deep anger and violence. He urged people to live in simplicity, yet he lived in extreme luxury. Just a few years later this rare talent was assassinated as he returned home one evening to his New York apartment near Central Park. Mark David Chapman was a disillusioned fan, and a sociopath that wanted to be famous. Chapman claimed that Lennon's music had misled an entire generation, and that Lennon had become a hypocrite to his own message.

Many of Lennon's songs remain as some of the greatest classics ever recorded. But his personal life was the living evidence of an existence in pursuit of excess, yet unable to find any lasting happiness. He was a model for a song written by his close friend, Mick Jagger, of the Rolling Stones, which says, *"I can't get no satisfaction, I can't get no satisfaction, but I try . . . and I try . . . and I try."*

Neil had just finished his day-shift at Tulagi's, and planned to stop by Magnolia's Thunder Thighs Restaurant to get something to eat before heading back to his downtown Boulder apartment. It was a beautiful August day, and a perfect Boulder afternoon for a bike ride. But as he approached the downtown area, he was shocked to see that everything was in gridlock. Every street had a police roadblock, and cars were being turned away by a line of officers in complete riot gear. Bike riders and pedestrians as well were not allowed to enter or exit the 12-block area. It looked like total mayhem.

Neil got off of his bike and walked it through the throng of confused people.

"Does anyone know what's going on?" he asked, without directing his question at any specific person.

"I don't know, man," one hippie finally replied, "but this has to be some serious s—t, because this has been shut down for a couple of hours, man."

It didn't make sense. There was no protest, there were no marchers, and there had been no bomb or fire. Yet there seemed to be hundreds of uniformed police surrounding this section of town that included commercial and apartment buildings.

Neil finally got through the crowd of on-lookers, and reached an armed policeman.

"Excuse me, officer," he said with a forced smile. "I live about three blocks in that direction. Is there any way I can please get to my apartment?"

The officer looked at him carefully before he replied. "Sorry," he said, "I can't let you do that just yet."

Neil wasn't satisfied with that curt response. "Well," he responded, trying to use his nicest voice possible, "can you at least tell me what's going on? I live right over there. When can I get to my apartment?"

The officer listened to a short broadcast on his emergency band radio before he replied. "OK, listen up," the officer said as he turned back to Neil. "We have this area of town on total lockdown right now, and we have agents that are going door to door into every apartment, as well as searching every store in this area. As soon as that is completed, everyone can get where they need to go."

"So, what's with the search party?" Neil persisted. "What's the big deal?"

"Just give us a little more patience," the officer assured him. "We received a random call earlier today that someone may have seen Patty

Hearst leaving Magniolia's Thunder Thighs today around lunchtime. So right now we are searching every building in this downtown area."

A chill went down Neil's back. *'Could that really be? Is Hearst and the SLA really here in town?'* he thought.

It was another hour before the police removed the barricades. No substantive clues were ever found, but at least three people had very similar stories of seeing the young heiress in the restaurant. The police and the FBI were convinced that she had been there. But once again the radical gang had managed to stay one step ahead of the authorities.

Reports hit the local news the next day, and everyone in Boulder was talking about the failed search. Patty Hearst and her captors had actually been in town for two days, but had returned to their mountain hideaway west of town before the barricades were set up. Another neighbor in Ward tipped off the SLA members as to what had happened. They realized they needed to get out of town right away, and move elsewhere as quickly as possible.

After a few brief phone calls, they headed east from Boulder the next day, and drove non-stop to Pennsylvania. A friend of Bill Walton, star basketball player at UCLA, was sympathetic to their cause, and once again offered that they could stay at his family farm out in the Amish countryside. It had a furnished barn that would be quite comfortable for the four of them.

And it was in that secluded Pennsylvania setting that the SLA was able to remain "invisible" into the spring of the following year.

Fred was born into wealth, and would not have needed to work a day in his life. His childhood had been dominated by two repeating themes: lots and lots of piano lessons, and lots of bullying from other kids. He chose to become a Christian while in high school, then finished college and seminary, and became an ordained minister in the Presbyterian Church. All of those factors not only combined to change his life, but also change the entire country.

Rather than pastoring a local church, Fred Rogers felt his "ministry" should be positioned to influence young children everywhere through the medium of public television broadcasting. Television would be his daily "sermon." His convictions were that all children desperately needed to know that they are loved as well as loveable, and that someone could be there to help them through the modulations of life. Starting in Pennsylvania, *"Mr.*

Roger's Neighborhood" was birthed as a daily children's hour on the local PBS station.

Families quickly fell in love with this soft-spoken man who began his program every day by taking off his coat and putting on a sweater, and singing *"Would you be my neighbor?"* The morning show grew rapidly in popularity, but suddenly was threatened with cancellation when President Nixon asked to reduce government support of public broadcasting so that those funds could be transferred to the war effort in Viet Nam. Fred Rogers – along with nine others who had regular PBS programs – was summoned to Capitol Hill to appear before a Congressional panel. As the final speaker, Rogers stressed the urgency of adults knowing that the most important things in life are invisible. He pleaded his case that children needed to know that they were fine just as they were, and that they should love their neighbors. His sincerity won the hearts of the panel, and they approved the necessary funding in opposition to the President's wishes.

Even though his audience was very young, Fred knew that he could influence lives for decades to come with an attitude of equality if those same children could truly understand that love is at the root of all learning. Over the years, *"Mr. Roger's Neighborhood"* was willing to tackle such difficult topics as war, death, divorce, assassination, and anger. But one topic that was particularly important to him was the racial hatred that he saw in America's adults. How could he speak – as well as demonstrate – equality and love to people who had a skin color different than his own? How could he communicate to such young minds that everyone is special, endowed by their Creator, and worthy of being accepted just as they are?

In 1974 he had the answer. He invited an African American friend of his to appear on his TV show wearing the uniform of a police officer. When the officer happened to "stop by" his studio during the filming of Mr. Roger's neighborhood, Fred was sitting in a chair with his shoes off, his pant-legs rolled up, and his bare feet soaking in a big tub of cool water. The police officer lamented to Mr. Rogers that it was so hot outside, and he still had a lot of walking to do on his beat. Mr. Rogers politely asked the officer to take a break, take off his shoes, and join him for a few minutes by soaking his feet in the cool water with him.

As the camera panned in on two pair of feet – one black and one white – soaking side by side in the tub, the men's conversation ceased. The silent image of their feet remained on the screen for more than 15 seconds. The indelible lessons in that moment were many. . . prohibitions of mixed bathing were unnecessary, blacks and whites could get along fine, they enjoyed similar things, and anyone can be a friend – even a policeman.

Fred Rogers used his platform to reach the hearts of millions. He took a long-term perspective in choosing how to impact the country. Regardless of differences in ethnicity or physical ability, a person could say "I like you as you are." Young boys and girls did not have to absorb the racial hatreds of their parents. The vision of ethnic equality was gaining momentum, one (young) heart at a time.

Boulder was host to a weekly protest march unlike any other in the country. One of the national government research labs was located just a few miles south of town, and it secretly provided a very unique function for the Defense Department and our U.S. weapons systems. It was here that the manufacturing of plutonium triggers for nuclear bombs was taking place.

Dow Chemical Company had managed the original contract when the lab was first built for the Atomic Energy Commission, but when their contractual time had been completed, the facility went under direct control of the Department of Energy, and the name of the facility changed to Rocky Flats. Under the highest levels of security, hundreds of engineers willingly worked every day in an environment of plutonium and radioactive components. While they certainly appreciated their well-paid positions, they really had no idea of the true danger to which they were exposed, nor to the permanent damage being done to the environment as residual water was left to drain into the porous soil on their 2500 acre property.

Passionate citizens began to rendezvous every week on the south edge of Boulder, and march together to the entrance of the lab. The protest group ranged in size from 100 to 15,000 people. Once the entourage had arrived at the armed security entrance, they would hold a quiet prayer vigil, calling on God, government, and the Defense Department to shut down the facility in a step toward world peace.

The complexion of these marchers was strikingly different from any other protests. This was not exclusively students, or hippies, or anti-war activists. This band of people was a most eclectic mix of the citizenry . . . young and old, liberal and conservative, people from all faiths and political persuasions. Catholic nuns could be seen walking alongside Buddhist priests. Grandparents were marching with their grandchildren. Because of the routine nature of these weekly marches, the news media became somewhat calloused to the presence of a group of marchers, or the newsworthiness of their actions.

In typical fashion, the government first denied what was actually taking place there. But when former employees confirmed the primary function of producing nuclear bomb triggers, the ensuing government statements insisted that everything was completely safe. Another misstatement of the facts.

By mid-1974 the FBI raided the facility with 70 armed agents due to secret "whistle-blowers" telling of a plutonium fire and numerous toxic spills. Independent tests showed that the presence of radiation in the water and air surrounding the lab was as great as the fallout from a nuclear bomb. After years of legal maneuvering and further denials, the plant management finally pled "guilty" to criminal violations of environmental law. The government façade was over.

Radiation doesn't just "dry up or go away." Nuclear waste doesn't magically disappear. When the lab was eventually closed in 1992, the remaining level of radioactive contamination was still a major problem. The Defense Department spent $10 billion in the cleanup efforts, which still stands as the most expensive ever. Hundreds of trucks shuttled in convoys between Boulder and a remote location in southern New Mexico, carrying the radioactive waste materials into a vast network of underground caves for permanent storage. Over 800 buildings on the lab property were destroyed. Some soil contamination was left unresolved, hoping that remaining radiation would not seep into the ground water, and thereby contaminate suburbs of Denver that exist on the down-slope from this former weapons facility.

The Defense Department converted the property into a "wildlife refuge", which they had also done with 21 other military and cold war sites. Given the government's previous deception with other poisons, the surrounding public has been wary of the general safety of this area. Agent orange. Insecticides. Hexavalent chromium. Toxic fertilizers. Aerosols. Radiation. Nuclear waste. In the late '60's and early '70's the government allowed Americans to be exposed to all of these even though most men and women had little or no idea of the severity of what was around them. Ignorance is bliss. Although by '74 America was just now beginning to recognize such environmental problems, actual correction or removal would take many years.

Abbie Hoffman had already made a name for himself as a political activist and anarchist. As one of the "Chicago 8", he avoided a lengthy prison sentence when his "GUILTY" verdict was overturned. He continually sought opportunities to get behind a microphone if there was an audience who might hear his message of revolution. At Woodstock, for example, he snuck on to the stage during the musical set by *"The WHO"*, and began a rant over the sound system about a friend unfairly sent to jail. His words were cut short when the lead guitarist smashed him on the back with his guitar, sending Hoffman sprawling into the front two rows of the audience.

In '71 he had written a book entitled *"Steal This Book"*, which provided instructions on how a person could live for free by scamming or freeloading at the public's expense. The contents were filled with some of his many infamous quotes, such as "I believe in compulsory cannibalism. If people were forced to eat what they killed, there would be no more wars." Bookstores soon refused to carry the book in stock because fans were stealing the book instead of buying it. As a result, total actual sales were very disappointing.

But in the summer of this year, his life reached a new low point. Hoffman was arrested again in July of 1974 and charged with selling and distributing cocaine. Before final sentencing, he paid for cosmetic surgery to change his facial appearance, and went underground to avoid prison. Hoffman had once stated, "The first duty of a revolutionist is to get away with it." He now was living that philosophy by going incognito. In the process he had to abandon his wife and young children. Friends said that his most frequent disguise was dressing as an Orthodox Jew. He managed to elude law enforcement in this way for nine years.

When he finally was caught, he ultimately served less than a year in prison, then returned to a life of protest against such hated targets as the CIA, random drug-testing, and capitalism. As one writer described, his passion was always to comfort the afflicted, and to afflict the comfortable. But within a few years he chose to end his life by suicide, taking a large overdose of Phenobarbital.

On July 27 the United States judicial bulls-eye narrowed further on its aim at the Office of the President. By a vote of 26 to 11, the House of Representatives Judiciary Committee passed three articles of impeachment against Richard Nixon, including obstruction of justice and failure to uphold the laws of the land. What had once been unthinkable now seemed inevitable – impeachment, and the forced ouster of an American President.

Eleven days later, on the afternoon of August 8, Senator Barry Goldwater, a former Republican Presidential candidate, and three other key Republicans were escorted into the Oval office. With no pleasantries or small talk, they delivered the somber news to President Nixon – after privately polling every member of Congress, the President did not have the needed votes to escape impeachment. His storied political career was at a tragic end. The only question was exactly how he wanted to do so officially.

The final tipping point came moments later when Nixon made one final phone call, reaching out to George Wallace, asking if he still had Wallace's support. When the Alabama Governor said "NO", the President hung up the phone, slowly turned to Alexander Haig and said, "I've just lost the presidency."

To avoid the deeper humiliation of impeachment, President Nixon decided to willingly resign from the office which he cherished so. It was historic in its own right, since no President had ever been disgraced to the point of stepping down in the middle of a term. He spent that afternoon in quiet conversations with his wife, Pat, and occasionally chatted with his speech writers on specific phrases to use in his resignation address. In a television address later that evening he spoke to all of America while seated in his Oval Office, and in very halting phrases thanked the American people for the privilege of serving as President. He reiterated his love for his country, and promised to quietly step down from office the next morning. It was over. Although any further impeachment vote by Congress was subsequently avoided, the following 24 hours were likely the most humiliating for any man that has held the office of President of the United States.

On the following morning of August 9, the President asked that all of the personal staff of the White House join him in the East Wing. Janitors, chefs, White House tour guides, secretaries, chauffeurs, and anyone else with direct responsibilities for the President solemnly filed past the entire Nixon family. Many tears were quietly shed as their President forced a smile and thanked each one for their faithful service to him and to their country. Individual handshakes then followed for everyone in the room before the Nixon family exited, walking across the White House lawn without a word, and stepped up into the awaiting Presidential helicopter. As Richard Nixon reached the final step, he turned and gave one final victorious wave to the media. That iconic moment represented the lowest point in the history of the office of the presidency. Simultaneously it represented the highest point in the history of newspaper reporting.

As painful as it may have been for so many in Nixon's inner circle, that peaceful transfer of power demonstrated once again the greatness of our country and our Constitution in withstanding a crisis.

The Watergate break-in itself did not take down a President, but the repeated attempts at the ensuing cover-up did. For the rest of time, this was certainly a crucial lesson for every political or business leader to take to heart. No one was killed in the break-in. No one profited financially, other than the fees paid to the burglars themselves. But the extensive attempts at a cover-up shifted this scheme from a misdemeanor into "the crime of the 20th Century."

The final tally from the Watergate investigation had become a political "blood-letting" of historic proportions. Not only had a U.S. President been removed from office in disgrace, but several White House staff members had their political careers abruptly ended as well.

- John Mitchell, U.S. Atty General (and former director of Nixon's re-election campaign): Guilty of conspiracy, obstruction of justice, and perjury. Served 19 months in prison.
- H.R. Halderman, White House Chief of Staff (2nd most powerful man in government): Guilty of conspiracy and obstruction of justice. Served 18 months in prison.
- John Erlichman – President's Asst. for Domestic Affairs: Guilty of conspiracy, obstruction of justice, and perjury. Served 18 months in prison.
- Charles Colson, White House Legal Counsel: Guilty of obstruction of justice. Served seven months in prison.
- John Dean, Legal Advisor to the President. He negotiated a plea deal in exchange for providing extensive evidence to the Watergate Commission regarding other White House staff. Found guilty of obstruction of justice. Permanently disbarred from practicing Law in the future. Served four months in a "half-way house", so that he could continue to meet with members of the Watergate investigation panel.
- Dwight Chapin, Deputy Asst. to the President: Guilty of lying to a Grand Jury. Served nine months in prison.
- G. Gordon Liddy and E. Howard Hunt, head of the "Plumbers", and personal consultants to the President. Guilty of the conception and implementation of the break-in itself, and receiving bribery payments in exchange for silence. They were given stiff fines of

$40,000 each, and sentenced to prison. Hunt served three years before being released from an eight-year sentence. Liddy was sentenced to 20 years, but President Carter later commuted his sentence to eight years, to be more consistent with others that were involved.

The actions surrounding the Watergate break-in remains as the greatest embarrassment to the White House collectively in the history of our nation. It demonstrated that no person should ever be above the law.

As second in command, Vice President Gerald Ford was hurriedly sworn into office as our nation's 35th President, without ever having been elected President or Vice President. Just a few months earlier Ford had been appointed to the office of Vice President because of his highly respected career in Congress. He had served 15 terms as a U.S. Representative from Michigan, and was always seen as an honest man who was willing to dialog with opposing views in an effort to seek compromise and resolution. He had abruptly replaced Vice President Spiro Agnew, and now – less than a year later – stepped into the office of President of the United States of America.

In his acceptance speech after being sworn into office, Ford firmly stated, "Our long, national nightmare is over." His strong desire was that the American people could somehow begin to heal and move on. But exactly 30 days later, as one of his first official acts in his new role in the Oval Office, Ford stunned the entire country by announcing a full and unconditional pardon to Richard Nixon for any crimes he *might* have committed against the U.S. while in the White House.

A vast majority of Americans were incensed. They had felt that a trial was not only expected but also necessary, to allow the judicial process to determine the proper legal outcome for every person involved in the scandal, no matter what their office may have been. It seemed a *fait accompli* in order to truly allow our nation's healing to begin. Consequently this presidential pardon appeared to be so premature, so unfair, maybe even manipulated or – at worst – pre-arranged. The cynics stated, "Roosevelt had his NEW DEAL, Truman had his FAIR DEAL, and now Nixon had his CROOKED DEAL." When White House Press Secretary Jerald ter Horst learned of the Presidential pardon, he was so angry that he resigned on the spot.

In the weeks that followed, President Ford was forced to testify before a joint Congress regarding his pardon of Richard Nixon. It represented the first time since Abraham Lincoln that a sitting President had to testify before Congress. But there was no way that the Legislature could rescind what had been done.

Richard Nixon faded into quiet seclusion, exiled to an elegant estate on the southern California coast. America thought – and hoped – he was gone for good, never to be seen or heard from again. But they were wrong. He would return once more in the coming years, only to deepen his lasting legacy of disgrace.

Gerald Ford irrevocably doomed his own political career in that single decision to pardon his predecessor. Even some of the most loyal members of his Republican party felt personally betrayed and abandoned. That "act of grace" came back to bite Ford just one year later in his own campaign for a new term in the White House.

An incumbent President is rarely challenged from within his own party in the primaries. Yet when Gerald Ford began to campaign for re-election as president the following year, his party nomination was seriously threatened by California's governor, Ronald Reagan. Ford narrowly won the position of presidential candidate at the next Republican Convention. And when he did run in the national election that fall, Ford was soundly defeated by a peanut farmer from Georgia, an "outsider" that had no Capitol Hill experience whatsoever, whose most compelling credential was that he was a Sunday School teacher at a small-town Baptist church, and stood out as a man of absolute integrity. That was what the country wanted more than anything. America still had not forgiven Richard Nixon for his blatant disregard for the law, nor had they forgiven Gerald Ford for pardoning Nixon, and consequently Ford never stood a chance at the ballot box. The nation knew that our greatest need in the White House was the restoration of honesty and trust as paramount.

Americans wanted closure on the Watergate debacle, but it would be slow in coming. A high degree of unresolved anger remained, which needed a means of healing.

Richard Nixon had won his re-election in 1972 by one of the largest margins of all time. Yet with that Republican landslide victory only two years removed in the rear-view mirror, the November mid-term elections this year were a crushing success for Democrats. Clearly it was an emotional retaliation on the part of the voting public. Significant gains were made in both Houses of Congress, as well as at the state levels, including 49 new seats in the House of Representatives. It became one of the greatest "political backlashes" in history.

As a city, Boulder wanted to be progressive on most issues. The time had come to elect an African American as Mayor. Penfield Tate stepped into office as a very articulate and educated black man. Some voters supported his liberal political stand. Some voters just wanted to make a statement, that they supported civil rights in general for all black people. Either way, the city was proud to be on the cutting edge once again.

It was a political "fad" that began that fall. Over the next few years, numerous cities followed in electing black men and women to serve their communities. L.A., Detroit, Chicago, and Washington, D.C. did so, by electing a Black mayor. Even Atlanta joined this movement, in spite of being located in the heart of the south. This national trend provided a tangible vindication for the many years of civil rights marches, sit-ins, or other protests on behalf of African American people.

There was an additional political marker in the mid-term elections of this year. As a reaction against the scars of Watergate as well as the prolonged frustration of the Viet Nam war, many young adults chose to run for local office for the first time. Their simple campaign focus was to reach out to their peers as new voters, and unite them in a voice for change. In spite of their youth and inexperience, they won in great numbers, and were collectively given the moniker of "Watergate Babies."

That political shift was an added indictment that Richard Nixon had to carry for the rest of his life.

For a rock & roll musician, life was often about the benefits of being a music star, not the joy of the music itself. Fast cars. Fast women. Lots of drugs.

Neil Young came to Boulder in the fall of the year to do a concert in Balch Fieldhouse, which was an indoor basketball arena at the University. It was a general admission concert, so once the entrance doors were open, CU students and fans would have to make a mad rush to find the best seats possible. Unfortunately, demand exceeded capacity, and a small riot ensued outside of the venue by students that were unable to get a ticket. Bricks were thrown, numerous campus building windows were broken, and more than two dozen arrests were made before the waiting crowd would calm down.

Inside the venue, it was quite calm prior to the beginning of the concert. Young joined one of the production team and climbed up on a catwalk among the rafters that overlooked the auditorium floor. Together they sat there and watched as the doors opened and crowd rushed in, able to assess the attractiveness of the young women in particular. "This is Boulder, so tonight, I want to find an 'earth chick'," Young said to his assistant.

Once his "plan A" and "plan B" selections had been made, he returned to his back-stage room, then proceeded on stage for his concert. During the show, his assistant made the necessary inquiries with the two women in the crowd, and following the show a cooperative young lady with long blonde hair, bell-bottom jeans, a tie-dyed T-shirt with no bra, and "granny glasses" was escorted to the dressing room door.

It was a routine that was repeated in countless cities by countless musicians. Stardom had its perks.

For politics in general, the changing social attitudes of American culture by now produced a new environment where "image" or "celebrity" became just as important as mere "leadership" or "policy." Skillfully using or manipulating the new-found power of the media also developed into a specialty science of it's own.

An Arkansas candidate for Congress during the fall of 1974 stated "If a President of the U.S. ever lied to the American people, he should be compelled to resign." Brash words indeed. This candidate's name was William "Bill" Clinton. What is of historically significant is that he ultimately became the first "baby-boomer" ever elected to the White House, and correspondingly brought with him this boomer mentality of self-defined acceptable social and moral standards. Certainly he would not be the first – nor the last – occupant of the White House blatantly to lie to the American people. Certainly he would not be the first – nor the last – occupant of the White House to have sexual affairs while in the Oval Office. It was those very factors, however, that would ultimately overshadow his political successes and become his most lasting legacy as America's President.

While in office, Bill Clinton balanced the federal budget one year. Yes, he even passed landmark legislation to reduce welfare expenditures. Yes, he successfully passed the "line-item veto" for the Commander-in-Chief. Each of those accomplishments was historic, to be sure. But his greatest legacy would directly reflect the "open freedoms" mindset and profile that had become commonplace from this boomer-driven generation, namely his numerous sexual indiscretions, frequent lies which attempted to cover those bad habits, and the tolerance of regular drug usage amongst some of the appointed White House staff. The Clintons' "baby-boomer attitudes" which were rooted from the late '60's brazenly moved against the commonly accepted standards for those holding public office, skirting the law too frequently. As a result, "scandal management" became the most lasting trademark for both of the Clintons throughout their careers.

The 1960's mindset of "sex, drugs, and rock & roll", accompanied by its moral relativism, would one day be escorted by a baby-boomer from the youthful rebellions on the college campus into the highest office in the world. In classic Boomer-fashion, the Clintons chose to live – and almost die – by selecting their own set of chosen rules. By adeptly handling such extreme successes and extreme failures while in office, "Baby Boomer Bill Clinton" proved himself to be the most skilled American politician in more than a century.

It was early December, and Russell had to drive carefully down the snow-packed streets of Boulder. He didn't want to have an accident, and miss out on his company's Christmas party. The car parts company that he worked for always provided an elegant meal with an open bar and dancing at one of the nicest hotel lounges in town to celebrate the holiday.

Russell had struggled to finish high school two years earlier, and decided to find a job rather than considering college. For him it was a good choice. He loved tinkering with cars, and this company was a good fit.

When he arrived at the Broker Inn, most of the company employees and their spouses were already there. By the time he got his first complimentary drink from the bar, he discovered that one of the few dinner seats left unclaimed was at the table with the company owner and his wife. Russell didn't mind, as long as he could have a few drinks and a big steak.

The evening held much more in store for him. His table of co-workers was having a lively conversation with lots of laughs. But during the main course he was shocked to realize that the owner's wife was starting to play "footsie" with him under the table. She was almost 30, and was the second wife of his boss, who was 35. Russell went along with it, not sure if it was just meaningless flirtation.

After the main course and before the dessert, several people got up on the dance floor to enjoy the music. The company owner was occupied "working the room", visiting with some of the other employees at another table. The owner's wife excused herself to use the restroom, and as she did so, she leaned over and whispered into Russell's ear. "Meet me in the elevator, next to the restrooms," she said.

Russell nodded, and gulped down the remainder of his drink. He waited a minute, and then hesitantly headed down the hallway. Sure enough, she was waiting in the elevator with the door held open. As soon as he stepped into the elevator, she let the door close and immediately pushed the "Emergency Stop" button.

"Let's do this," she said with a seductive grin. "We only have a few minutes."

It didn't take him that long. As she turned around, she hiked up her mini-skirt, and braced herself against the elevator railing. It was the fastest "quickie" he had ever had. Moments later she stopped into the women's restroom while he rejoined the party. He definitely needed another drink.

What Russell learned that Christmas was that many married people also wanted to be a part of the radical cultural changes that were taking place.

The integrity of America's government took another "hit" in the late fall. During his last few months in office, former President Nixon had secretly promised $1,000,000,000 in aid to South Viet Nam's President Tho so that South Vietnamese troops could continue to fight. But once Nixon was forced to resign, that unwritten promise disappeared.

When President Ford went to Congress to ask for the approval of additional financial aid for President Tho and his military, both Houses of the legislature – for the first time since the war had started – voted "NO." It was now apparent that any further support was just chasing good money after bad.

President Tho felt that he had just been cut off at the knees, and knew this consigned his country's government to an imminent collapse. Within days he resigned from office. International television and radio carried his speech around the world, declaring that he had been unfairly betrayed by the United States. After ten years of bloodshed, that blunt statement solidified the outcome of total defeat. It was now only a matter of time.

During the last week of December Brian needed to make a quick road-trip to the west coast to meet with other leaders of the Weather Underground. Major changes were on the drawing board for the coming year, so crucil that they needed to be discussed face to face. As he passed through Colorado, he called his younger brother, Tom, to meet him for breakfast.

"You got time for some pancakes?" Brian asked, once Tom roused enough to answer the phone.

"Sure," Tom said with sudden excitement, when he realized who was on the phone. "Where are you?"

"I'll meet you at IHOP in 30 minutes," Brian said, and hung up the phone.

Due to their age difference, Tom and Brian had never been "playground pals." There may have been little in the way of companionship or affection, yet there was a deep mutual admiration simply because they were brothers. For two brief hours they elevated each other's energy with their optimistic endeavors, oblivious to anyone else in the restaurant.

"Can you believe it?" Tom asked with a tone of glee. "Finally 'Tricky Dicky' Nixon is out of office, the Viet Nam War is actually ending, and America can now begin to recover. All my friends are done with peace marches or sit-ins because we've won! You and the thousands of university students actually made that happen."

"It's a drop in the bucket," Brian replied, somewhat to Tom's surprise. "REAL change has just begun." He took a sip of his coffee before continuing. "The Weathermen are going to make a strategic shift, and I think it's a good one. I was never convinced that all the bombs in the world would change people's mind-set anyway."

Tom was more than curious. "So what are your next plans?" he asked.

"We are going to have to take a much longer-term perspective, but we are convinced it will have a much more lasting effect on the country," Brian said with a tone of urgency. "We are going to train and radicalize people with the expressed purpose of infiltrating politics and higher education. That is how real change is going to happen. It will certainly take longer, but it will be more permanent and more pervasive."

Tom thought that sounded a bit grandiose, but didn't say anything. He would rather pursue a path that made lots of money for himself. As they said their final good-byes in the parking lot, they had no idea it would be the last time they would ever see each other. They also had no idea that both of them would ultimately accomplish their respective goals.

President Jimmy Carter

Abbie Hoffman

Patricia Hearst

E. Howard Hunt   G. Gordon Liddy

1st Lady Betty Ford and President Gerald Ford

President Nixon's final farewell from the White House

CHAPTER 12

"1975 – CLOSURES AND NEWFOUND HOPE"

"We gotta' get out of this place
If it's the last thing we ever do . . .
We gotta' get out of this place,
Girl, there's a better life for me and you."
the Animals
"When the moon is in the seventh house
And Jupiter aligns with Mars
Then PEACE will guide the planet
And LOVE will steer the stars.
This is the dawning of the Age of Aquarius . . ."

- the Fifth Dimension

Boulder witnessed a tragic headline in their local newspaper in early January of 1975. Jake had grown up in Boulder, and graduated from high school just 18 months earlier. He was a bright young man, good looking, athletic, and the youngest of five boys in a loving family.

Like most of his classmates, he matriculated to CU even though he had no specific plans or goals for a college degree. That decision meant he could stay in town with all of his friends, but not have to live at home. This was his chance to get away from very strict parents and live on his own. But it was that college dorm life that started to eat him up. Drugs and alcohol became a daily component of his activities, and after one semester he felt no need to go any further with a formal education. Jake dropped out of school, and took a job with a small construction company in Boulder County.

His choices were very disappointing to his parents, but they continued to help him with some of his rent payments in hopes that he would get tired of the manual labor life-style and decide to return to school. Neither of his parents smoked or drank, and both were very religious, so they had very little understanding and even less patience with him when he would stop by their house in a stoned or drunken state.

A few weeks before Christmas Jake had just received the devastating news that his girlfriend was pregnant. Neither of them wanted to consider an abortion. The prevailing social presumption of that era was that any such couple "had to get married." Yet both Jake and his girlfriend knew that they really weren't ready for that either. They didn't want to face the responsibility of trying to set up a home together.

Worse than the financial dilemma that faced him, Jake could not stand to think of the shame and social pain that this would bring to his parents as well as his girlfriend's parents. He feared what might happen if he told his father in person, but he also knew he must tell his mother in person. He could not find a clear answer.

On New Year's Day, Jake invited a large number of friends over to watch the Rose Bowl. USC was playing Ohio State once again, and the college football #1 ranking was on the line. He hoped that an apartment full of people and a party atmosphere would cheer him up. Instead it had the opposite effect. So many friends were having such a great time, and it reminded him more and more that he was about to resign himself to a life of emotional pain that he was bringing down on his parents and on himself, a degree of shame to a young woman that he really didn't love, and a financial burden beyond his ability. It was too much.

After drinking seven or eight beers, he made a slow pass through the living room, chatting one last time with several of his best friends. He then made his way to a back bedroom and closed the door. As he sat on the bed, he pulled a 9mm pistol out of the night-stand. There was no need to write a note . . . his parents would never understand him anyway. Maybe his girlfriend could say the right things on his behalf.

Jake took a deep breath, placed the cold barrel against his temple, and squeezed the trigger. An hour later the police completed their investigation, and sent a squad car personally to inform his parents of what had just happened. Their worst-case scenarios could never have anticipated such news. Grief and confusion enveloped them for the next several years.

Boulder's newspaper, The Daily Camera, carried articles on the story for four days in a row, trying to answer a myriad of questions. Why was this drastic choice necessary in Jake's mind? Why were so many parents losing touch with their kids? Why were kids so careless with their choices of sex, drugs, or alcohol?

Life often presents "WHY?" situations to a person, and every individual must learn how to process those moments, even when there are no easy answers. There certainly were no easy answers surrounding the life of Jake. His 19 ½ years on this earth only reminded the Boulder community that the carefree mantra of "sex, drugs, and rock & roll" occasionally had some horrible consequences.

On January 29 the Weather Underground detonated another bomb, this time in the headquarters of the U.S. State Department in Washington, D.C. True to their original objectives, no persons were killed, but the damage was extensive. More than 20 offices on three floors were virtually destroyed. Once again, this was meant as an "exploding press conference", declaring the need to incapacitate the "evil empire" of capitalism, as well as white supremacy and the military industrial complex. It would be one of their last such statements via terrorism.

With the diminishing U.S. presence in Viet Nam, their primary cause for protesting as well as recruiting was fading. Their prime rallying point for organized dissent was no longer sufficient. Both the Weather Underground and the SDS quietly began to disband, unable to sustain any committed leadership for the purpose of other public protests. That decrescendo was aided by the fact that several key instigators had been killed by law enforcement, others had frequently been arrested, legal costs were mounting, and an internal battle was taking place because of too many diverse opinions within the ranks regarding which priorities to focus on next.

Instead, the true radicals who remained took the advice of Brian and made a strategic decision to infiltrate politics and education, taking a long-term perspective to achieving their goals of changing dramatically America's attitudes from within. Their message could be leveraged, and the country would quietly begin to shift without resistance from law enforcement. The mindset of these passionate young people would win.

In January of '75 Richard Nixon was rushed to the hospital with a severe case of phlebitis. Doctors worked feverishly around the clock to reduce the swelling and diminish the risk of a fatal blood clot. He narrowly survived. Because he was necessarily in the news, the recent memories and anger surrounding Watergate once again returned to the front page.

Verdicts were handed down that same month for the top aides to the former President. Over 40 people were ultimately indicted and given prison terms for their part in the Watergate break-in and the subsequent cover-up. John Mitchell, H.R. Haldeman, John Ehrlichman, and Charles Colson were all found guilty in assisting in the cover-up, lying under oath, and obstructing justice. John Mitchell spent 19 months in prison, and is the only U.S. Attorney General to ever serve time in prison. Haldeman spent 18 months in prison for his role in these crimes. Ehrlichman was sentenced to 2½ to 8 years as a concurrent sentence because of his specific role in the '71 break-in of Daniel Ellsberg's psychiatrist's office. He actually served 18 months in prison. Colson received the shortest sentence, and spent 7 months in prison. Even though these men had held some of the loftiest positions in our nation's government, their prison time served as a sound reminder that no person is immune from the law. And in so doing, America began to feel only a partial sense of vindication.

Richard Nixon was still the "big prize", however, and the media wanted to find a way to generate their own trial for his role in these cover-ups. Somehow they had to find a process to "hang him" via the printed press. The final opportunity to do so came unexpectedly because of Nixon's enormous pride. He was always convinced that if he was given a chance, he could "set the record straight", and could salvage his own reputation. So he sought to have an extensive TV interview that could provide the controlled setting for him to do so.

David Frost was already a popular TV host in England and Australia, but virtually unknown in the U.S. He out-bid the other networks for the Nixon interviews, and salivated at the chance to make a name for himself in this country. And with that contract in place, former President Nixon felt he had already scored a coup by side-stepping all of the American TV network reporters, whom he despised vehemently. He was now certain that he would be given the national platform he needed, and that Frost would be a "pushover" since he had no political investigation experience. With two such egos careening toward each other, at least one was going to be severely disappointed.

The format was set for four shows of 90 minutes each, and the identified topics respectively devoted to each show segment were (1) Nixon, the man; (2) his domestic affairs; (3) international policies; and (4) Watergate.

Nixon's handlers made sure he was in control of every minute detail, and for the first three interviews he handled himself admirably. Compelling anecdotes regarding other heads of state. Amusing insights into his personal childhood. Presidential accomplishments in opening the door to new relations between the U.S. and China. He actually seemed quite impressive.

But his attempt to salvage any self-respect from the American public collapsed in the final interview. As Frost grilled him about the Oval Office tapes, and the missing 18 minutes that had been erased, and the fact that all of his aides had been found guilty and received prison terms, Nixon unexpectedly departed from his "coached" remarks. He began to rationalize that illegal actions were permissible by the President if they were for the good of the country. He candidly talked about serious errors that were made, how he had personally let down the American people, personally let down his friends and supporters, and personally let down the high office of the Presidency. And he publically apologized for his serious mistakes. Watergate, he said, remained his recurring nightmare.

Frost briefly stared in stunned silence. There could be no actual prison time for this man, but the "trial" had finally taken place. He had been "undressed" on national television, and left as a very sad and lonely man, tragically suffering in exile as a pitiful "has-been" who recognized his culpability. Frustrated Americans finally had a satisfactory bit of revenge, and with that the healing process could slowly begin to move forward. His admission of guilt finally offered some closure on the Watergate drama.

Richard Nixon remained on his isolated California estate for almost 20 years, carefully protected by a security team that sealed in his obscurity until his death in 1994. Ironically the most lasting legacy from his presidency was that any ensuing political illegality or suspicion of corruption since that time has been given the suffix "-- GATE."

Nine-year-old Nguyen (pronounced 'win') awoke on April 30th, 1975, as if it were any other day in Saigon. He ate his breakfast of Mien – a combination of noodles and vegetables – and prepared to go out to play with his friends. But as he was heading for the door, his father unexpectedly returned from his office. Dad was a General in the South Vietnamese Army, and typically never came home before dinnertime, so Nguyen knew that something was terribly wrong this morning.

His father had a focused glare on his face that Nguyen had never seen before. Without saying a word to Nguyen or his younger sister, the man took his wife by the hand and quietly walked into their back bedroom. Moments after door closed, Nguyen could faintly hear his mother sobbing throughout their conversation.

Less than ten minutes later, his parents stepped out of their bedroom. His father sat down on their large chair and plopped his son onto his knee. "Nguyen," the man began with a tone of urgency, "today I need you to be a man, OK?" He paused, trying to choose his words very carefully. "You and your sister are going to go on a trip with your mother, and I'll catch up with all of you in a few days."

He gave a long hug to both of his children, then wiped a small tear from his wife's cheek before kissing her good-bye. As he hurried back to his military vehicle waiting for him in the street, he turned and gave one last wave to his family. It was the last time Nguyen would ever see his father.

The message delivered to Nguyen's mother that morning was that the last remaining Americans in Saigon were secretly evacuating the city that day in emergency fashion. It was expected that North Vietnamese troops would be occupying Saigon within three days. She was told to pack two small suitcases that she could carry herself, and immediately leave the country with her children. Otherwise any family such as his that was loyal to the South Vietnamese government could very well be slaughtered when the Viet Cong arrived.

There were 7,700 Americans remaining in Saigon that week, including U.S. embassy officials, military officers, news media personnel, spouses and children. The Defense Department had quietly been developing an emergency evacuation plan throughout the previous month, as it became clear that North Vietnamese troops were advancing closer and closer to Saigon from three directions. The most critical elements of such an evacuation were that it must be both orderly and discreet. It turned out to be neither.

The secret code was broadcast on American radio that morning in Saigon, so that every U.S. citizen living there would know this was the prearranged final alarm, giving the signal for a complete and immediate evacuation. The announcer said, "Good morning, the temperature is 105°

and rising", and then immediately played Bing Crosby singing *"I'm Dreaming of a White Christmas."* The hidden alarm had been sounded.

"Plan A" for the evacuation was that everyone could leave from the main airport, Tan Sun Nhut, with 200 – 300 people at a time filling large cargo and transport planes headed for the Philippines or Guam. But Viet Cong troops had advanced more quickly than expected in that sector, destroyed the runways with mortar shells, and left several planes in flames on the runways. The airport was completely inoperable.

"Plan B" was to shuttle everyone in convoys of buses and vans to large ships anchored at the coast, and get everyone off-shore as quickly as possible. Several troop ships and an aircraft carrier were ready and waiting to make that run to Clark Air Force Base in Manila, as the central transfer point back to the U.S. The idea only looked good on paper.

By mid-morning word had spread throughout Saigon that the Americans were all hurriedly leaving, and trying quietly to do so at once. Americans tried to evacuate in secret, leaving 150,000 loyal Vietnamese employees to be at the mercy of the North Vietnamese soldiers. Every vendor with a close relationship to the Americans, every girlfriend of an American officer, and every family of the South Vietnamese military wanted out as well. So many people frantically congested the streets that the entire city was in absolute traffic gridlock. Consequently the easy movement of large buses and vans as shuttles became impossible.

"Plan C" was to use a convoy of helicopters to make as many trips as necessary to get everyone to the large ships just a few miles off shore. These helicopters – coincidentally called "Chinooks" – could carry 40 to 45 people at a time. It certainly was more time-consuming to work with such relatively small numbers for each load, but it was the only remaining option that could work. More than 50 such helicopters were utilized for the coordinated removal of American personnel.

The first Chinook was instructed to carry U.S. Ambassador Graham Martin to safety, along with a few of his key staff, but he refused. Ambassador Martin was in a state of denial, unable to believe that the situation was so dire. He had lost his only son on the Viet Nam battlefield, and could not accept the idea that such a humiliating defeat was possible after America had invested so many precious lives into the conflict. He chose to stay in his office until the final minutes, helping his staff to shred confidential documents.

Two beautiful mature trees in the center of the American embassy grounds were quickly chopped down to make room for helicopters to land safely on the central lawn. The Chinooks began arriving on the newly-created landing pad as well as the roof of the U.S. Embassy in 10 – 12 minute intervals. They would load up to 40 people as quickly as possible, and make the flight to a waiting ship. Round-trip was 70 minutes, and they would do the process all over again.

By noon more than 40,000 citizens of Saigon had jammed the streets surrounding the American Embassy, begging for permission to pass through the security gate and await their turn on to a helicopter. Desperation set in. Men offered their silver coin collections or other valuables to the embassy guards. Women offered sexual favors. Those that were young and agile enough tried scaling the ten-foot cement walls that were topped with barbed wire. Armed U.S. guards tried to maintain a sense of order at the front gate, but fights were occurring frequently.

And all the while, the helicopter pilots just kept loading up their cargo space with the next segment of people from the embassy lines, and making another run to the waiting ships. Most shuttle runs had only six to ten Americans at a time, and the rest were Vietnamese, because everyone knew that once the Americans were all gone, the evacuation effort would stop. Some pilots flew more than 17 hours that day without a break.

Nguyen, his sister, and his mother were three of the lucky ones. Their home was within a mile of the U.S. embassy, so they walked with their suitcases in hand. One of the strangest sights they observed on that walk was dozens of young Vietnamese men walking around bare-footed, wearing nothing but white underwear briefs. These happened to be South Vietnamese soldiers that had panicked at the thought of the impending occupation by the North Vietnamese. They assumed they would be killed if they were found in uniform, so they hurriedly discarded their army boots and green uniforms in small piles in the gutters of the street. Almost naked, and nowhere to run.

Once Nguyen and his family arrived at the Embassy, they had to wrestle their way through the throng of agitated people that packed the street. Their family credentials were strong enough to be approved by the guards, and they were allowed to enter the Embassy grounds. More than 2,000 other Vietnamese people were already inside the Embassy ahead of them, so they had to wait most of the day – without any food or restroom facilities – seated on the central lawn with the others. An additional 1500 locals would join them before the day ended.

Two very peculiar memories remain etched in Nguyen's mind from that afternoon. Once they were inside the Embassy grounds, it was announced repeatedly that no weapons would be allowed on any of the Chinook helicopters. Before he and his family were flown out late in the day, Nguyen counted more than 100 pistols that had been tossed into the bottom of the Embassy swimming pool that was in the middle of the waiting area.

The other oddity was a strange-smelling smoke wafting all afternoon from a small shed next to the Embassy machine shop. He knew it was not food of some sort that was cooking, and it did not smell like any wood that was burning. He would not learn until many years later that he had been smelling . . . money. Lots of smoldering money. The U.S. Embassy had more than $1.5 million dollars in cash ready for their payroll coming up in the next week. When the emergency evacuation decision was announced, two U.S. employees were assigned to burn all of the paper money that afternoon before they could leave. It took them the better part of the day to finish.

Other South Vietnamese families had to be extra creative in finding different ways out of the city. Many military men had been trained to fly U.S. Hueys, which were combat helicopters that could carry 6 – 15 people. Dozens of those had been abandoned at the airport when the final American ground troops had left in the previous year. Using scooters to get in and out of city traffic, these men took their family and friends to the airport, crammed 20 or more into each of the small helicopters and headed east. They assumed once there were in the air, they could follow the larger Chinooks to the waiting flotilla of boats. Once there, they intended to land on any boat that had sufficient deck space for a helicopter. As soon as the passengers were removed, the men would then push the helicopter over the edge of the boat and let it sink to the bottom of the ocean. It was a strange necessity in order to make room for more helicopters and more passengers that were coming in right behind them. One helicopter pilot found a boat too small to handle the weight of his aircraft. The pilot deftly hovered about six feet above the deck of the boat, and his twenty passengers jumped out one at a time. One infant had to be tossed to the arms of its waiting mother. Once all passengers were unloaded, he intentionally crashed the copter gently into the water, and swam to the surface, treading water until a life raft could pick him up.

Boats and ships of all sizes began to load more and more people to safety. Small fishing boats. A garbage skow. Even a stolen U.S. gun ship that had been in dry-dock because it had only one out of four engines functioning. Most boats were carrying ten times their capacity, i.e. a

357

20-passenger houseboat had 200 people sandwiched on its decks. By the end of the day, more than 80,000 people had managed to leave Saigon successfully. Another 120,000 were left behind, wanting desperately to get out, but unable to find any transportation that had room for them. These were loyal Vietnamese that had served as faithful employees, but were now abandoned in the moment of crisis. They were left to the mercy of the North Vietnamese, and were considered "dead men walking." They quickly destroyed any ID's or badges that they had, hoping to appear as innocent civilians.

Other than two media representatives that insisted on staying behind for a few weeks, the last U.S. citizens were headed home that evening. Americans throughout the U.S. watched the live news footage with an utter sense of helplessness. For the next 24 hours there was extensive looting in the Embassy as well as all U.S. offices and apartments. Within 48 hours the Viet Cong were riding through the streets of Saigon in jubilant celebration. Although the American military presence had been vastly superior in their weaponry, they were now entirely gone, having left with a final image of complete futility and disgrace.

Nguyen, his sister, and his mother finally boarded a Chinook just before sunset, and landed on a U.S. cargo ship 20 miles off shore. Their drama, however, was far from over. Only minutes after disembarking from the Chinook helicopter, an announcement was made over the intercom system that the ship was partially disabled, that it was now taking on water, and slowly sinking. The boat captain pulled along side another ship nearby, and everyone was instructed to walk across a ten-foot plank carefully to get to safety on the other vessel. There were no guide ropes or hand-rails, so walking that plank was precarious as the ships would occasionally roll slowly with the ocean swells.

As people proceeded to walk single-file from one ship to the next, one man panicked and pushed the woman in front of him to move faster. She stumbled and fell 40 feet into the ocean below, and drowned before she could be rescued. A South Vietnamese officer immediately shot the guilty man with a pistol to restore order, and pushed his body into the water as well.

An hour later they were all boarded on to a Vietnamese cargo ship, headed for Manila. As they watched the coastline fade with the diminishing daylight, they said good-bye to their homeland. They had no idea that good-bye was going to be forever. By the time their ship arrived in the Philippines two days later, they were not allowed to unload because the ship was sailing under a South Vietnamese flag, and that country was no longer recognized. Because there were several Americans on board, they were able to get emergency provisions for everyone from Clark Air Force Base. It was enough to survive for three days until a U.S. aircraft carrier sailed into port, and everyone was transferred to that ship. Each passenger on board was issued a temporary passport, and then flown to the U.S. Nguyen and his family were ultimately assigned by the U.S. government to live in Boulder, Colorado, with a volunteer family for two years. Both Nguyen and his sister were excellent students, and in the ensuing years grew up to be hard-working and successful business people in metro-Denver.

Their father was never able to leave Viet Nam. Once captured by the Viet Cong, along with thousands of others who were deemed loyal to the previous South Vietnamese government, he was sent to a "re-education" camp. The communist indoctrination there could take two to five years, at the discretion of the instructors. Although punishment was a part of the re-education process, it was not meant to be a torture or concentration-camp facility. Everyone was expected to survive and become a loyal worker for the unified state. Viet Nam would need every able-bodied man to help rebuild the war-torn country. Because of a poor diet, however, his father became ill, which soon turned into pneumonia. And because of the lack of sufficient health treatment, he died just before his 45th birthday.

In the months that followed the evacuation, President Ford and the Congress refused to vote for any emergency funds to pay for the aid or additional transfers of South Vietnamese friends. The political consensus was that America had already wasted too much time and money in Viet Nam, and any further funds would be good money chasing after bad. Consequently some U.S. soldiers created a "black market" list of specific key friends and associates to sneak out of the country. Bribery is a universal language, and during the next few years several thousand more men and women were able to leave Viet Nam secretly for a new life in the West, usually finding passage in the cargo hold of a supply ship.

On June 26, violence broke out once again at the Pine Ridge Indian Reservation in South Dakota. Since the shoot-out of two years ago at Wounded Knee, the U.S. government had done nothing of substance to respond to AIM's demands for reparations to Native Americans because of numerous broken treaties.

Leonard Peltier and Russell Means were self-appointed leaders of the AIM. They took several local law enforcement officials as hostages, and demanded that the government begin negotiating with them. This time federal authorities did not ignore their threats, and responded by immediately surrounding the compound. AIM members and local residents of the reservation fired high-powered rifles at federal airplanes that came within range, as well as any federal agent that stepped from behind cover. In the brief exchange of gunfire, two FBI agents and one AIM member were killed before the uprising was squelched.

All surviving AIM supporters were arrested. Leonard Peltier was found guilty of first-degree murder, and received a sentence of two consecutive life terms. AIM disbanded in the coming months because most of its leaders were in prison. The chants and prayers of the Native American people slowly faded like a smoke signal being dispersed in a breeze.

Congress never acknowledged any fault or need for changes. In the state courts, however, some tribes won major concessions from their local governments in cases involving land claims. But those victories seemed like a pittance.

In the coming years, Russell Means was a presidential candidate for the Libertarian Party, and later attempted to run for Governor of New Mexico. His passion for justice for Native Americans, however, seemed to die with him. America's treatment of our Indian tribes remains one of the two greatest scars in our nation's grand history.

By the arrival of summer, Patty Hearst and friends were getting restless. Not only were they running very low on funds, but they were also lonely and wanted to get back to some of their California friends. Their decision to head west once again was hastened when one of their California friends got drunk and told his local police that he knew where the SLA gang was hiding out. The FBI rushed to search the Pennsylvania farmhouse, but missed them by two days.

After a long drive by way of Las Vegas, Patty was once again back in northern California, and with her other two remaining members of the SLA chose Sacramento as their new home. It was close enough to San Francisco and their network of relationships at Cal-Berkeley, but far enough away to feel secluded. Again, Patty could have walked away an infinite number of times, but was now committed to the SLA's vision of complete and total cultural upheaval. A few new friends were recruited from Cal to join them there, and the group started making plans for the next steps of the revolution. Since they had to have more money before they might attempt any radical statement or action against the establishment, the first piece to the puzzle was to rob another bank.

A small bank on the out-skirts of Sacramento was carefully chosen. Four members of the SLA went into the bank with guns loaded, while Patty and one other friend stayed outside as drivers for the two getaway cars. It should have been easy, since the bank had no security guard and no electronic surveillance cameras. But "Murphy's Law" hit them in disastrous fashion.

As the four SLA members entered the bank and announced the hold-up, demanding that people step aside while they emptied the cash drawers, one of the shot-guns went off accidentally, instantly killing a female customer in the bank. Moments later the gang raced out with a large shopping bag full of cash and drove away. But now they were once again wanted for armed bank robbery, and murder in the first degree.

Within a few weeks the police and FBI had received enough new leads that they were able to make their arrests. As the entire SLA group was hand-cuffed and driven away in police cars that September afternoon, Patty and the other SLA members kept shouting "Death to the Pigs" and "Capitalism Must Die." Closure had finally come to one of the greatest man-hunts in U.S. history. What was troubling to every parent in America was how this apparent behavioral change could have happened to Patty. How could a young woman with everything going for her – beauty, wealth beyond most people's dreams, and highly intelligent – make such radical choices which might destroy her character and even her life? What was happening to America's youth?

Once in court, the prosecution sought to make a vivid example to all protestors in the country that would try to circumvent the law. Although the death penalty had just been outlawed in California, lengthy prison terms were given to each member of the SLA. Special treatment, however, was given to the young heiress. Her family hired F. Lee Bailey, considered to be the top trial lawyer in the country.

Going into her trial, the jury might have assumed that Patty had willingly helped to rob three banks, was aiding and abetting in two murders, and remained on the lam for more than a year because of her support of the SLA. However Bailey moved the courtroom in a new direction. He convinced the jury to consider that Patty was a victim of kidnapping, brain-washing, and mind-control. He asked the court to consider her "as innocent as the wind-driven snow." In the end she was found "Guilty" on lesser charges than the other SLA members, and was sent to prison for two years.

President Jimmy Carter then commuted the remainder of her sentence, and she was released from the rest of her prison term. During his last week in office Carter then pardoned her from the original sentence entirely, so that the felony would not even be on her permanent record. Since then Patty has lived a quiet and comfortable life as a model citizen in New York City. But it's no wonder that some people remain convinced that "justice can be bought", or that "the judicial system is not about truth, but about winning."

By mid- 1975 two major transitions had begun to take place in the news industry relating to what was now deemed necessary for thorough news coverage. First, news anchors began to offer opinions and analysis instead of limiting themselves to factual reporting. That new niche was very subtle at first, but has slowly and steadily encroached on news desks to where we are today. Now we have several cable channels that spend 24 hours a day analyzing the news and telling viewers how they should think.

Secondly, television and newspaper reporters were now willing to pursue more titillating stories which had once been off limits. The Washington Post had just won the Pulitzer Prize for Public Service, and deservedly so. The Post helped change the course of history by bravely publishing the Pentagon Papers, and by finding the story behind the story in the Watergate drama. Now every news outlet wanted to emulate that new standard by finding exclusive stories of any kind that would gain new viewers or readers.

Formerly the press cooperated with politicians, and vice versa. There had been a sense of trust or respect with each other. They even "covered" for each other, and allowed for one's privacy. When Presidents Kennedy and Johnson had multiple affairs while in the White House, the press respected the office of President too much to mention it. Such chivalry was part of the privilege of reporting news on Capitol Hill.

But now it was a new era, which required a willingness to look for "dirt." The press began to hold politicians accountable. Reporters sought to create news if necessary to get a scoop on the competition. There was little hesitation in embarrassing an elected official to satisfy the curiosity of the public. And lusty material always seemed to be available.

Arkansas Representative Wilbur Mills was the most powerful member of the House as Chairman of the House Ways and Means Committee. But his 38-year career in Washington crashed in just a few weeks. In October, when he was stopped for speeding at 2a.m. on a D.C. street, a stripper known as Fannie Foxe the "Argentine Firecracker" jumped out of his car and began splashing in the basin of a large water fountain. One reporter happened to get a photo before Mills and Foxe left the scene. Suddenly the news sharks were chasing some fresh meat. Just one week later a drunken Mills staggered onto a Boston stage while Foxe was performing, and began clumsily dancing and fondling her. The Congressman was arrested for public indecency.

The story as well as the accompanying photos went national. Democrats were so angered they forced Mills to resign. Something that the media would not have touched five or ten years earlier was now a national spectacle. News reporters celebrated their role in revealing such character flaws of the rich and powerful.

Just a few months later Ohio Representative Wayne Hays met a similar fate. As the head of the House Advisory Committee he had more than two dozen people on his private staff. But some of those employees complained that Hays' personal secretary, Elizabeth Ray, did nothing. In an interview with the Washington Post, Miss Ray said that "she did not know how to type, did not know how to file, and didn't even know how to answer the phone." Her only responsibility, she confessed, was to have sex with Representative Hays several times a week. Once again the Post had a news scoop that went national.

The House Ethics Committee was required to conduct an investigation into Hays entire office. Some taxpayers may not have minded an elected official having an affair, but no taxpayer was happy that they were paying her $14,000 salary just to be a mistress. Elizabeth Ray was terminated immediately, and Wayne Hays was forced to resign within days.

The Hill was on notice. There was no longer anything off limits for a good news story.

That summer U.S. relations with the Soviet Union took a surprising turn in a positive direction. With the Viet Nam War now in the rear view mirror, gentle attempts were made to solidify a peaceful co-existence.

Mikail Baryschnikov was a Russian ballet dancer, widely considered the best in the world. When his dance troupe was asked to tape a TV special in Canada, he agreed. But upon completion, he shocked the world by announcing his intent to defect. Within a few weeks he moved from Canada to the United States, and joined the New York City Ballet. While it was considered a major coup for the free world, government response was cautiously muted to avoid unnecessary irritation of the Russians.

On July 17th, a "public relations gesture" was successfully executed to ease any further tensions between the two countries, although it had to take place in outer space. The Russian capsule Soyuz rendezvoused with the U.S. space craft Apollo and carefully negotiated a docking maneuver. The world watched as the two captains met each other 160 miles above the earth. Soviet Commander Alexei Leonov and America's Apollo Commander Thomas Stafford shook hands and smiled for the camera.

The symbolic statement was profound. The world's two super-powers could peacefully cooperate in a worthwhile mission. Maybe the cold war was easing.

Prior to August of 1975, women in the corporate workplace were expected to endure any mistreatment quietly with little or no room for recourse. In prior decades any uninvited sexual advances were not reported, and any improper sexual behavior was ignored by the press. Women's only advice had been to quit their jobs if they were unhappy with their company's work environment. This summer, however, the women's movement took an historic stand.

A group of women at Cornell University founded "WORKING WOMEN UNITED." Together they filed a court case on behalf of a former Cornell employee, Carmita Wood, who chose to resign from her job and attempt to apply for unemployment benefits due to unwanted sexual advances from her former supervisor.

This case was the first to coin the phrase "sexual harassment." National news media chose to pick up the story when Wood's lawyers presented evidence of widespread abuse of a similar nature to women in manufacturing, education, restaurants, and airline industries. The prosecution identified two types of harassment: first, a hostile working environment in general, i.e. crass language, teasing, or touching; and secondly, a 'quid pro quo' type, where career advancement might be offered to a specific woman in exchange for sex.

Thousands of women issued statements of support for Miss Wood, reiterating the sexual harassment that they themselves had experienced at their own jobs. The prevalence of this work environment on a national scale made this case a landmark trial. Ultimately the Equal Employment Opportunity Commission (EEOC) developed laws to recognize such harassment as a violation of a woman's rights.

Although a worthy legal precedent was set, some men have proven that these habits are difficult to change. The recent "MeToo Movement" has helped to reveal such continued practices in the workplace, and the crying need for sufficient enforcement and punishment to begin to alter bad behaviors.

It was a very difficult year for President Gerald Ford, as well as the First Lady, Betty Ford. In his 1975 State of the Union address, which traditionally has an optimistic spin to every circumstance, the President instead opened his speech to both Houses of Congress by saying "The state of the union is NOT good." He proceeded to lament about "stagflation" that was choking the country. That new economic term encompassed a stagnant economy drowning in high inflation, high unemployment, slow economic growth, and a declining Gross Domestic Product.

Betty Ford quietly shared her husband's anguish from the dismal economy and the "highly unfavorable" rating given them by the American public. Somewhat hidden from the media, the First Lady began to drink excessively. The Secret Service was fully aware of her growing addiction, but political etiquette meant that they assisted in keeping that a secret. It would be several years after the Ford's were out of Washington before her disease was truly addressed. Her most valuable legacy was the establishment of the Betty Ford Clinic, which challenged men and women to acknowledge alcoholism as something that could be treated openly and honestly.

Gerald Ford became nothing more than an "asterisk" in the history of U.S. Presidents. He is the only man to serve as both Vice President and President without ever being elected to either office, and only served in that capacity for a total of two years. To counter the growing negative image that came as a result of his unconditional pardon for Richard Nixon, he made a determined effort to create a positive legacy for himself in some other decision. In the fall of '75 he declared inflation as "public enemy #1", and unveiled a national program called "WIN", which stood for "Whip Inflation Now." The inflation rate had been between 8 and 12 % for several years, and the "prophets of doom" were predicting imminent economic collapse for America, accompanied by the prospect of mass starvation, and gold going from $250 to $6000 per ounce.

The grandiose roll-out of "WIN" proved to be little more than wishful thinking, along with a few bumper stickers and lapel pins. The program itself entailed a list of voluntary suggestions, contrasting President Nixon's mandatory price controls and wage-freezes. Citizens were asked to begin saving money rather than borrowing money. Practical steps were offered for reducing personal expenses, such as car-pooling whenever possible, turning down the thermostat, and growing a private vegetable garden in one's back yard. Alan Greenspan, Chairman of the Federal Reserve, later said it was one of the "stupidest efforts" in the history of the U.S. government. Actual demand for borrowing more and more money would not voluntarily diminish until the Federal Reserve raised the prime interest rate to an astronomical level of 22% a few months later.

Ford's other moment of negative notoriety came this year when he survived two assassination attempts within less than three weeks of each other. "Squeeky" Fromme had just been released from her five years in prison as part of the Charles Manson family murders. She showed up at a political gathering in Sacramento, California, when President Ford was on his way to see Governor Jerry Brown. Carrying a small pistol, Fromme managed to get within four feet of the President as he walked by. However her gun failed to fire. Luckily, alert security guards noticed the gun, and within moments Squeeky was whisked away in a police car. She would spend the next 34 years in prison for her final attempt at notoriety.

Just 17 days later, Gerald Ford was in San Francisco to deliver a political speech at the St. Francis Hotel. As he walked past the crowd from the grand Hotel entrance to his waiting limo, Sara Jane Moore raised a pistol to shoot the President as he came by. A citizen standing next to her happened to see the gun, and instinctively pushed her arm to the ground. The gun went off, but no one was wounded. For this failed attempt, Moore also spent the next 30 years in federal prison. Interestingly, five years after her incarceration, she escaped. But after two days of freedom, she voluntarily turned herself back in, where she was transferred to a more secure facility for the duration of her sentence.

The heroic San Francisco citizen that saved the President's life that September afternoon was Oliver Sipple, a former Marine and Viet Nam veteran. Plans for a formal "Thank You" ceremony at the White House were scrubbed when it was discovered that Sipple was gay.

As the presidential campaign began later that year, California Governor Ronald Reagan ran against Ford in the Republican primaries, claiming that our foreign policy was aimless. Reagan trounced Ford in the Texas primary, and the GOP remained divided for the rest of the campaign. Reagan had won the hearts – and financial support – of most of the conservatives. Much of the party abandoned Ford, and the rest of his campaign efforts were futile.

America certainly wanted economic changes, and certainly needed a new direction. But America also wanted that new direction to come from someone other than Gerald Ford. The public was not about to elect any Republican this time around. He had opened the door for a man of complete integrity to come into the White House as the "national redeemer." After completing his partial term in the White House and failing in his re-election bid, Ford retired to his vacation home in Colorado where he tried his best to avoid the lime-light. Until the day he died, the general public never forgave Ford for his presidential pardon of his predecessor. He was remembered as a two-year band-aid on a deeply wounded White House.

American culture had dramatically changed in just ten years. Youth's focus on sex, drugs, and rock & roll had quickly normalized some choices which had been absolutely taboo just a few years earlier. Such a conflicting shift in standards was awkwardly displayed in Boulder in the summer of '75.

Boulder's Chief of Police had maintained a phenomenal record of integrity with his officers. In spite of the abrupt and heavy influx of drugs into the city, there was never a known incident where a Boulder police officer was secretly selling drugs on the side, or accepting money under the table to allow a drug dealer to operate. Few cities in the entire country could make such a claim. There was an outstanding level of respect between the officers and their Chief, and vice versa.

But that line was breached this summer when it was discovered that one of the younger officers was "living in sin" with his girlfriend. The Chief of Police called the officer in question into his office, and confronted him with the concern of whether or not this was true. The officer unashamedly confirmed what he was doing and – to his surprise – the Chief promptly fired him. The explanation was that every member of law enforcement must be absolutely trustworthy. Anyone who would live with a woman outside of marriage could not be fully trusted in their relationships, and thus could not be fully trusted in other areas of their life either.

The decision was final, and the young man lost his job. But the public outcry in his defense was very strong, much to the surprise of the popular

Police Chief. By now the predominant attitude was that if the relationship was consensual, it was nobody else's business. The debate left a deep blemish on an otherwise stellar career for the Chief.

Yes, the pendulum of moral standards had moved faster and farther than traditional America could understand.

In October a new chapter began in the expression of political criticism. Campus sit-ins or marches had become passé. Instead, television was learning that it could use its mass influence much more effectively and much more efficiently to impact people's thinking.

NBC debuted a program called *"Saturday Night Live"*, featuring the "Not-Ready-For-Prime-Time-Players." The format allowed for a mix of inane sketches, cutting-edge music and weekly celebrity guests. Also woven throughout the show was a tone of political satire and mockery. The regular segment called "Weekend Update" took its cues directly from *"Laugh-In"*, which had aired ten years earlier. News anchors were able to poke fun or criticism toward any politician as well as any issue of the day.

The show found great success by targeting the demographic of adults under the age of 35. Its slant on current issues motivated more young people to vote than any other television program. Consistently using that recipe of relevant humor as seen through a progressive worldview, SNL subsequently became the longest running show in television history.

In addition to SNL coming on the air in the fall, that same October was also the starting month for another pillar in American history.

A major shift had quietly begun to take place in the U.S. economy over the past few years, moving away from agriculture and manufacturing, and moving toward technology and information. For 300 years the family farm had been at the very foundation of American culture. Now the trend was toward corporate farming. In its place, a new importance was being given to engineers, scientists, and professors. Rural living began to diminish rapidly as a way of life.

Bill was a college student nerd who could see the future. He realized that if computers were going to have a greater presence in both corporate and personal use, those machines could work much more effectively if there were a standardized software format that allowed users a simpler and consistent means of operating those machines.

That month Bill Gates and another college friend started a company called Micro-Soft in his parent's garage. More than IBM or any other company, this company accelerated the transition from an agricultural and manufacturing based economy into a technology-based economy. Within 30 years Micro-Soft would become the largest company in the world. These advances in technology would not only change how most people worked, but this transition would also change how people related to each other. Although technological breakthroughs provided quantum leaps for productivity and efficiency, these improvements caused people to work in isolation and to distance themselves from their co-workers.

But the new universe was unstoppable nonetheless. STEM – or science, technology, engineering, and math – became the new foundation for America's growth. Mankind rapidly moved from haystacks to smokestacks, and from smokestacks to information stacks.

Sam Giancana was beginning to draw too much attention to himself. As the head of The Outfit (organized crime) in Chicago, he began bragging about his position of influence. It was exactly the opposite style of what the crime network had promised to themselves. He bragged about his previous partnership with Joe Kennedy, as dominant boot-leggers during Prohibition. He bragged about winning the presidential election for John Kennedy, and then sharing mistresses with the President while he was in office. He began to crave any publicity, and was so self-confident that he allowed chosen members of Chicago's news media access to his office to interview him.

Although the city's police and the FBI had tried more than once to find a legal charge that could send him to prison, their efforts always failed. Murder. Extortion. Illegal gambling. Tax evasion. Giancana's lawyers were always able to out-maneuver the law on his behalf.

But his lawyers could not out-maneuver The Outfit itself. With another court trial looming in the near future, several of the lieutenants within the crime organization decided it was time to silence the Boss so that he wouldn't say something in court that could put them all in prison.

On a warm July morning, two of Giancana's trusted associates called him asking if they could pick him up for lunch. When they arrived at his modest home in a west-suburb of Chicago, Sam was waiting in his driveway. But instead of letting him into their car, the two men stepped out of their vehicle with guns drawn. The first man fired two blasts from a sawed-off shotgun. Giancana dropped to the cement with gaping holes in his abdomen. The other man then stood over him, pointed a pistol at his face, and fired five or six times.

The message had been delivered. As the car sped away, neighbors began to gather around the body before the police could arrive. If anyone had actually witnessed the "hit", they were not about to come forward, and in so doing put their own life at risk. No arrests were ever made.

A significant chapter in the legend of Chicago's organized crime had come to a close. The Outfit quietly resumed control of its legal and illegal businesses. The Mayor's office resumed its rigid efforts to manage the city. Neither organization realized the precipitous decline that was pending for the great city of Chicago.

Life as a rock & roll musician was a serendipitous choice for some. Rod Stewart could have been a professional soccer player, but picked up guitar playing while nursing a severely sprained ankle. Elton John could have been a professional tennis player, but instead opted for a career that might succeed while indulging in drugs and alcohol. Vincent Furnier enjoyed the "rush" of gaining the attention of others, but mostly was driven to get away from the poor neighborhood that surrounded him during his elementary school years.

"Poor" was an understatement. Vincent grew up with his parents living on the outskirts of Phoenix, Arizona. He frequently saw Native American families living in abandoned cars that were held together by nothing more than mud and cardboard. These were called "wickiups", and sometimes contained as many as eight people in one such car. Temperatures in those shelters could exceed 120 degrees F in the summer, and 0 degrees F in the winter.

Vincent's rebellion started in grade school when he and his friends would go to the store to buy cigarettes for his parents. Stores would sell tobacco to those kids because every parent in their community smoked. Thus smoking was the norm for him by the 7th grade. As he sought other ways to live his life counter to what was expected, he was expelled from high school on two different occasions because his hair was too long.

Vincent also discovered something in high school that would carry him for the rest of his life. If parents and school administrators hated something, that meant kids liked it. That became the single driving principle for the next twenty years of his life.

Like many high school kids, Vincent and a few friends had started a band while in school. In general they played cover tunes of some of the popular rock & roll bands such as the Beatles. With three days notice they were asked to play for their high school's Homecoming Dance because the original band had to cancel. A career was born.

As soon as their H.S. graduation was completed, the band pooled their allowance money, bought a van, and moved to L.A. They eked out an existence in the Landmark Motel with seven other rock & roll bands, begging for any gig that would give them a little grocery money. To find their own niche, they decided they needed to be a "shock" band, aiming for something that would even jolt the hippies. Their hair grew beyond shoulder length, they wore dresses and face paint in their concerts, they used a live boa constrictor as a prop while on-stage, and – even though they were an all-male band – chose to call their group "Alice Cooper."

Fate was about to smile on them. Shep Gordon was staying at the same motel, and had just decided to quit his accounting job to become a free-lance agent and manager for musicians. The synergy was instantaneous. Shep soon became the most successful agent in history for musicians, movie stars, and celebrity chefs. And with his help, Alice Cooper became the most notorious shock rocker of all time.

Shep sent the band on tour to try to sell some albums. The stage antics of Alice Cooper quickly became legendary. In the middle of a performance he supposedly bit the head off of a live chicken and drank some of its blood. His two snakes became a mainstay in their shows, named "Boa Derek" and "Julius Squeezer." An album cover pictured the band wrapped in women's panties. The album cover was banned, but the publicity was great. Anything for shock value.

The financial success of the Alice Cooper band was meteoric. Their song *"School's Out"* became an instant #1 hit. In South America they played the largest indoor concert in world history, when 158,000 screaming fans crammed into a soccer stadium to hear their songs and buy their albums. Demand for tickets was so high that two people were killed in the press conference. Their rebellious look spawned similar careers for KISS and Marilyn Manson, seeking gaudier make-up and costumes.

But by the middle of 1975 Alice Cooper was unable to maintain the lifestyle he had created for himself. Endless drugs, alcohol, and women were about to destroy him physically. Walking to his suite in New York's Chelsea Hotel, he saw the hallways littered with dope addicts, druggies, and transvestites that were too gone to get their room key into the keyhole.

Alice spent the next four days in his room, drinking a quart of whiskey each day, and consuming no food. His body finally shut down.

For the next month, Alice was confined to an emergency rehab facility with truly insane people – murderers, rapists, arms-suppliers, and schizophrenics. Thankfully, he "cleaned out." Like many other musicians, celebrities or athletes on the verge of sudden death, he turned to Jesus for help. His original career goal had been controversy and rebellion. Now the most controversial decision of his career was to announce his transition into what he called "morality and common sense." He risked his entire fan base in doing so.

By late 1975 a new Alice Cooper returned to the stage. He broke uncharted ground once again by creating rock and video production, and adding dancers. He started a Foundation in Phoenix called "Solid Rock", for the purpose of helping young men and women to get off the street. He started an annual golf tournament to help raise extra funds for that purpose. And because he regained his physical strength, he continued to tour worldwide with his band for the next 44 years. His "baby boomer fans" never left him.

April 30, 1975, has been recorded as the official date for the end of the Viet Nam War. Although the finale had come rather abruptly, there was no instantaneous sense of closure. Just a national sense of relief. Why had it taken so long, when for many it had always seemed so pointless? For some, the answer was that Presidents Johnson and Nixon did not have any sons, and consequently were personally immune to the anxiety or hatred that parents felt when they watched their sons being drafted into unwanted military service. For some, the answer was that LBJ might have benefited financially because he had an exclusive contract with the U.S. Army to provide beef for the soldiers from his cattle ranch in Argentina. For most, the simple answer for such a prolonged war was America's naïve arrogance in believing our forces could NEVER lose in any military action. Depending on ones individual emotional involvement, people had to process for themselves how they would move forward. It would be necessary for many years to pass before America could truly heal from such a monumental disaster.

Comedian Dick Gregory had joined numerous marches and sit-ins to protest the war, but had also created his own distinction by fasting to create a greater sense of urgency for ending the war. News media personnel chronicled his extreme discipline to a "liquid-only diet", and even going 40 days at a time living only on water. Over the span of the previous two years his weight had gone from 280 to 90 lbs. Once the war was over, Gregory did not return to eating solid foods. He was now convinced that his body had been cleansed, and that he would live a longer and better life by consuming only fruit or vegetable juices. His opposition to the war had helped him discover something unexpected.

Although our country experienced unprecedented dissention during the ten-year window of the war itself, as soon as the Viet Nam conflict was over there were very few who hesitated to remember respectfully those young men and women that had given their lives by serving their country. Toward the end of 1975, discussions began in earnest around Capitol Hill to commemorate this war in a solemn and tangible way. Various proposals were immediately drafted for a memorial of some kind to be added to the historical sites of Washington, D.C. It would take seven years for the selection process and construction phases to be completed. But when the finished product was unveiled in 1982, the end result was stunning as well as numbing to every observer. Engraved into a stark stone wall were the full names of the 58,195 individual American lives that were ended in Viet Nam. That simple yet blunt presentation created a collective sense of reverence and loss.

From major cities to rural farm communities, every neighborhood in America experienced a portion of this deep pain from its war casualties. Every corner of the United States was represented on that wall, and Boulder County was not immune to this marbleized symbol of sacrifice and death. These are the local individuals from the cities within Boulder County that are listed on the Viet Nam Memorial Wall.

From the city of Boulder:
James Willie Adkisson, 31, Air Force
Donn Peter Arina, 21, Army
Ladd Robert Condy, 20, Army
Thomas George Dietsch, 36, Air Force
Ronald Thomas Hoffman, 20, Army
Michael Lewis Hyde, 28, Air Force
Robert James Lawlor, 21, Air Force
Charles Frank McGowen, 23, Army
Manfred Bertold Miller, 19, Army
Scott Thomas Nelson, 23, Army
James Douglas Peschel, 24, Marine Corps

Michael Robert Shapard, 20, Army
Roger Horace Stearns, 28, Air Force
Frank "Crick" Marion Streamer, 21, Navy
Dr. John J. Saunders, 28, Navy
Jon Edward Swanson, 29, Army
From Lafayette:
Charles Edward Manzanares, 23, Army
From Longmont:
Carlton Barry Halcomb, 23, Marine Corps
James Edward Hamm, 30, Air Force
Paul David Rodriguez, 19, Army
Kenneth Earl Stetson, 22, Marine Corps
Larry George Trevarton, 20, Army
From Hygiene:
Stephen Wayne Day, 22, Army
From Lyons:
Mickey Lee Hawkins, 19, Marine Corps
From Nederland:
Eric Doran Jenkins, 18, Army
Gary W. Platt, 22, Army

Every name is a painful reminder of what might have been. A healthy young adult raised in a free country where limitless opportunities were set before them. Instead, their lives were ended much too early in a cause that seemed unwarranted. And each life listed on that wall undoubtedly has a story worthy of remembering. Mickey Hawkins happened to be the first Viet Nam casualty from Boulder County. James Hamm had a Community Park in northeastern Longmont named after him. Eric Jenkins had only been in Viet Nam for one week when a Viet Cong bullet ended his life. "Crick" Streamer was a freckled redhead with a good singing voice whose life was taken – not by enemy gunfire – but in a fluke accident while putting out a fire at an American military base that was under attack.

The exhaustive list of names on the Viet Nam Memorial Wall provides a moment of honor to every life that was sacrificed. Yet there are thousands of other names and stories that are entirely missing from the wall. Mark's good friend, Jimmy Buczkowski of Nederland, was severely wounded in Viet Nam, and returned home as a double amputee. It was a miracle that he even survived the shrapnel that had riddled his body. But once he was back in the United States, discouragement devolved into deeper and deeper depression, until Jimmy ended his life by choosing suicide. The names of

Jimmy – and the other 20,000 Viet Nam veterans who also died of suicide – are not listed on that Memorial Wall . . . but they should be.

The year 1975 came to an end in a relatively quiet manner. Tom – along with millions of others – was suddenly quite excited that America might begin to work once again. The war was over. The corresponding protests against the war were over. The Nixon presidency was over. The Watergate investigation and trials were over. Maybe the nation could collectively move from these points of pain to newfound opportunities for optimism. But before those issues could be replaced completely with other national passions, there was one surprising "benefit" that surfaced this year out of the fiasco surrounding Watergate.

As the former legal advisor to President Nixon, Charles Colson had spent the majority of 1975 in prison because of his complicity with the Watergate cover-up. While incarcerated, he became "born again", meaning that he claimed to have a dramatic new-life-change experience in choosing to become a Christian. Cynics would say that this was nothing more than a strategic move in seeking pity and compassion from the American public upon his release. His ensuing legacy would seem to prove otherwise.

Colson's prison experience exposed him to the improper – and even inhumane – conditions that existed for many American men and women behind bars. The list sounded like something from the French Foreign Legion. Unwarranted physical abuse from the guards. Undesired sexual abuse from other prisoners. Inadequate heat or sanitation. Yes, if a person in America had committed a crime, he or she should be punished. But that sentence should be carried out in a humane manner. Once Colson was released from prison, he made a personal commitment to spend the rest of his life in an endeavor to change those factors surrounding prison inmates.

In October he founded an organization called *Prison Fellowship.* Hundreds of like-minded people began to join his team, offering counseling and hope to individual prisoners, as well as legislative initiatives to upgrade facilities that had fallen below standard building codes. Individual inmates were taught work skills, reading skills, and English as a second language. The most significant outcome from these efforts was an 80% drop in the rate of recidivism compared to those prisoners that did not have any such connection with Prison Fellowship. As paroled ex-cons found better ways to fit back into society on a permanent basis, Colson's organization created a cost-savings to state and federal prison budgets of hundreds of millions of dollars.

Prison Fellowship's vision ultimately spread globally. Their staff members are currently working with inmates in all 50 states, as well as 120 foreign countries. For the rest of his life, as strange as it may sound, Charles Colson thanked God that Watergate had sent him to prison.

The activists and hippies of Boulder began to splinter after the Viet Nam war had ended. No longer were there any marches or other national causes to keep them unified. They now had to find a new avenue for personal expression.

There was no way that these "seekers of complete freedom" were about to enter corporate America. It was too inhibiting. Too "clean." Too rigid. They did not want to give up their casual clothes, their long hair, their flexible schedule, or their personal prerogative to get stoned any day they felt like it.

The solution for many hippies was to become skilled, self-employed artisans in a wide variety of trades. A renaissance began to take place in every imaginable field of manual labor as these flower children began to embrace commerce. Exquisite wood-working, candle making, stained glass features, custom tile work, pottery, knot-tying, oil painting, photography, office furniture, and specialty T-shirts. To get started, their earliest customers were often each other.

Tom never had a problem with thinking BIG. In 1975 he began working fervently on a "Beatles Reunion Concert." Numerous promoters had already offered the band up to $20 million for such an event, which seemed astronomical at the time. Tom had a different approach, and offered the "Fab Four" $250 million, as well as another $50 million toward humanitarian aid, and a potential $50 million for himself. To date, only professional boxing had used closed circuit TV to sell live tickets world-wide. Tom also gained major sponsorship from Playboy Magazine and Marlboro tobacco as potential partners. After a few years of fine-tuning the financial details, two of the four members of the band said "Yes." They in turn were asking the other two to make the same commitment, which appeared imminent. But an assassin's bullet ended the life of John Lennon, and also ended Tom's dream. His creativity would have to be channeled elsewhere.

Mo was a little more "down to earth." He hired a few hippies to help him gather herbs and leaves from wild flowers growing in and around

Boulder. At first he thought there might be some proprietary recipe he could discover to create an hallucinogenic tea from these items. That dream never happened. But in the process he found a niche market for herbal teas that had never existed before. He named his company "Celestial Seasonings", and ultimately his 300 employees helped him become the top producer of herbal teas anywhere in the world.

Wanda went in a very different direction. Before graduating from high school, she had learned to be an accomplished seamstress. In recent years she had made most of her own clothes while living in a commune. Now it was time to branch out. Because her funds were very limited, she needed help in getting her start-up inventory of fabrics. Her solution was to go to every hotel and motel in Boulder County, asking if she could have any draperies, linens, bed spreads, or table cloths that they might discard when it was time to have them replaced. It worked.

Using such a hodge-podge of fabrics, her first products were floor-length patchwork skirts and patchwork vests for women. No two items looked exactly alike, which became part of the allure. It was a very limited line, but her timing was perfect. Two local clothing stores asked to carry her designs. And as a result, she had a hard time keeping up with demand.

In December of '75 she took another chance. It was time for "Weaves by Wanda" to have its first official fashion show. She rented the lobby of the historic Boulderado Hotel, home to Allen Ginsburg and other notables, and asked several of her friends to be her runway "models". The invitation list included numerous clothing stores in the metro Denver – Boulder area, as well as a smattering of random friends to help make the room to appear full.

Cases of champagne were flowing freely before and during the show. Each model took her respective turn by descending the grand staircase, walking the full width of the lobby as the "runway", and then returning by the same route to change outfits and be ready to go again a few minutes later.

About a third of the way into the show, one of the models got daring. Maybe it was the ten cases of champagne kicking in. She chose to wear one of the "Weaves by Wanda" vests, but with no blouse or bra underneath. When she reached the far turn of the runway, she took off the vest. The audience applauded loudly as she retraced her steps while naked to the waist. A new "normal" had just been set. For the rest of the show, every model either began topless, or removed her top while on the runway.

It was a fitting statement to demonstrate the melding of the era of sex, drugs, and rock & roll with the world of free enterprise. People that day witnessed a merger of the attitudes of sexual freedom, rebellion, and selfish individualism intersecting with the established business culture at large. It is likely that none of those creative artisans could have succeeded outside of the Boulder community that they shared. But together, they made a compelling example for the rest of the country to follow.

America was resilient, and once again found a way to work through the mayhem with new solutions for progress. The war had ended, thanks to Henry Kissinger. Nixon's career had ended, thanks to The Washington Post. Violent protests were now taking a more pragmatic direction, thanks to some legislative successes. And rock music was broadening into a wider spectrum of directions, even including a more civilized and moral component, thanks to Alice Cooper.

Yes, massive changes would continue. And yes, America would survive.

H.R. "Bob" Haldeman

John Ehrlichman

Mob boss Sam Giancana

Panic of Evacuation Day, Saigon

Discarding Helicopters, Saigon

Charles Colson

Viet Nam Memorial Wall

CHAPTER 13

"LOOKING BACK, AND LOOKING AHEAD . . ."

"Sometimes it feels like this world's gone crazy,
When the line between right & wrong didn't seem so hazy. . .
Did lovers really fall in love to stay?
Did families really bow their heads to pray?
Did Daddies really never go away?
Grandpa, tell me 'bout the good old days."

- the Judds

When Naomi and Wynonna Judd first performed that song on *"The Tonight Show"*, Johnny Carson began to cry. Whatever the "good old days" may be to any given person, it is those particular memories that have the power to reach into one's very soul.

Many "baby boomers" think of this time window from 1965 to 1975 as the "good old days", while others consider it as the era of abrupt transition "away from the good old days." Regardless, this short span of time impacted everyone, and laid the groundwork for the cultural tensions and changes that are continuing to unfold today. It was comedian Robin Williams who once said, "If you can remember the '60's, then you didn't really experience the '60's." For too many, including the mega-talented Williams, the relentless pursuit of the '60's experience ultimately destroyed them.

Mingled with happy memories of youth, there are so many regrets carried by these baby boomers as they reflect on those dramatic years of 1965 to 1975. Most of those young adults were just seeking fun and freedom, and in so doing followed the crowd in opposing everything, often just for the sake of being different. While many of the "causes" may have been honorable, the chosen "means" were all too often unreasonable for the purpose of bringing about any rational or substantive change. Violence. Marching. Sit-ins. Destruction of property. Frequent drug abuse. Revolting against personal moral constraints. The rude and crude treatment of almost anyone in authority. Today many of those women in particular often regret their sexual mistakes of excess. Men in particular regret having arrests or jail time on their record. For most, those acts of rebellion were all simply part of growing up, of maturing, of slowly learning to manage their individual emotions.

Any careful reflection on that memorable season in American history obligates one to ask at least two critical questions. First, *"What did we learn from the unprecedented cultural tumult and chaos of that specific time period?"* And second – at the risk of sounding prophetic – *"Would it ever be possible for our country to experience a cultural and societal upheaval of such magnitude again?"* And if we can answer both of those, then we must also develop a guiding principle for moving forward.

CRITICAL QUESTION 1 : WHAT DID WE LEARN FROM THE CULTURAL TUMULT AND CHAOS OF 1965 TO 1975

Looking back on this era of monumental change in America, there are at least three major takeaways that can give us useful instruction. First, *"CHANGE" IS ALWAYS AN ABSOLUTE CERTAINTY WITHIN AN ENVIRONMENT OF FREEDOM.* Freedom is the single greatest platform of our founding fathers that has made our country the unequaled world leader that it is. Freedom and change must logically go hand in hand. There is no way to avoid that. It just goes with the territory if you choose to live in a free country. And every new generation must have its unique voice. Yes, change may at times be unpleasant or even painful, and it almost always is controversial. But change in America is constant. Unstoppable.

Baby-boomer attitudes were – and continue to be – different from previous generations in their expectation of change. Their rebellion against social and moral norms became a cultural avalanche, demanding change in every area of life. Their obsession with individualism accelerated the rate of change to unprecedented levels. According to the Institute for Research on Intercultural Cooperation (IRIC) that studied employees in 53 countries, the U.S. now ranks #1 as the most individualistic nation in the world.

Individualism has become a greater influence on our society than diversity and multiculturalism. It is the ultimate mindset. Advances in technology have accelerated that move toward individualization with the availability of leisure time pursuits such as television, the internet, smart phones, and "virtual reality helmets." Individual pursuits have weakened or diminished the need for "communities." Social media has replaced personal conversations and direct social interaction. As an example, the actual number of people that currently go bowling has doubled since 1975, but there are fewer people today that bowl in a league compared to league bowlers from that same time period.

The outgrowth of the youth-driven revolution of the late '60's and early '70's has given our society an instruction manual with "no givens, no rules, and no limits." Here is a quick over-view of some of the major changes or trends that baby-boomers have brought to our current culture:

CHANGES IN ATTITUDES REGARDING SEX AND SEXUALITY – Baby-boomers never relinquished the sexual rebellion of the late '60's. Today, consensual hookups are condoned, and "open" relationships are defined as "friends with benefits." The highest levels of STD's in the 21st Century are in retirement communities and senior living centers as Boomers remain comfortable having unprotected sex with multiple partners.

An even more dramatic shift has taken place regarding sexuality itself. In the late '60's gay or lesbian relationships were considered a perversion of nature, worthy of expulsion from the military, and even punishable by prison in some states. Now these relationships are celebrated, and activists are defending laws for legalized same-sex marriage on a state-by-state basis. Advocates for the LGBQT community have asked to be addressed by the pronoun "mx" in an effort to eliminate any confusion of male or female gender identification. A "Rainbow Floor" has been established as a part of the University of Colorado dormitory system. On that particular level, any two persons can choose to live together – gay, lesbian, transgender, bi-sexual, etc. The only combination that is NOT allowed is a heterosexual man and woman.

CHANGES IN ATTITUDES REGARDING MARRIAGE AND REPRODUCTION – In the '50's and '60's, the average woman was married and had her first child by age 23. Divorce was the rare exception with married couples. "Prenuptial agreements" did not exist. Now marriage is typically postponed until after age 30, or avoided entirely. More than 60% of couples live together before getting married. Divorce occurs in over 55% of all marriages.

Birth rates were slightly more than 3.5 children per household, and many homes had five or six children. Since Catholic couples were not supposed to practice any form of birth control, it was not uncommon for them to have eight or more children. But those numbers have declined significantly. Today the average American family has 1.8 children. A national birth rate of 2.1 children per household is necessary as a "replacement rate" for any country's population to break even. China's birth rate, for example, is now government-mandated at 1.0, and Russia's is 1.4. The only reason the total population of the U.S. is growing today is due to immigration. For U.S. women ages 16 to 45, the number of births last year was 60.2 per 1000, which is the lowest in more than a century.

CHANGES IN ATTITUDES ABOUT AGING - When Social Security was first created, the average life expectancy of an American male was 64. If a person was fortunate enough to reach retirement age, it was expected that he or she would have a rather sedentary life for just a few years, and then die. Most large companies offered pensions for their life-time employees, and the funds required to meet those obligations were more than adequate because of shorter life-spans. The majority of medical research was focused on reducing risks of childbirth or childhood diseases.

Today, most childhood diseases have been conquered, so more than 90% of all medical research pertains to the extension of life for the elderly. Over 10,000 baby-boomers now reach the age of 65 every day, and their life expectancy at that point is 85 for males and 87 for females. Actuarial tables for pensions as well as Social Security benefits have not kept pace with changing life expectancy, which is why government-backed retirement funding for police, firemen, and school teachers is severely threatened. Trend lines for all those persons expecting a full pension appear to be ominous at best.

The age wave of baby boomers is causing a dramatic demographic shift in America regarding the proportion of older people to the general population. Currently the ratio of adults over the age of 65 to teenagers is 3: 1, and within 12 years that ratio will be 6: 1. This "pig-in-a-python" of aging baby-boomers continues to dominate the American stage. At 70 they are healthier than any septuagenarian in history, and still expect to live active and productive lives. Yes, they may be getting "older", but they refuse to let themselves get "old." Many choose to continue to work, rather than retire. Many others are forced to continue to work, because they have outlived their savings. The optimistic mindset for baby-boomers is "there is no need to age or slow down." One's age is no longer determined by chronology, but rather by "attitude." As an example, an 80-year-old woman recently got braces for her teeth because she wanted to be more attractive the next time she got married. Wall Street does not want to miss out on this phenomena. At least three start-up pharmaceutical companies have been funded to develop a process to eliminate senescent cells, which could halt or even reverse aging of the human body.

This obsession with staying young has also produced the plastic surgery industry, a business which now exceeds $16,500,000,000. in annual revenues. Driven primarily by breast implants, face lifts, and tummy tucks, doctors have found dozens of surgical procedures to modify any hint of a human body in decline.

CHANGES IN ATTITUDES REGARDING PERSONAL HEALTH – Tobacco and sugar have become major enemies of all those seeking healthy lives and sound nutrition. Tobacco was chosen as the first public enemy because its effects were more immediate and more severe. Found "guilty" of willful suppression of evidence that cigarettes were addictive and the direct cause of lung cancer, major tobacco companies had to pay $206 billion in fines over 25 years for their harm to users. No further cigarette advertising has been allowed on television. Every cigarette carton is required to include this statement – *"WARNING: Surgeon General has determined that smoking is hazardous to your health."*

In a parallel manner, sugar is now the next public enemy of health. Numerous communities have added a targeted "sugar-tax" on soda or candy. All grocery food items are required to list the ingredients within their packaged product so that the consumer can choose to avoid sugar or other harmful elements if they so desire. Health campaigns are now in place to fight obesity among children because of their high intake of sugar-infused products. The trends are eerily similar to what confronted the tobacco industry just a few years ago, such that sugar will likely be demonized to a greater and greater extent, forcing it to be removed from products, and forcing the sugar industry to pay enormous penalty fines for its negative impact on humanity.

Gluten-free, dairy-free, sugar-free. People have customized their own diet needs, and are attentive to nutrition and fitness as never before. In a direct connection with this focus on personal health management, there is a new trend of young adults participating in the organic diet and sustainable food movement by buying small farms. The number of farmers under the age of 35 has increased for the first time since the end of WWII. These are highly educated young adults, seeking control of their personal health that is often jeopardized by GMO foods and processed foods.

Boomers have popularized the expression "60 is the new 40." A conscientiousness regarding proper diet, stretching, and regular exercise has created a retirement generation that is intent on continuing to live life to the fullest. It's no longer acceptable merely to add "years to one's life", now everyone wants to add "life to their years."

CHANGES IN ATTITUDES SURROUNDING RELIGION – Approaching the mid-1960's, America was still considered a "Christian nation." Our currency says "IN GOD WE TRUST." Bible verses or biblical characters are permanently etched into numerous monuments and office buildings in Washington, D.C., reflecting a respect and adherence to the Bible which had existed since our nation was founded. The phrase "under God" was added to the Pledge of Allegiance in 1954, more than 60 years after it was first written. But baby-boomers pushed away from our Judeo-Christian heritage, seeking self-expression. The net result has been a pervasive world-view of "tolerance toward all, exclusivity of none." Boulder, as an example, is now the home to more than 300 religions or cults.

Buddhism and New Age thinking were barely present in the U.S. prior to the rebellion of the late '60's. Buddhism had found enough traction by 1970 that their participants established a commune and learning center in Boulder. Eventually their followers began offering classes on the tenets of Buddha, and Naropa University was officially formed in 1974. Located just ½ mile from the University of Colorado, Naropa now is the base campus to more than 950 undergraduate and graduate students, and boasts the largest Buddhist Temple in North America.

Although Harvard University was founded as a church-affiliated school, the majority of their students today identify themselves as "atheist" or "agnostic." Nihilism became the predominant worldview of young adults by 1975. That philosophy graduated from the college dorms and moved into general education, politics, and entertainment. Any remaining influence of religion on our current culture has diminished greatly, and public prayer was officially and legally removed from public schools. The greatest source for cultural influence is now centered on the entertainment industry, which has had to become more explicit in scenes of sex and violence to fill the appetites of its audience.

CHANGES IN ECONOMIC AND CORPORATE CULTURE – By the mid '70's a company's loyalty to its employees had begun to dissolve. Instead, those companies chose to focus on stock price, with a higher obligation to shareholders. Mergers and acquisitions became commonplace. Companies then had to be willing to lay off employees in large numbers to improve their bottom line. Pension commitments have had to be reduced as life expectancy began to sharply increase. As a logical consequence, employees were no longer loyal to their employers either, and developed a pattern of numerous job changes within a person's career. Corporations forced their union membership to accept less and less in benefits or to dissolve completely. The voice of organized labor has become a whimper compared to 50 years ago.

This era of '65 to '75 ultimately created a generation of narcissism and self-centeredness, moving from self-control to self-expression. It was a collective movement that broke down the traditional cultural values, and was replaced with the sole measuring rod of MONEY. This focus has ultimately created a concentration of wealth in upper management compared to the '60's and '70's, moving the new generation of young adults today to question if in fact capitalism is the best system of opportunity. Socialism is now seen as a viable alternative to a growing sector of young people. These 20-and-30-somethings are now better educated but deeper in debt, with far less job security than their parents once had, and half as likely to own a home.

Another trend has recently surfaced. As corporations demand longer and longer hours, as the workplace holds no loyalty for employees, as stress has become a recognized threat to quality of life, and as individualism seeks more self-control, many young adults have targeted a "FIRE" mentality, which is "Financial Independence, Retire Early." Individual freedom is once again the driving force.

CHANGES IN DRUG USAGE. Experimentation with illegal drugs is no longer limited to young adults. Government programs such as "JUST SAY NO" have been a miserable failure, and the war on drugs appears to be fighting a tsunami with a plastic bucket. The variety of drugs – and the delivery of those drugs – continue to expand with incredible ingenuity. Thanks to the skilled drug network under El Chapo's Mexican drug cartel, there is now a deadly surge in the use of Fentanyl, which is an inexpensive synthetic opioid, almost 40 times stronger than heroin. It's a pandemic problem that is killing 160 young people each day by over-dose. A few federal prisons that practice capital punishment have begun using Fentanyl as an alternative lethal injection because it is readily available and less expensive than previous drugs used for State sanctioned executions.

Science has also created a few "super drugs" for professional athletes. Doping is particularly rampant in bicycling, track & field, major league baseball, and select Olympic events. Misuse of various prescription drugs or medicines has included Xanax, hydrocodone, or soda mixed with codeine syrup, as well as steroids and human growth hormones. Greedy pharmacists have frequently been bribed with the objective of masking illegal drugs so that the athlete's personal usage cannot be detected under the most stringent testing methods.

Boulder became the origination point for the national trend toward legalization of marijuana. Proponents are fueled by the conviction that people should have the freedom of choice, and to support those patients that rely on its medical benefits for pain management. Although defendants of marijuana say that it is not addictive, opponents have statistically demonstrated that regular use diminishes the body's immune system and also proves to be a "gateway" to heavier drug usage, particularly heroin addiction and alcoholism. Several states have now followed Colorado's lead. The trend of legalization on a national scale will slowly become a reality because of the "trump card" of tax revenues. The potential two-fold windfall of taxation from both marijuana and sports betting will be too great for the tax collector to ignore. It is evidence once again of how American culture continues to change.

Principle #1 : In a free country, change is guaranteed and change is constant.

Why change from "the good old days"? There are many baby boomers that have never really left the '60's – in both appearance and mindset. They have attempted to hang on to that life-style of abandon, incorporating drugs and recreational sex into their routine as if they were still in their 20's. Associated with that is an unbending attitude of opposition to any government regulation or law enforcement agency that would inhibit their choices. It's a quiet refusal to let go.

One unusual example of this "mindset-locked-in-the-past" is David Ansberry. When he first moved to Boulder in the late '60's, he became best friends with Guy Goughnor. Almost every day they hung out together at the Golden Cue, and eked out a living trying to get high as often as they could. They purposely chose nicknames for themselves that would allow them to live "off of the grid." For more than two years David went by the name "Sandman", and his friend Guy was only known as "Deputy Dawg."

They lived in a tent on the edge of town during their first summer in Boulder, and in the colder months they tried to crash with the STP family of hippies because ample drugs and group sex were always available. Life was so simple and carefree.

But in early spring of '71, his best friend "Deputy Dawg" mysteriously disappeared without even saying "good-bye." David checked every day at the Golden Cue as well as Tulagi's to see if anyone had seen or heard from him. He finally stopped by the Boulder Police Station to ask the same questions. Nothing. It was as if his closest friend had moved to another planet without leaving a forwarding address.

David continued to stay in Boulder for almost eight more months. But he was rudderless. No other real friends. Never enough food. It wasn't fun anymore, and life had become a real bummer. As Christmas approached, and the looming challenge of living in the colder weather again, David decided to hitchhike back home to suburban L.A. At least his parent's house gave him a roof over his head, and he could fend for himself there.

For 45 years his lifestyle never changed. Shoulder-length hair, grungy clothes, and as little responsibility as possible. While he quietly worked in an auto-body shop to pay his bills, he smoked marijuana daily and lounged at the California beaches every weekend. Only on rare occasions did he tell any of his co-workers about the "good old days" of Boulder. But those fading memories unexpectedly came crashing to the forefront for him in 2016.

Back in Boulder County, a stunning news story was breaking. Former Marshall Renner Forbes had long since retired from law enforcement, and was now living in a Denver Assisted Living facility where he was being treated for a terminal disease. As a gesture of love and encouragement, a couple of retired police officers took Forbes for a leisurely afternoon drive through Boulder and Nederland, giving him an opportunity to reminisce about their days together in law enforcement.

The scenery was wonderful. The memories were plentiful. The nostalgia ran deep. But as they turned around to return to Denver, Forbes asked the driver to take a left turn instead and head south from Nederland on the Peak-to-Peak Highway. About two miles out of town he asked the driver to come to a stop on the shoulder of the road, right next to a small bridge and box culvert. As he got out of the car, he vomited and then began quietly crying. The retired officers rushed to his side, thinking that he was dealing with bad reactions to his most recent chemotherapy and radiation treatments. That was not the case.

Once Forbes was able to regain his composure, he began to confess his entire story with a sad and repentant voice. This was the very spot where he had shot a young man in the back of the head who was known only as "Deputy Dawg." This is where he began to live a duplicitous life. But now – before his own impending death from cancer – he decided he needed to come clean. The burden of guilt had been profoundly heavy for more than 40 years, but somehow he wanted to be able to die in peace.

In the next few weeks Forbes was tried for manslaughter. Since the crime had occurred more than 40 years ago, since there was no tangible evidence, and because his life expectancy was now less than 6 months, the judge released him on probation.

The stunning story wasn't exactly front-page news outside of Boulder and Denver, but the wire services did pick it up as a human-interest item for the weekend editions. Most major newspapers carried an abbreviated synopsis of the murder mystery of 1971 and how it was finally solved 45 years later. Boulder and Nederland assumed that the drama surrounding Sheriff Forbes and "Deputy Dawg" was now a distant moment in the annuls of their local history. But they were wrong as well. Fate had other plans.

Twelve hundred miles away on a balmy Sunday morning, David Ansberry settled into his lounge chair at Newport Beach with another joint and a day-old newspaper. His level of interest was minimal as he absent-mindedly skimmed through the national and international news. The constant coverage of America's war against terrorism reminded him of the futility of Viet Nam. The news obsession with the 2016 presidential campaign reminded him of the frustration of seeing Richard Nixon elected – twice. Newspapers were usually tediously boring. But when he got to a section of small miscellaneous news items, his blood froze as he read a headline: "DEPUTY DAWG DONE IN BY LOCAL MARSHALL."

At first he just felt numb, but as he read the article for the third time he began to feel nauseous. Memories of Boulder and his dear friend swept over him in waves. He never imagined that his best friend could have been secretly murdered by someone in law enforcement. As he rode the city bus back to his home, he immediately began plotting his revenge. Within two weeks he was driving northeast on Interstate 15 in his 12-year-old Toyota, determined to get back to Boulder. It was his first time out of California in 45 years.

Once in Colorado, he wasted no time. He constructed a crude bomb just like the STP family had taught him when he had originally lived there. The only change was that now the detonating device would be the electronic signal from a new cell phone that could not be traced to him. At dusk he carefully placed the bomb into his backpack and deposited the entire package at the entrance door to the Nederland Police office. His mind was racing. *Even though that former Marshall may actually be dead, the entire police department would forever regret their connection to that man. Justice would prevail. Blowing up the entire Police building will be such sweet revenge. And Deputy Dawg will finally have an unexpected hand in avenging his own death.*

David quickly drove four blocks away and settled into a corner seat at the coffee shop. Just before paying his bill, he pulled out his personal smart phone and called the number of the other phone which was still nestled in the bottom of his back pack. He waited. And waited. What he anticipated was the impending confusion from a loud explosion, allowing him to leave quietly without paying his bill, and quickly begin his drive back to L.A. But incredibly bad luck intervened in his life once again. He heard no explosion. David did not realize how poor the cell phone reception could sometimes be in the mountains. In spite of six attempts at calling the other phone, it failed to detonate the bomb.

David panicked, and headed east to Chicago instead of going home. Once the police began carefully to unpack the contents of the suspicious backpack, they identified several significant clues of who they were looking for. Video surveillance cameras from the grocery store parking lot next door gave them a decent image to go along with the other information. The FBI executed a nation-wide manhunt, and two weeks later arrested David in Chicago. It was a quick trial. Guilty on all counts. At age 66, he probably could not live long enough to ever see the outside of a prison again.

The twists and turns of the entire story of "Deputy Dawg" would seem too bizarre to be real. But it is a sad reminder of what extremes were present in the '65 to '75 timeframe: young adults that were radicalized and living without boundaries, and demanding extreme change; ultra-traditional adults that could not tolerate the cultural upheaval that was rapidly occurring around them, and resistant to change; men and women acting on those opposing ideologies without concern for the consequences; and a rigid refusal ever to let go of their chosen narrow worldview.

The second important takeaway from this segment of U.S. history is to recognize that *NOT ALL CHANGE IS NECESSARILY PROGRESS*. Bertrand Russell said, "Change is scientific, progress is ethical. Change is indubitable, whereas progress is a matter of controversy." Numerous elements point to this sobering assessment.

The socio-cultural earthquake pushed many young adults to over-reach. That drive has had some unintended consequences. Sociologists describe that outcome as "the pursuit of Utopia by means of Myopia can bring about Dystopia", which is to say that pursuing an ideal perfection from a viewpoint that is too narrow or lacking careful foresight creates lives that are fearful and all too often dehumanized. Crime rates, violence, drug usage, loss of family structure, a shrinking middle-class, and extreme political polarization are just a few of the factors that reflect this finding.

Crime and violence are at pandemic levels, particularly in our larger cities. In 2010 the World Health Organization released statistics that gun homicide rates in most first-world countries ranged from .1 to 3 deaths per million citizens. The exception is the United States, where that gun homicide rate is 36, or 24 times the global average. The frequency of mass shootings has become inexplicable. In the last 50 years there have been 106 on American soil. By closest comparison, the Philippines had 18, Russia had 16, and France has 12. The U.S. now has more people in prison than any other country, yet our crime rates continue to increase. Chicago has surpassed Detroit and New York with the dubious title of "murder capital of the civilized world."

Senator Moynahan was accurate in his warnings from 50 years ago. The government's well-intended welfare system has accelerated the burgeoning strata of single moms who choose to have more and more children. Within the African American community, more than 75% of all children are born into a single-parent home. If those single moms were to get married, they would lose their welfare support. Statistically, young boys that have no solid male role model are much more likely to get into trouble with the law. For those same children, rates for dropping out of school more than triple. One of every three Black men born in a U.S. city today will end up incarcerated. An attitude of hopelessness has consumed the inner-city populace, and fueled a pervasive sense of fear and anger.

Yes, we wanted equal rights for everyone, but the pendulum has swung into the dysfunctional zone. Suicide and sexual abuse are more prevalent.

Men are no longer seen as "care-givers", so the role of "father" has greatly diminished, or lost its value entirely.

The explosion of technology was supposed to make life easier for the average worker. Instead it has created an overload of information. Computer capacity certainly allows the individual to be more productive, but companies require more working hours from their staff than they did 50 years ago. The access to limitless information has moved people toward isolation, choosing to text rather than talk, searching for data on their smart phones rather than experiencing community. This addiction to technology has led to increases in insomnia, anxiety, and depression. In spite of an increased population by a factor of three, loneliness has also multiplied. Major tech companies have begun to seek ways to force users to REDUCE time spent on their websites. In recent years there has been a disconcerting increase in the use of anti-depressant drugs, and a correlating eight-fold increase in the rate of suicide as those meds create an emotional "roller-coaster" frame of mind. Suicide is now the 2nd leading killer among young people.

Drug usage is no longer limited to our nation's university students and young people. Its pervasive grip reaches into all ages and classes of society, in the inner-city as well as the suburbs, in the white-collar offices as well as the blue-collar assembly lines. There are many high paying manufacturing jobs that are now unable to be filled because no applicant can pass the mandatory drug test. Opioid overdoses kill more young people on an annual basis than were killed in Viet Nam in any given year.

It's a wonderful privilege to live in a free country, but elements such as these cannot be considered as "progress." Change is not always necessarily moving in the right direction. That is Principle #2.

There is a third component of this syllogism that follows logically.

First, CHANGE is a "given" in a free country. And second, not all change is "PROGRESS." Following the extreme changes which occurred through the late '60's and early '70's, many individuals as well as many group entities were entirely destroyed. But the United States did not self-destruct as some of the doom-sayers had predicted. It is a reminder that *EVERY PERSON and EVERY ENTITY MUST BE WILLING TO ADAPT SELECTIVELY to CHANGE, OR SLOWLY MOVE TOWARD IRRELEVANCE AND POSSIBLE EXTINCTION.* The ability to adapt will not only facilitate survival, but can lead to greater success. Conversely, history has also taught us that an adamant refusal to change – like Marshall Forbes and his ilk – will lead to great destruction, possible irrelevance and even oblivion. Hindsight gives us the privilege of looking at two corporations and two cities that inadvertently demonstrated that truth.

IBM is still functioning in Boulder, but as a transformed re-design of what it once was. For several decades they were the largest technology company in the world, and more than once were sued by the U.S. government for having a total monopoly of a certain market segment, such as the Selectric Typewriter. Economically they were always seen as the big gorilla in a small cage. But by the mid-1990's IBM finally had to go against its proud tradition of "never laying off an employee" and painfully reduce its payroll by eliminating thousands from their world-wide work force. They also had to sell off two major printer divisions from the Boulder location in an effort to maintain desired levels of profitability. Today they focus on technical service and support rather than the manufacturing of actual hardware. In 2014 they were removed from the Dow Jones Industrial Average on the New York Stock Exchange, which consists of the 30 leading companies in the country, for being unable to keep pace with the DJA at large. Yet IBM can be applauded for successfully adapting in a rapidly changing world, and thus being able to survive.

Kodak, on the other hand, represents the "poster-child" for complete corporate failure to make such necessary changes in a shifting marketplace. They too had once been included on the Dow-Jones because they were the world's largest manufacturer of cameras as well as film. But when the first digital camera prototype was offered to them, they chose to ignore it – and even tried to hide it – thinking it would eliminate their revenue stream from repeat purchases of film. That managerial decision was nothing short of fatal. Kodak's former massive world-headquarters building in Rochester, New York, is now completely abandoned, and stands as an eerie and hollow monument to rigidity and closed thinking. Their refusal to adapt moved them into oblivion.

The cities of Boulder and Chicago provide another stunning contrast for this same principle, in a "tale of two cities" as it were.

Chicago is a sorry remnant from the days when it was known as the "city that works." Unable to shed its politics by cronyism, its choke-hold from Labor Unions as well as "the Outfit", gang warfare, excessive police violence, continued racial hatred, a failed public education system, and a dependence on out-dated industries, today its crippling corruption and crime have subsequently become the norm. Chicago is now ranked as the most unsafe city in the U.S., having surpassed New York and Detroit in the annual number of murders. People who can afford to do so are moving away from the city as well as the state. As the net population continues to decrease by one person every five minutes, taxes on the remaining populace have necessarily had to rise correspondingly to make up the growing deficit. As a result, Chicago also has the highest tax rate of any city in the U.S.

Actual bankruptcy of the city – as well as the entire state of Illinois – is rapidly approaching because of these factors. This death spiral appears unavoidable. In the late '60's and early 70's, Rev. Jesse Jackson had offered a simple, two-step recipe to prevent most of these societal trends by challenging all young people to "stay in school, and stay off of drugs." Sadly, the city fathers – including the first Black Mayor – secretly asked him to get out of town. When actual bankruptcy does occur, all of Chicago's Policemen, Firemen, and public school teachers will have their pensions decimated. The ensuing public revolt that is likely to follow will strike fear into every other city in the country.

In spite of being at the very hub of so much of the upheaval and rebellion of the late '60's and early '70's, Boulder became stronger. As a community Boulder not only was able to survive but even grow and flourish through the sweeping tide of cultural transition that took place during that era. Today Boulder County is consistently chosen as one of the top three most desirable locations in the entire country in which to live and work. Although the city of Boulder is not even big enough to have its own commercial airport, it has had an inordinate presence and influence in America. A panel of sociologists appeared on the *"Today Show"* in 2017, and, as part of their findings, revealed that Boulder was the "happiest city" in the U.S.

Following those tumultuous years of 50 years ago, any resident of Boulder today no longer needs to say "Colorado" when describing where they live. Just "Boulder" is sufficient. Yet our nation knows only a fraction of the unique as well as diverse personality that is now Boulder. The compelling climate, ample recreation opportunities, and highly skilled workforce make it a magnet to both businesses and individuals that want a stimulating, active and healthy lifestyle. The eclectic mix of Boulder continues to be the home to more PhD.'s, more women with Graduate degrees, more Master Sommeliers, more classically trained chefs, more world-class runners and bicyclists, more health food stores, and more restaurants per capita than any other city in the country.

Boulder is also the origination point in America for both the legalization of marijuana (discussed later in this chapter) and abortion rights. Where abortion was once a forbidden secret, today Boulder is home to one of the busiest abortion clinics in the country, available to women at any time in the nine months of their pregnancy. Because of the national controversy surrounding the termination of a full-term fetus, frequent protesters have appeared at their doorstep, and numerous death-threats have been made against the primary doctor. But their services continue to increase because a majority of the community demands it to be so.

Same-sex marriage found one of its earliest proponents in Boulder's City Hall. Before any states had passed actual legislation on that issue, the County Clerk of Boulder was performing same-sex marriages in the '70's because "it seemed the right thing to do." Frequent editorials in the local paper expressed their support or opposition to the Clerk's actions. One "red-neck" citizen vehemently argued that if two persons of the same gender could choose to get married, he should also be able to choose to marry his horse. After numerous threats to do so, one summer day the man and his appaloosa showed up on the Court House lawn, and he insisted that the Clerk come outside to perform the wedding ceremony. In a moment of cleaver spontaneity, the Clerk declined because the horse was only eight years old, and the Clerk would not perform a wedding with anyone – or anything – that was under-age.

In the midst of its aggressive counter-cultural thinking and anti-capitalism voices, Boulder is also the home for a conservative judge most recently appointed to the U.S. Supreme Court, a nationally renowned venture capitalist for technology start-ups, and a highly sought business consultant that helps corporations move from "good to great." Vastly different philosophies for living, but they are able to co-exist peacefully.

Boulder was also the origination point for a Christian men's ministry called *"Promise Keepers."* Men from any religious background were invited to fill dozens of football stadiums for a weekend of music and teaching which challenged them to be men of integrity – humbly loving their wives and children, seeking racial reconciliation, and living in their communities as model citizens. A record attendance of over 1.4 million men gathered at the Washington Mall for a single PK event in 1997. (that record has since been surpassed by the 2,000,000 that attended the inauguration of President Barack Obama in 2009) In so doing, Promise Keepers changed the face of the Protestant Church in the 20th Century. Such a "traditional" organization interspersed in such a "progressive" community stands as another example of Boulder's wide spectrum of tolerance and willingness to adapt.

Conversely, Chicago has become the national model of a city that has refused – or at the very least failed – to successfully adapt to an evolving national culture. The opulence and beauty along its Lake Michigan shoreline provide only a thin veneer covering the cancerous underbelly of a city that is spiraling downward. Its jobless rate now ranks #51 out of the 51 U.S. cities with more than 1,000,000 residents. Racial divide and hatred have only worsened since 1975, moving from segregation to "ghettoization." Like most major cities, whites have fled from the inner cities in massive numbers. Drug usage, welfare dependency, and single-parent households are at record levels. Any opportunity for economic growth is constrained by a dependence on outdated industries. Property taxes have risen much faster than real estate values. The city ranks as the very last in desirability of where to live. It represents a complete failure in the necessity to successfully adjust.

Principle #3: Selectively adapt to change, or you will slide toward insignificance and possible oblivion.

To fill the void once held by IBM, numerous other technical companies have entered the conversation to take their place. Innovators such as MicroSoft, Apple, and Facebook have dominated their respective realms, both nationally and internationally. Recently Google and Amazon have attained the highest valuations of all companies in the world. Given their mammoth size and abundance of cash respectively, both Google and Amazon could locate their offices anywhere in the world that they might choose. So it is most interesting that both companies recently announced they are locating their newest business campuses in Boulder because of its many attractive elements, to position more than 3000 jobs there. The local impact on residential real estate, retail, ancillary support businesses, and local traffic will likely be even greater than when IBM moved to Boulder 50 years earlier.

Celestial Seasonings – once a haven for hippies – continues to grow in its world-wide distribution of tea products, employing more than 275 men and women. Their corporate philosophy has successfully melded with that of the community, seeking to be eco-friendly while simultaneously being creative in the process of identifying new customers and new markets.

The chemical and nutritional naivete of the late '60's has been replaced by a national focus toward healthy foods and natural ingredients. Once again Boulder has become the nation's leader in this arena. Founded in Boulder, both Whole Foods Grocery and Wild Oats have become the national trend-setters in providing high-end foods and supplements that are regionally and organically grown, chemical-free, and comprised of only the most natural and healthy ingredients. McDonald's Restaurants remains profitable, but its former dominance is often lost in the maze of every possible fast-food franchise now sharing that stage. The "Happy Meal" – which was birthed in Boulder in the 70's by its local franchisee – is still on their menu, and continues to generate at least 8% of the corporation's worldwide profits. As an example of successful adaptation, McDonald's has recently revised the components of the Happy Meal to be more nutritious for children. All of these companies continue to adapt and flourish.

At the same time, traditional Christianity has also evolved in Boulder but certainly not disappeared. As with the rest of the nation, denominational distinctions have blurred or become virtually invisible. Instead of seeking standard denominational labels, those persons that identify themselves as Protestant Christians in Boulder are generally choosing to find a church home based on such consumer-driven variables as its programs for children and youth, or the quality of the music, or the charisma of a teaching pastor. As recently as 1988, Flatirons Church was started by a dozen young adults in Boulder County. In a relatively short time it has now become the largest church in all of Colorado, and the 3rd fastest growing church in the entire U.S. More than 30,000 people attended their Easter services last year. Somehow they have been able to maneuver through changing culture by creatively and effectively adapting their methods without diluting their core message.

The institution of the University of Colorado now has a greater international appeal, and draws students from more than 100 countries. The general political mindset of the faculty has shifted so far to the Left since the '60s that the University Regents recently created a search team specifically to recruit one professor for the sole purpose of teaching from a Conservative world-view. This created significant vocal debate on campus as to whether or not such a perspective was in fact a genuine and legitimate need within higher education.

In stark contrast to the '60's, the men's football and basketball rosters today are predominantly African-American men. They often feel isolated as they live and compete in a community that is disproportionately white. They frequently refer to their campus as "the plantation", where they work hard at football and basketball, earning so much revenue for rest of the CU students and faculty. Major college sports such as these have become a monster money machine on a national scale. Quality education for athletes has taken a back seat to that of a "farm system" for sports on the professional level. At high schools as well as colleges, participants in any competitive sport are given an "Athletic Letter" or a Certificate of Recognition during one of the student assemblies, but there is rarely any secret initiation or hazing ceremony for lettering in a sport. Now deemed illegal in many states, the legitimate fear of a major lawsuit regarding possible sexual harassment or physical abuse from hazing has virtually ended that practice nationwide.

The university continues to adapt in a changing world.

CRITICAL QUESTION #2 : WOULD IT EVER BE POSSIBLE FOR OUR COUNTRY TO EXPERIENCE A CULTURAL AND SOCIETAL UPHEAVAL OF SUCH MAGNITUDE AGAIN?

The answer is becoming very clear, and it is not a pleasant one. While the contributing variables would certainly differ from the '60's and '70's, the alarming trend is that the United States is on a trajectory for another cultural upheaval of even greater dimensions than any in our history. Voters of all ages have become more and more self-absorbed, and are choosing with a fierce rigidity to focus on their singular issue that is most dear to them. Civil discourse has become a lost art as opposing factions yell louder and louder, opting for vitriolic debate instead of reasoned dialog. With rare exception, any personal comment on current issues is like playing hopscotch in a mine-field. Society seems to be unraveling due to the inability to find civil conversation on key issues. The Weather Underground once held a radical vision that they needed to bomb the U.S. into a new era. Fifty years later, that vision may become a reality – but for different reasons.

Bumper stickers used to be an innocuous way to express one's preference. Maybe it was to endorse a specific political candidate, maybe it was backing a specific social issue. But it was a simple way of saying "Here is one more American that supports " __XYZ___." Today, more and more drivers are choosing not to make such a statement on their bumper that expresses any position on the political spectrum because they are fearful they may get "keyed" or have a car window shot out.

There are at least ten divisive issues where the gap of separation is widening rather than narrowing, with a desperate attitude of "winner-take-all." Hostility, property damage, and death threats have become routine on every one of these variables as they have become an "Us vs. Them" mentality, and a person's identity is often determined solely by who they hate. Sadly, an environment of political Manichaeism is now the norm. As an example, opposing factions helped to make the most recent national election cycle the most vitriolic in history. Rather than voting FOR a particular presidential candidate, a majority of voters on both sides exercised their franchise by voting AGAINST the opposing candidate. Our very constitution is about to be tested as never before, to determine if we still have any national character of decency, and to see if we are willing to be ruled by the laws of the land.

Without suggesting any prioritization in this list, here are some of the major points of contention that are pushing people to higher and higher levels of separation and animosity:

- the "Right" vs. the "Left" / or Conservative vs. Progressive. Partisan voters for either side of the aisle no longer consider their opponent to be "different". No longer do they consider their opponent to be misguided or merely "crazy." Instead, they now literally believe their opponents are "evil", and as such, represent a serious danger to the future of our country.
- "Black Lives Matter" vs. White Supremacists. Racial hatred is brewing with new energy, and the extremities of both sides now consider violence as a valid and necessary option. "Racial cleansing" is openly discussed.
- Hispanic Immigration – legal or illegal – vs. Closing the Border. One extreme demands that California and parts of the southwest be returned to Mexico. The other side wants thousands of people that have lived and worked in the U.S. for more than 20 years to be sent back to Mexico or Central America with or without their children, and start over.
- "Pro-Life" vs. "Pro-Choice." One voice says all abortions are murder. The other voice says "freedom" is the sole issue, and a woman must be protected in her legal option to choose for her own self. Abortion proponents claim this is a valid tool for population control. It demonstrates a polarized debate on when life truly begins, with little or no constructive dialog.

- Gun Control vs. the NRA (National Rifle Assoc.). Mass shootings have become commonplace, unlike any other civilized country in the world. Cries for some practical limitations or total banning of guns – particularly assault rifles – is met with an adamant shield by the 2nd Amendment of the U.S. Constitution, and the insistence that more guns rather than fewer guns may be the solution.

- Jew vs. Gentile / and Israel vs. Palestine. Although the geographic area in question is off-shore, the debate is growing throughout the U.S. as anti-Semitic statements become more frequent. Advocates for either side use the threat of violence as justified revenge as well as persuasion.

- Christianity vs. Atheism & Agnosticism. Are Christians focusing on the love and forgiveness that Jesus taught, or are they "self-appointed morality police"? Are atheists and agnostics exercising the "tolerance" that they claim to adhere to, or are they operating with as much "exclusivity" as their opposition?

- Global climate change vs. Cyclical shifts. Is global warming "human-caused" or a normal ebb and flow of nature? Are temperature trends due to man-made increases in carbon dioxide emissions, or by the sun's magnetic field interacting with increasing cosmic rays? Both camps claim they are committed to studying science, but the critical need for continued government funding prevents either side from seeking common ground.

- "Old" vs. "Young." Life expectancy has risen sharply, with a corresponding demand for increased medical care and other services. Sky-rocketing healthcare costs and shrinking Social Security balances have pushed young adults to promote euthanasia as a viable option, even though the "65+" demographic vastly out-numbers any other age segment in the country.

- Radical Islamists vs. all non-Muslims. Terrorism is certainly not limited to the U.S. but the domestic concern is growing exponentially as Muslims immigrating into America quietly support their terrorist brothers worldwide and demand to be governed by Sharia Law in defiance of our Constitution.

This list is by no means exhaustive, but is extensive enough to paint a grim picture. We are now living in an era of "intolerance and disrespect" – not just in income levels or political persuasion or religious affiliation, as stated above, but even in allowing which voices should be given a platform from which to speak. University campuses – meant to be a bastion for open-minded learning – are ridiculed by their students because of the selection of particular graduation speakers. Students have frequently demanded that schools rescind their invitation to those guest speakers prior to commencement exercises, or at the very least arrange a coordinated mass walk-out as soon as the speaker approaches the podium to begin his or her address. What does higher education consist of when there is an absolute refusal even to listen to a differing set of ideas?

Abuse through social media has become a plague for some websites. Growing hatred for any opposing points of view has created a new world of "keyboard courage", where persons can anonymously attack any person, political party, or entity they choose without risk of self-identification. Once again, heated debate but no rational dialog.

Hatred and paranoia today are so prevalent that *ANY* public expression pertaining to politics, religion, entertainment, or the arts must presumably be placed somewhere on the partisan spectrum of "Right" or "Left", i.e. to stand or kneel for the National Anthem, to offer aid to new immigrants, or to acknowledge that one likes or dislikes a situation comedy TV show that has a particular niche for its humor. We have become a society deeply fractured by politics, religion, and class, with no tolerance for opposing views.

America's upheaval during the late 60's and early 70's was a counter-cultural rebellion, fueled exclusively by the demographic of young adults. Today's social schism is a philosophical rebellion, fueled by ideologies put forth from men and women of all ages. Unless the trajectory changes, a national class war or civil war is feasible.

As voters continue to become more and more rigid in their affiliation with any singular perspective, at least one specific outcome of CHANGE becomes more and more likely. Unless the public will embrace civil "DIALOG" instead of vitriolic "DEBATE", in the not too distant future we will see the unraveling and splintering of our two-party political system. If major candidates happen to choose NOT to support the specific issue of a particular special-interest faction, those voters will feel forced to select their own captive candidate.

As hypothetical examples, there are at least three scenarios where this disintegration could easily unfold. First, on the far Left, the voice of Socialism is gaining more and more momentum. Those tenets are vastly different from the vision of our nation's founders. But if the Centrists of the Democratic Party are not willing to shift farther and farther to the Left, a new Socialist Party candidate may emerge with a strong following.

On the other side of the aisle, the solidarity of the Republican Party is threatened by the group known as "evangelicals." This enormous voting block is comprised of very conscientious men and women who consider it their duty to vote as a demonstration of their role as American citizens. Even when the candidate choices are perceived as the moral equivalent of voting for Nero or Caligula, they will still enter the voting booth while holding their noses. But a repeated vacuum of desired character or integrity could quickly force them to produce their own Party and their own candidates.

A third such scenario is a singular issue that could decimate either or both major political parties. As mass-shootings and mass-murder continue to plague our nation, there is a ground-swell of support for some practical form of gun control. The National Rifle Association (NRA) is the largest political lobby in this country, and stands in adamant opposition to any such legislation. If an introductory form of gun control were to be adopted by both major parties, NRA members would not simply abstain from voting. They would establish their own independent candidate for that office. Such "single-issue voting" could become the norm, and splinter the vote outcome into multiple directions.

Skeptics of this particular notion should be reminded that George Wallace already did this very thing under the singular issue of segregation, and – to our nation's embarrassment – actually won the majority of votes in five states. His 45 Electoral College votes in 1968 were not quite sufficient to disrupt the final outcome in favor of Richard Nixon. In typically close presidential elections, those 45 Electoral votes could be enough to force the necessity of a brokered election. Other "third-party candidates" have previously qualified for government funds for their campaign, such as H. Ross Perot, John Anderson, Ralph Nader, and Rev. Jesse Jackson. The freedom to vote as an individual so chooses is one of the great privileges of this country. But if such diluted voting from so many special interest groups were to begin to take place in higher percentages, no single candidate would be able to win the necessary 51% majority of the Electoral College. It would force a major shift in our process for electing a President.

Hatred in our nation is on the rise. Sokespersons for any cause seem to think their only solution is to raise the volume of anger. Continuing on that game plan only accelerates an ominous downward spiral that soon will lead to selective assassinations, deeper hate crimes, and ultimately could lead to physical war. If that happens, by comparison, the '60's will look mild.

Other than expanding hatred and name-calling toward the opposition, the remaining option is civilized dialog, and a sincere willingness to seek middle-ground. William Falk, Editor-in-Chief of *THE WEEK Magazine*, reiterated this warning when he published an editorial at the end of 2017 with the following assessment of our cultural condition. "Never in my lifetime – even in the late 1960's – has the country felt so fractured, and so close to a civil war. Our one nation, allegedly indivisible, has cracked open along fault lines of culture, class, religion, and partisan identity, creating chasms of mutual incomprehension and disdain. Politics has devolved into a winner-take-all blood sport. Virtually everything is politicized, from football to wedding cakes . . . Our democracy will be sorely tested; in the crucible, we will discover whether character, decency, truth, and the rule of law still matter."

For some, Viet Nam never fully went away.

The aftermath of the ill-advised war forever changed our Defense Department, not only in how America might engage an enemy force on the ground, but also in how our military leaders would communicate our status and strategies while a war effort is underway. During the Gulf War, for example, General Norman Schwarzkopf held a live daily press conference in front of the cameras to personally convey up-to-the-minute details of how the war was progressing. Thanks to Viet Nam, war is no longer exclusively a military undertaking, but now has a public relations component as well.

Lt. Hugh Thompson had grown tired of the controversy and hate mail that followed him out of Viet Nam. Getting assigned to other military locations allowed him the chance to become anonymous again, and not let his associates know of his role in the My Lai incident. But 20 years after his retirement from the Army, British television forced him to re-surface.

London reporters had chosen to produce a documentary series on random heroes. They specifically searched him out, as well as his co-pilot Larry Coburn, and reported in detail on the number of lives that he had saved under the threat of gunfire from his own fellow soldiers. The story of My Lai and Thompson's heroic effort once again became front-page news.

However it would take another ten years following that report before the U.S. Army could swallow its remaining pride and political reputation, and finally agree to hold a public ceremony at the Viet Nam War Memorial Wall to honor Hugh Thompson and Larry Coburn with the Soldier's Medal for Heroism. On the official Pentagon record, his daring decision to save the lives of helpless civilians ultimately had become a part of U.S. military ethics manuals, and was later added into some European military training manuals as well.

As demonstrated in the lives of Thompson and Coburn, integrity in the face of great adversity will always – eventually – rise to the surface.

But now, more than 40 years after our troops left southeast Asia, a new Vietnamese killer is quietly taking the lives of U.S. Veterans once again. The name is cholangiocarcinoma. It is a rare cancer that comes from parasites that were once ingested along with raw or poorly cooked river fish. Those minute liver flukes tend to attach themselves to the lining of the consumer's bile duct, causing scarring, inflammation, and infection. Over decades of time that rare infection progresses into this form of cancer.

More than 700 Viet Nam veterans have filed for medical benefits from this cancer. As one such vet, Michael Baughman said, "It's hard to believe. I spent two tours of duty dodging all those Viet Cong bullets, and now I'm getting killed by a bad fish." To make matters worse, three out of four such claims have been denied by the VA healthcare system, arguing that there is no direct proof of a connection with this ailment to their time of military service.

Once again the horrible blemish of Viet Nam continues to find ways to do damage to the reputation of our military as well as our government, at the expense of those brave men that were simply following orders.

CRITICAL QUESTION #3:
WHERE WILL THESE DIVISIVE FACTORS OF CHANGE LEAD US?

As terrorism becomes more and more sophisticated on a world-wide stage, there is one more ominous trend to consider regarding the future of all humanity. It is a scenario "looking down from 40,000 feet", and with far greater ramifications than the potential civil war that William Falk and others have contemplated. This potential outcome is a three-step scenario that is particularly poignant for those that are familiar with product marketing on a large scale.

Any product has three general stages, namely proto-type and design, then "beta-test", and finally product roll-out. In the first phase, an inventor must develop a concept with a clear set of specifications that might meet a particular need in the marketplace. In the second phase, that initial design must actually be tested in real-life applications to see if and where some variables may need to be adjusted in order to assure success. The third phase is when those final changes have then been implemented, and the product is ready to be fully and successfully utilized for its customers.

That three-step sequence may already be in play regarding the future of mankind. The notion of "lasting peace" has eluded every civilization, in spite of great efforts to pursue it. Immanuel Kant wrote of "Perpetual Peace", or the *Pax Perpetua*, as the ultimate aim of all humanity. Could there not be a way to end all wars and establish permanent peace on a global basis?

This utopian dream had been addressed by numerous great minds throughout history, and became the focal issue for a 19th Century German philosopher named Friedrich Nietzsche. He was a profound thinker and writer in his day, and sought to understand the influences of government, religion, and personal survival that deeply influenced individuals as well as entire nations. His analysis created a "product design" or a set of specifications for a world system that could entirely eliminate war and its destructive end.

Nietzsche envisioned a "one-world government", eliminating the drive for nations to fight other nations on a geographical basis. To implement such a ruling authority, there would need to be a layer of "UberMensche", or "super men", an elite ruling class that would be designated to control and manage the masses. Nationalism would no longer exist under such a world-wide system. Religion of any kind would also need to be removed, to prevent dissention based on differing spiritual world-views, and thus eliminate such "psycho-graphical" dissention. And the shortest route to get there would be to identify a common enemy that would rally the vast majority of men and women to offer their whole-hearted support for such a ruling government. That design concept was Phase I.

Phase II, or the "beta-test", for Nietzsche's theory took place in the mid-20th Century. A young man spent time every week in the Central Library of Germany, staring at the bust of Nietzsche, and thinking about his philosophical prescription for world government. The young man was convinced that those writings from more than 50 years earlier could be implemented into reality, and he would be the ideal leader to do it.

This young man's name was Adolf Hitler. He created a plan for the

Aryan race to help him rule the world. Breeding camps were established to produce an elite populace of young men and women with specific desired physical traits. And by choosing a common enemy he was able to rally the masses to support him in this quest. Those selected enemies of this idealized state were Jews and gypsies. Total annihilation of both people groups was his platform as his troops began to capture surrounding countries.

Tocqueville once said, "One of the most ordinary weaknesses of human intellect . . . is to purchase peace at the expense of logic." Winston Churchill narrowly convinced Great Britain to avoid that mistake in the early days of World War II, and his courage ultimately – if only briefly – helped to save the free world. Thankfully, Hitler's attempt at implementing Nietzsche's masterplan was narrowly defeated. But that was only the "beta-test" for the ultimate vision of world government, or Phase II.

There are now numerous students of history who are convinced that a Phase III is coming, and this time the undertaking of world-peace via world government will succeed. "The world is FLAT" has already become a descriptive principle in the arenas of communication and commerce. Satellite links allow us instantaneous conversations to all corners of the planet. World-wide commerce and trade is underway, as small businesses in remote locations are now able to have global distribution of their products. Manufacturing and sales from one corner of the world to the other will only increase. And Phase III – which is a one-world government – may be close behind.

John Lennon was one of the three most prolific song-writers of the 20th Century, and his greatest selling song described this coming phenomena. "Imagine" a world with no countries. No religion too. No cause to kill or die for. No heaven or hell. Everyone living in peace, and the world will be as One. Such a compelling image from Lennon has already been embraced by millions of his fans.

As terrorism and war continue to ravage the world at an increasing rate, "peace at any cost" begins to sound more and more appealing. "Futurists" foresee a day when a majority of people will beg for such a peace at any price because they are exhausted with the alternative. Futility in trying to stop suicide bombers or other acts of terrorism will motivate people to desperately bargain for peace. And if a charismatic leader were in the right place at the right time, he or she could offer to provide that total world-peace in exchange for total world power.

Such a world government will not come about by military coercion, according to these writers. That model of worldwide surrender which was

409

once pursued by Alexander the Great could not succeed because nuclear weapons would destroy mankind before that would happen. Rather, such a world government will be a collective and voluntary transition.

Here is a recent example of why this could be true. In 1999, with the stroke of a few government pens, 12 European nations agreed to abandon their respective currencies in lieu of the new "Euro." Overnight the Deutschmark disappeared. No more British Pounds. No Francs. No Lire, Schillings, or Pfennigs. Within a few years seven more nations followed them. There was no military takeover that forced this transition. Government leaders voluntarily chose to cooperate in a pragmatic step of change. So it would be someday with a one-world government.

Those readers who are familiar with Bible prophecy know that this world leader of the future is described as the "Anti-Christ." Other futuristic writings claim that this "governor of the planet" will in fact set up a world government, and – for a short time – successfully implement peace for everyone. However, according to these same seers of the future, human pride will quickly cause this world leader with complete and total authority to become the most feared tyrant in human history.

More than 100 years ago William Butler Yeats seemed to gain a glimpse of this future world, when he wrote his most famous poem, *"The Second Coming."* His description of the approaching age looks like this:

". . . Things fall apart, the center cannot hold;
Mere anarchy is loosed upon the world,
The blood-dimmed tide is loosed, and everywhere
The ceremony of innocence is drowned;
The best lack all conviction,
While the worst are full of passionate intensity. . . "

Yes, the free world was able to survive the "beta" phase II of Hitler's onslaught, but if these prophetic writers are at all accurate, the next time around humanity won't be as fortunate.

It started in Boulder. Then it won over a majority of Coloradoans. And now it marches across America.

Legalization of all marijuana originally became a dream for students at the University of Colorado. Then they began circulating petitions, gaining more and more signatures. Because of the special connotation of "420" to pot smokers, they held large "smoke-outs" on April 20th each year (4 / 20) on the football practice field. Other supporters from around the state joined them, until the annual gathering had more than 25,000 participants getting buzzed together. In ensuing years, the City of Boulder and University police departments ultimately refused to let any non-students gain access to the campus on that date.

Amendment 64 regarding legal use of weed reached the Colorado state ballot in 2012, and was finally legalized for recreational purposes in January of 2014. Many non-smokers also chose to vote for the bill as an act of support for those that needed daily relief from chronic pain or nausea, as well as the political promise that a healthy percentage of the pending tax revenue increase would go to benefit the public school system. Although approved by the state, local communities were allowed the leeway to prevent dispensaries from locating in their immediate area. About half the cities and townships of Colorado chose to do so. Following the passage of this bill, the Denver-Boulder corridor quickly gained a new reason to be called the "mile-high" city. Such a community-by-community debate is similar to those states that allow "gaming", or legalized gambling, as long as it is restricted to select locations. Many voters want the revenue benefits for their state, as long as the casino "is not in their back yard."

In the immediate aftermath of the implementation of this Marijuana Amendment in Colorado, two positive surprises have occurred for the benefit of the state: first, tax revenues have significantly exceeded the early projections, and second, a new industry for Colorado has been birthed called "Cannabis tourism." There is no way accurately to measure the incremental revenue from people making vacation trips to the state so that they might legally enjoy the use of pot. Thus this voter's initial outcome has been a financial wind-fall for the state.

But the national debate had grown more intense as to whether or not this has truly been a wise decision. Proponents argue that it is a simple matter of freedom. Anything else would be hypocritical, particularly if doctors can prescribe marijuana as a useful treatment for the relief of pain, and its use is considered non-addictive. The general public certainly seems to agree, in that there are now more dispensaries in Denver and Boulder than there are Starbucks Coffee locations. And Boulder has more marijuana stores than Denver, even though it is less than 1/10th the size in population, and is now known to many as "cannabis Camelot."

Roadblocks to legalization elsewhere are many. First, there is a disconnect between federal and state laws, and both claim power over the other on this issue. Courts are able to cite examples where either side is correct. There is also an increasing debate as to whether or not marijuana is really "medicine." There are countless stories of families that are "forced" to buy the product illegally in order to find needed medical relief. States that are straddling the fence by offering only "medical marijuana" have merely kicked the can down the road, waiting for other states to take the lead. This has created confusion and inconsistency within the legal system as more than 45,000 individuals are currently in prison – some with life sentences – for marijuana-related arrests in one state that are legal in others.

Supporters contend that freedom of choice for both medical and recreational use of pot would generate an economic boom for any state in terms of agricultural growth, retail jobs, and tax revenues for the state. The University of Colorado is participating in the Cannabis Genomic Research Institute to create marijuana recipes that can reduce opiate dependencies. Medical research in Canada and Israel is showing promise for marijuana usage to fight cancer. Other scientists claim that this "miracle weed" could ultimately replace aspirin and echinacea as well as anxiety-reducing prescription drugs. Movements are underway to plan national marches in Washington, D.C. to build a ground-swell of support for freedom instead of restriction, just as Martin Luther King, Jr. did for civil rights more than 50 years ago.

Opponents contend that "freedom" is not the issue, but insist that there are numerous factors that make legalization a very poor choice. Evidence shows that marijuana can have disastrous effects on young children by limiting their brain development, diminishing motivation, and reducing ones ability to make decisions. Youth under the age of 24 are uniquely negatively impacted, particularly in their driving skills. Currently 8% of all traffic fatalities in Colorado are now marijuana-related. Hidden costs such as these may out-weigh the tax revenue benefit. Adults over 24 are not as effected because they have developed a greater capacity to anticipate consequences.

Those that oppose legalization also claim that regular use of pot is in fact addictive, and it is a "gateway drug" which multiplies the likelihood of future use of hard drugs. Clinical studies have shown that smoking marijuana inhibits motor skills as well as academic performance. Recent research in California discovered that the negative effects of second-hand marijuana smoke lasted three times longer than second-hand smoke from a regular cigarette. Smoke in both cases causes arteries to contract, and limit blood-flow. Repeated exposure can permanently damage artery walls, and cause blood clots, heart attack, or a stroke.

Legislative proposals for legalization had made two major promises

412

to the public: passage of the marijuana bill would provide new tax revenue to benefit public schools, and it would eliminate the "black market" for marijuana sales. Both factors have since been proven to be untrue. A recent survey of 25 Colorado school principles found that not one has seen a nickel of new support from the state, even though marijuana tax revenues have spiked far higher than expected. Marijuana demand has skyrocketed among young people – using both legal and illegal sources – for medical treatment of minor injuries. Without significant new restrictions for younger adults and teens, opponents feel the state has sold their children down the river for the sake of the promise of new tax revenues.

Now a new trend has surfaced that is causing deeper concerns for parents as well as law enforcement officials. Vaporizing – also known as "vaping" – and "dabbing" of cannabis concentrates has become a rage amongst minors. The process of these e-cigarettes eliminates the need for inhaling smoke and the corresponding damaging effects of the tar carried in that smoke, but allows for the intake of straight THC (tetrahydrocannabinol) vapors which can produce a more intense "high" by a factor of 3 or 3.5.

Where will all of this controversy ultimately take us? Several states have already followed Colorado's lead and legalized pot for their own residents. Currently 16 additional states have appointed a task force to make a study and recommendation whether to put this on their state ballot or not. The debate may continue for some time, but the ultimate trend is clear. Federal, state, and local governments have an insatiable appetite for new tax revenue. Without new increases in tax revenues, reducing or eliminating some state or local services becomes a necessary consideration. But any such reductions would be unpopular, and create a direct threat to their job security. Billions (yes, with a "B") in new untapped annual taxes are being seductively waved in front of them. So the debate continues. Personal freedom, compassion for those in chronic pain, health risks, increased traffic fatalities, or a gateway drug to more severe addictions. Ultimately none of those factors will carry as much weight as the guarantee of so much new money coming into their tax-revenue coffers. Slowly but surely, legalization on a national scale is likely. Users need only be patient.

It has been 50-plus years since Martin Luther King, Jr. left this earth. His "dream" was that one day his African American brothers would be judged by the quality of their character instead of the color of their skin. Would he be pleased with the progress that has been made since then?

Collectively civil rights and equality for minorities in America has inched forward in that time span. While there are certainly great examples of monumental progress in this regard, there are also painful reminders that we still have a long way to go.

Without question the greatest visual statement of racial equality took place in November of 2008, when America's voters chose to place Barack Obama in the White House. Millions of African Americans took to the streets in celebration. Others sat in their living rooms and quietly wept for joy. Two million gathered at the Washington Monument to witness his inauguration. After centuries of slavery, abuse and hatred in America, a black man had become the president of the greatest country in the world.

More than the influence that any words could accomplish, Barack and his wife, Michelle, led via their example by first getting an education, second choosing to get married, and third having children. Most commendable priorities, regardless of one's race, religion, or political persuasion. Sadly, the opposite pattern has become the norm. Young people have children first, don't bother to get married or stay married, and thus have no time or money to get a quality education. Sociologists have calculated that 60 – 70% of our nation's social and economic ills would be eliminated if young men and women emulated the Obamas.

Another momentous victory for racial equality occurred in Hollywood in March of 2002, as the Academy Awards for Best Actor and Best Actress – for the first time ever – went to a black man and black woman. Denzel Washington and Halle Berry respectively broke new ground in their esteemed arena of entertainment.

One of the most moving examples of stepping toward ethnic reconciliation is currently taking place in Montgomery, Alabama. Located in the heart of the "Old South", the city and its surrounding counties have historically been home to some of the ugliest forms of hatred based on skin color. Following in the footsteps of George Wallace, who eventually repented and asked forgiveness for his many years of racial bigotry, his home town has erected the National Memorial for Peace and Justice. This monument commemorates the deaths of more than 4,400 African American men, women, and children that were murdered in the south between the time of Emancipation and 1950. Many were hanged, while others were shot, drowned, burned alive, or beaten to death at the hands of white mobs. Typically those killings were ignored by law enforcement officials. The architectural design of this memorial is 800 suspended steel columns that are 6 feet tall, representing one "hanging" column for each of the 800 counties where any such murder took place, with the names of the individual victims engraved on them. Hopefully this solemn acknowledgement and visual reminder will assist in the healing process that is needed for both blacks and whites.

But setbacks continue to cause the movement for racial equality to stumble. Specific isolated examples of police brutality or unwarranted killings of blacks in several cities have re-kindled the need for marches or protests similar to those led by Martin Luther King, Jr. The pendulum of hatred has swung too far at these times, causing blacks to target other police officers by trying to run them over with their cars, or ambush them with their pistols.

Steady minds must lead us, not just with flowery words, but with examples in action. Fairness in hiring. Fairness in housing or mortgage applications. Fairness in access to a sound education. Slowly but surely, hearts will be won over, and Dr. King's vision can someday become reality.

In the late '60's and early '70's there were a certain few young people that wanted to overthrow anything having to do with the existing establishment, like Tom's brother Brian and his circle of friends. At the other end of the spectrum there were a few that tried to avoid any change at all, like Mark and his cronies. The majority of those young adults in between were just seeking to go with the flow and have some fun. In the end, all those that did live through the seismic cultural shift of that era had to survive by selectively finding a way to sort through the clutter of choices in order to find their own purpose and their own unique path.

Today, Tom continues to pursue a materialistic dream that just might someday change the world. He is one of the rare individuals that truly experienced Boulder but chose to leave. After moving to the Silicon Valley area of California, he married later in life and opted to transition out of the music scene entirely. In recent years he has been consumed with the creation of a revolutionary marketing platform for the internet. The vision could someday generate billions in revenue, which may or may not give him the perceived level of acceptance that he needs. Or it could generate nothing. But the grand dream is worth the chase.

Tom somehow managed to avoid any addiction to the hard drugs that ruined the lives of too many of his friends back in Boulder. Like so many from that era, he eventually gave up cigarettes when it was no longer cool to smoke. Today he rarely chooses to have an alcoholic drink. Although he is not thrilled with his "man-boobs", he is still in relatively decent shape. But several days a week he will take an afternoon break to smoke some marijuana in an attempt to relax his mind from the stress of his 18 – 20 hour workdays. He has been smart enough to avoid self-destruction, and knows that he is one of the lucky ones.

When he takes time from his work for social interaction, he is always curious why any particular person holds any particular stance on an issue. He has become an excellent listener, and genuinely seeks dialog rather than debate.

Conversely, Mark still reverts to the habit of heated debate rather than civil dialog. He never left Boulder County, and never abandoned the mindset in which he was raised. Now retired and in failing health, he lives a simple life once again in the foothills just west of Boulder, between Ward and Nederland where he grew up. Any recreational drugs have long since been replaced with prescription medicine, using the local pharmacist as his drug dealer. He takes heavy doses of Percocet and OxyContin every day for pain management. Often he likes to curl up in his recliner chair and listen to his favorite LP's of the *Beatles* or *Buffalo Springfield*, yearning for those idealized days when a genuine handshake was more reliable than any notarized signature, when "heavy traffic" meant three cars at the same intersection, when commercial air travel was a total delight, when tomatoes had flavor, when trophies were only given out for 1st Place, when marriage really meant "till death do us part", when everyone read a daily newspaper to get the news, when car doors and houses were never locked, and when the Government was not meddling in every possible niche of his life.

But Mark's nostalgic wishes will never happen. There is no "reverse gear" when it comes to cultural change. And Mark has reluctantly resigned himself to the fact that he – like every other person as well as any other entity – must be able to selectively adapt or die. . .

EPILOGUE

On behalf of the author and the entire staff at History Publishing Company, we hope you have enjoyed this rapid review of the historic years of 1965 to 1975. Readers who were born before 1960 will certainly have their own memories of the profound events of this era, including the tragedy of the Viet Nam War, the drama of Watergate, demands from numerous sectors for equal rights, Woodstock, the national sorrow following the assassinations of Martin Luther King Jr., Bobby Kennedy, and others.

But one segment in this book that was undoubtedly new to every reader was the bizarre set of circumstances surrounding the murder of "Deputy Dawg" at the hands of Marshall Renner Forbes, and the attempted revenge 45 years later by Deputy Dawg's best friend. It revealed many variables of the time, i.e. young people searching for purpose and direction, and adults not knowing how to contend with the rapid changes that were engulfing them.

History Publishing intends to produce a follow-up sequel of this book by late 2021 which will provide an in-depth re-telling of that singular event, and the unusual personalities there were involved.. If you have an interest in reading about that unusual but true story, you are invited to respond in either of two ways. First, you may visit our company website, *'www.historypublishingco.com'*, from time to time to see when the book is actually released. Secondly, you are invited to send an email to this book's website, *'revolutionandrenaissance.com'* Upon publication of this sequel, you will receive a response notification that the book is available, as well as a 40% discount coupon to purchase the book. Please note that no other solicitations will be sent to those inquiries.

Thanks again for your interest in this book.

Warmly,

Don Bracken, Publisher

History Publishing Company

INDEX

CPSIA information can be obtained
at www.ICGtesting.com
Printed in the USA
BVHW062126020320
573873BV00012B/210